IN SUNSHINE
OR IN SHADOW

Charlotte Bingham

BANTAM BOOKS
TORONTO · NEW YORK · LONDON · SYDNEY · AUCKLAND

IN SUNSHINE OR IN SHADOW

*All of the characters in this book are fictitious, and any resemblance
to actual persons, living or dead, is purely coincidental.*

A BANTAM BOOK 0 553 40296 X

Originally published in Great Britain by Doubleday,
a division of Transworld Publishers Ltd.

PRINTING HISTORY
Doubleday edition published 1991
Bantam edition published 1992
Doubleday Canada edition published 1991
Bantam Canada edition published 1992

This book was set in 10pt Sabon by
Chippendale Type Ltd., Otley, West Yorkshire.

Bantam Books are published by Transworld Publishers Ltd., 61–63
Uxbridge Road, Ealing, London W5 5SA, in Australia by Transworld
Publishers (Australia) Pty. Ltd., 15–23 Helles Avenue, Moorebank,
NSW 2170, and in New Zealand by Transworld Publishers (N.Z.)
Ltd., 3 William Pickering Drive, Albany, Auckland.

Made and printed in Canada.

UNV   10 9 8 7 6 5 4 3 2 1

PRAISE FOR CHARLOTTE BINGHAM

TO HEAR A NIGHTINGALE
'A delightful novel ... pulsating with vitality and deeply felt emotions. I found myself with tears in my eyes on one page and laughing out loud on another' *Sunday Express*

THE BUSINESS
'Probably more sun-tan lotion will be spilled on the pages of Charlotte Bingham's *The Business* than any other book this summer ... the ideal beach read' *Homes and Gardens*

IN SUNSHINE OR IN SHADOW
'Bingham sweeps you along ... a must for lazy reading on the beach' *Company*

'Smashing' *Prima*

'A blockbuster ideal for summer reading. Yum-yum ...' *Sunday Express*

Also by Charlotte Bingham:

For the Duke – with love for the sunshine

From quiet homes and first beginning,
Out to the undiscovered ends,
There's nothing worth the wear of winning,
But laughter and the love of friends.

HILLAIRE BELLOC

Prologue

He stood outside the house waiting for the signal which was given exactly as arranged.

Let in by the back door, through the kitchen, he followed the maid's directions until he arrived at the door of the room. Easing the door open, he saw she was sleeping on a chintz-covered sofa by the fire. The dog was there as well, lying on the rug in front of a log fire.

'It's all right,' the maid whispered, 'he's as deaf as a post now. He won't hear you.' He nodded and eased the door open more. The maid left him, disappearing into the shadows of the hall back to the kitchen.

There were gifts on the floor, at least that's what he took them to be as he carefully tiptoed his way towards her. She was sleeping so peacefully, one arm draped above her tousled head, the other trailing off the sofa so that her long elegant fingers just touched the floor. They had to be gifts because there was wrapping paper in the waste basket and some hand-made tags on the chimney piece. The gifts were some small hand-carved models, figures, some embroidered linen napkins, a book bound in deep red leather, and a water-colour of the dog who still slept on, undisturbed by him.

It was her birthday.

The image before him was so beautiful that for a moment he caught his breath, the girl and her dog, asleep in an elegant room lit by the warm glow of the firelight. She was even lovelier than he remembered. And it was her birthday.

There was also an old-fashioned hat, which looked as though it had been retrimmed, lying on the arm of the sofa, and another book, but an old and much read one, which had fallen open on the floor.

He bent to pick the book up to look at what it was. It was a children's book, open at an illustration of a child in a bed, with a young girl with long dark hair standing at the foot in nightrobes, holding a candle. He read the caption. 'Who are you?' the little boy was saying. 'Are you a ghost?'

'Who are you?' the young woman on the sofa with the bright blue eyes said to him when she awoke and saw him. 'Are you a ghost?'

'No,' he said. 'Are you?'

1913

1

The man who was to kill her mother rode calmly up the drive of the great house. He was mounted on a chestnut thoroughbred who was already becoming over-excited at the thought of the day ahead. His companion rode side-saddle, a beautiful dark-eyed girl in a shiny top hat and immaculate riding habit, mounted on a pure bred iron-grey Arab.

As they rounded the final bend in the long drive and the house came into view, the man reined back his horse, as did his companion.

'I always think,' the man said, 'that Brougham is almost impossibly perfect.'

'I actually prefer Chatsworth,' the girl replied. 'If I had to choose.'

'Too grand,' the young man said. 'Superb but much too grand. The charm of Brougham is that one can live in it.'

They lingered a few moments more to admire the Palladian house which stood before them, beyond an ornamental lake crossed by a fine stone bridge, lying in a fold of the rolling parkland, as if held in the palm of a vast green hand.

'What I love about it,' the young man said, leaning forward in his saddle, 'is its symmetry. The balance of the two wings, those wonderful colonnades, and of course that exquisite pillared portico.'

'Yes,' his companion agreed, adjusting her top hat, 'it's very pretty. But I really would rather have Chatsworth.'

The young man's horse, grown fretful with the wait, pawed the ground and started to back away. 'Come on,' said his rider, 'or we shall miss all the gossip.'

As always with the opening meet there was a splendid turnout, with every invitation issued by the 4th Earl of Deverill, master and owner of the Brougham Foxhounds, having been eagerly accepted. The weather was perfect, and a small army of servants, dressed in plum coloured livery, moved through the mounted followers carrying stirrup cups borne high on silver salvers. The brindle hounds, John Deverill's speciality and obsession, stood well to order at one side of the drive with the whippers-in waiting as patiently as they could for the order to move off.

'Wonderful weather, Lady Deverill!' the young man called to his victim as he cantered through the iron gates and reined his horse back to a walk. 'Perfect, I'd say!'

Lady Mary smiled at the young man as he doffed his topper to her, and walked her horse on, uncertain for a moment of her guest's identity. She knew the girl who accompanied him well enough, but her companion's face escaped her.

'That's one of the Stanhope-Murray boys,' a friend told her. 'Charming and utterly feckless and, let it be said, a bit of a "thruster".'

Lady Mary laughed. 'Thank you!' she called over her shoulder. 'I shall do my best to avoid him when hounds are running!'

Looking back at the crowd at the foot of the great stone double staircase, she suddenly caught sight of the familiar blonde head of her daughter and called the nursemaid, who was holding her up to get a better view of all the excitement, to bring her over. The girl handed her charge to Nanny, who immediately straightened the child's dress and re-tied her hair ribbon.

'Thank you, Rosie,' Nanny said to her subordinate, before calling for a way through the throng of servants who had gathered to see hounds move off.

Lady Mary smiled when she saw her daughter, and bent down towards her from her horse.

'Do you want to stroke Capers' nose, darling?' she whispered. 'You know how Capers loves you doing that.'

Nanny walked to the front of the handsome grey gelding and the child put out a small hand to rub his silk-soft muzzle. The horse pushed his nose upwards and snorted, spraying the little girl and making her laugh with delight.

'You see?' her mother told her. 'You see how much he loves you? Nearly as much as I do, my darling,' she added. She bent down to kiss her child. 'But not quite, because I love you far too much.'

The little girl would always remember that moment, and the picture of her mother, so beautiful and so elegant in her top hat and long dark riding habit, mounted side-saddle on her famous grey hunter. It would stay with her for the rest of her life.

Nanny hoisted her higher in her arms as the huntsman blew his horn and the hounds moved off. For a moment she lost her mother in the crowd of horses and riders and foot followers, as people jostled for the best position, or to ride alongside their fancy. Then she saw her once more, as she checked her horse in the mêlée before easing him through to take up their regular position at the front.

There was one last wave as they crossed the stone bridge before swinging away right, up the long gentle pull which led to the first draw. Lady Mary Deverill, now clear of the pack and alongside her husband, reined Capers back into a half-rear, blew her daughter an extravagant kiss, raised her hand in the air, and was gone forever.

Early on that morning, that very same morning in October 1913, anyone walking or motoring down Westfield Drive, Boston, Massachusetts, would never have given any of the houses a second glance, so ordinary were they, and none more so than number 1015, a clapboard house like all the others in the street, only one which was in even more urgent need of repainting than most of its neighbours. The small grass lawn at the front was overgrown, the wooden verandah running from the porch along the front of the house had several posts missing, and the catch on the outer porch door was broken, so that it swung open and shut with a groan and a bang in the ever freshening wind.

A woman arriving at the house fiddled with the lock as she waited for someone to let her in, but finally, with a despairing gesture, gave up the attempt to fix it long before she was admitted.

Next door, in the house on the right, someone had been watching the visitor's arrival from the side of an upstairs window, a middle-aged woman with a startling mass of red hair piled high above a powdered face with a well rouged mouth and plucked and pencilled eyebrows, a woman dressed in a dark crimson gown, of the kind which some years before would have been described in fashionable circles as 'tea gowns'. She was holding a net curtain to one side with the gold-ringed fingers of one hand, while in the other hand she held to her mouth a long white ebony cigarette holder on which she drew constantly as she watched the visitor enter her neighbour's house. Then she waited with a slight frown on her pale white face, as if she might learn something by waiting. But when she heard or saw nothing more, she dropped the net drape back into place, to disappear once more into the darkness of her house.

Outside number 1015 the rest of the world came and went, while the porch door swung open and shut even more frequently, as the October wind strengthened, forcing the few passers-by to bend into what was now turning into a gale and to clutch at their hats. So when the cry came, that first cry which heralds life, had anyone been passing the house at that moment, it is doubtful that they would have heard it. What they might have heard however, had they been passing ten minutes later, even above the noise of the traffic and the raging of the wind, was a roar of someone in pain, a great and agonizing cry. The red-haired woman in the house next door most certainly heard it, and hurried to another upstairs window to look out the back, for the cry seemed to have come from the yard of her neighbour's house. And sure enough, there her neighbour was, standing half dressed in his yard, with both fists clenched and raised to the skies as he demanded to know of his God why He had chosen to take his wife.

No-one ever told Artemis Deverill that her mother had been killed out hunting that fine October morning, knocked from her horse by the young Stanhope-Murray boy as he tried to thrust his way past her, jumping a hedge and instantly breaking her neck. Later Artemis was told in many indirect ways that her mother was dead, but on the day of the accident she was kept in ignorance.

Of course, she was aware that something had happened, and that whatever it was, was wrong. She knew this from the hushed voices of the nursery staff and from the comings and goings far below her in the great house. Years later, all that she would remember of that fateful day were two things. First, the sight of one of the huntsmen galloping at full speed up the drive, over the bridge and in through the ornamental gates, throwing himself off his still cantering horse, and running into the house through one of the entrances below the main staircase.

'There's been an accident,' one of the nursemaids, catching sight of him, called excitedly. 'There must have been an accident.'

Artemis had been busy drawing, sitting on the window seat of the nursery, high up on the third floor of the family wing. She was drawing a house, a house which had just four windows, one chimney and one door, while Nanny, full of nursery lunch, dozed by the fire. Having finished it, Artemis then sat gazing at her drawing, trying to imagine what it would be like to live in a house with just four windows, one chimney and one door, with just her mother, and perhaps even her father. When she too heard the clatter of the galloping horse far below she went to the window, but there was no longer anything to see and only the sound of the nursemaids chattering.

The second thing Artemis remembered was being put to bed very early, so early that tea had hardly been cleared. That night, unlike other nights, Nanny sat and stroked her head and held her hand.

'There's been an accident,' she kept saying. 'There's been a dreadful accident.'

Artemis had a vague idea as to what accidents were. They were things like a servant getting shot in the chest when a big party went out shooting, or a boat capsizing on the lake, nearly drowning the four occupants. But this accident must be something far more serious, because all the nursery maids were crying, and so, when she looked through the bannisters on her way to bed, were the servants downstairs.

'What is it please, Nanny?' she tried to ask when Nanny was tucking her in. 'Please, what has happened?'

'Just go to sleep, child,' Nanny replied. 'Go to sleep and your papa will come and see you in the morning.'

Artemis lay in the darkened room. Her father never came up to the nursery floor. It was unheard of. She knew then it was her mother who must have been hurt. She called out for someone, but no-one came. She called again and again. Eventually Rosie, the youngest of the nursery maids, pushed the door open a fraction, a handkerchief to her face.

'Go to sleep, pet.'

'What's happened, Rosie?'

'You'll find out in the morning,' Rosie replied, her voice floating towards Artemis through the handkerchief. 'You just go to sleep, pet.'

In the morning her father arrived up in the nursery. Artemis knew it was him before she saw him, because even before he was in the room everyone stood up, and

Nanny as always straightened Artemis's dress, tugging it at the back. He dismissed the nursery staff with a peremptory wave of his index finger, leaving only Artemis alone with him.

'Yes,' he said, after clearing his throat. 'Look here, there's been a bit of an accident. Couldn't be helped. One of those things, I'm afraid.'

Artemis frowned, but said nothing, wondering what was to come. Her mother had fallen off Capers, that much she knew. And that was why everyone had been crying. For a moment her father said nothing more either, he just stood with his hands clasped behind him, looking up at the ceiling. Artemis attempted a smile to reassure him that she at least wasn't going to let him down by crying, but he paid her no attention. Instead, he turned away to stare at the picture of her mother which was on the chest of drawers. He picked it up and held it away from him while he looked at it. Then he replaced it.

'Nice picture,' he said finally. 'Very nice indeed. Anyway. About the accident.' He cleared his throat once more and resumed staring up at the ceiling. 'Happened when we were out, do you see. Nasty business. And the long and the short of it I'm afraid is, your mother's gone.'

He turned and walked over to the window where he stood looking out with his hands clasped behind his back. Artemis didn't understand what he meant, but dared not ask him.

'So there you are,' her father concluded, once again clearing his throat. 'Terrible business, I'm afraid, but there you are. These things will happen.' He left without turning back, without looking at her.

When Nanny returned at last Artemis asked her what her father had meant by saying her mother had gone.

'Because I'm afraid she has, dear,' Nanny replied. 'She's gone where we all must follow.'

'I see,' Artemis said, without seeing. 'But where, Nanny? Where's she gone?'

'She's crossed over, dear,' Nanny sighed, 'gone to Kingdom come. Your poor mother has been gathered.'

'Will I ever see her again, Nanny? If she's gone?'

'Of course you will, dear. We all will.' She nodded briskly. 'Time for your walk.'

That night Artemis prayed silently to God that if she was going to see her mother, then she hoped it would be soon.

They buried Lady Mary Deverill without her daughter knowing. It had been decided that the child was too young to understand and as a result she might suffer unpleasant after-effects, rather as people tend to do after eating something which disagrees with them. So prior to the funeral, which was to be held in the church attached to the great house, Artemis was despatched with her nanny to Scotland, to stay with relations in a remote castle, where once more no reference whatsoever was made to the tragedy.

It was all intended for the best. The reasoning behind it being that she would not be able to come to terms with the notion of her mother being dead, so by removing her from the place where the tragedy had occurred and allowing enough time to pass, she would better be able to come to terms with her loss. It was also to be hoped, her father told her nanny prior to their departure, that by the time his daughter was returned to Brougham, the memory of her mother would already be fading.

In the very same week as Lady Mary Deverill was being laid to her final rest in the family churchyard at Brougham, across the Atlantic Ocean, in the statue packed graveyard of the Church of St Peter and St Paul, Westfield, Boston, Massachusetts, the recently bereaved Patrick Milligan entertained a very different hope from the father of the little girl in England. For as he watched the cheap pine coffin being lowered into the frosty ground, Patrick Joseph Garrett Milligan vowed that the person responsible for the untimely death of his beautiful wife Kathleen should live to regret, forever and always, the moment of her wretched birth.

On the eve of her seventh birthday, Nanny told Artemis that she had been invited downstairs that very afternoon to take tea with her father. The thought of such a thing terrified the child. She had hardly seen her father in all the weeks since returning from Scotland, nearly five months after the 'accident' as it was known. Once the hunting season was over he had gone straight off to Ireland to fish, and then, on the outbreak of war, had promptly rejoined his regiment, and as their colonel-in-chief had made several sorties to France during the next three years. When he wasn't abroad, he was at his house in London. He rarely seemed either to have the time or the inclination to return to Brougham.

Artemis saw her father twice during all this time. The first time she was playing marbles with Rosie in the saloon, when the double doors swung open and he appeared as if from nowhere, a tall and very upright figure, still in his colonel's uniform. Rosie at once scrambled to her feet, the marbles she had in her lap dropping and clattering over the polished wood floors.

Artemis, down on her knees, just turned round and stared for a moment, before Rosie took her hand and pulled her to her feet.

'Excuse us, your lordship,' Rosie apologized. 'But, like, no-one said you was home.'

'Perfectly all right, girl,' Lord Deverill replied, after a moment spent staring at Artemis. 'That's perfectly all right. Carry on.' Then with a couple of brief nods at them both, he crossed the saloon and left through the other double doors.

Artemis and Rosie both stood in silent uncertainty for a moment before Rosie began to pick up the marbles and put them back in their small cloth sack. Artemis helped her and they both instinctively began to hurry, lest Artemis's father should return and find them still there, even though he had given his permission. Then they ran out of the saloon and up the backstairs as quickly as they could, to resume their game in the safety of the nursery.

The other time Artemis saw him was one day when she and Nanny were returning from a walk by the lake. Her father was just leaving in a blue Rolls-Royce. The car didn't stop as it passed them. It barely slowed down. Nanny held Artemis aside and told her to wave, which she did. Her father raised his hand once, hardly sparing a second glance. Artemis, on tiptoes, saw there was another person in the back of the car, a woman with bobbed blonde hair, wearing a pale fur coat, and smoking a cigarette. She too waved briefly at Artemis and smiled fleetingly, before the Rolls swept away and finally out of view.

And now Artemis was to go to tea downstairs with her father.

'What shall I say?' she asked Nanny.

'You won't have to say anything,' Nanny reassured her, smoothing down her best dress. 'Speak when you're spoken to, but otherwise don't say a word. Little children should just be seen, you know that. Seen but not heard.'

'I feel sick, Nanny,' Artemis complained.

'Of course you do, child,' Nanny replied. 'But never mind, never mind. Just speak when spoken to, that's all. Speak when spoken to and you'll be fine.'

Tea had been laid in the blue drawing room, a vast room dominated by two huge chandeliers and an enormous portrait of Henry VIII after Holbein, which hung over the fireplace. Lord Deverill was standing down the far end of the room, staring out of a window across the estate.

The butler had opened the door to announce them, but even before he had finished, Artemis's father cut him short.

'Thank you!' he called. 'That will do, thank you!'

Nanny left once she had pushed Artemis into the room. There was no-one else there, just a maid, whom Artemis couldn't remember ever seeing before, waiting to serve tea.

'Good,' her father called from his window. 'Come to tea, right? Good. So give her a lemonade, will you? And a fancy or whatever.'

In response to his instructions, the maid pulled up a chair for the little girl, and Artemis carefully sat on the edge of it, her legs still too short to reach the floor. The maid then shook out a large linen table napkin which she placed across the lap of Artemis's best frock. Still her father stared out of the window.

'Treating you all right, I suppose?' he asked suddenly.

'Yes thank you, Papa,' Artemis replied, not understanding at all what her father meant.

'Jolly good,' he said. 'Well done.'

There was a long silence, during which the maid offered her a muffin from under a silver dish. Artemis took one and quickly started to eat it. They never had muffins in the nursery.

'So there you are then,' her father said, breaking the silence. 'So it's your sixth birthday tomorrow then. Jolly good.'

'No it's my seventh, Papa,' Artemis said. 'Tomorrow I shall be seven.'

'Oh well,' her father sighed, without looking round. 'It'll all be the same in a thousand years.' He paused and reclasped his hands behind his back. 'Expect you'd like to make a day of it, yes?'

Artemis frowned at her father, away up the room and then nodded. 'Yes,' she said. 'Yes please, Papa.'

'Good. Point is, won't be here for tea. Got to get back to London.' Her father took a silver case from his pocket and withdrew a cigarette, which he tapped on a thumbnail before putting it in his mouth and lighting it. 'No, got to get back to London, do you see. For dinner. So thought we'd go for a ride in the morning. Jenkins says you're quite useful on that pony of yours. Yes?'

'I don't know, Papa,' Artemis answered, brushing some cake crumbs off her dress.

'What Jenkins says.'

'I'd love to go riding though. Please.'

Her father tapped the ash off his cigarette into his cupped hand and then blew it into the air. 'Good. That's all fixed then. Good.' He cleared his throat and continued to stare out of the window for a couple of moments longer. 'Good,' he said finally, then turned on his heel and left the room.

Since her father had not stipulated the exact time when they were to ride, Artemis was dressed and in the stables at first light lest she miss her treat by being late. Jenkins, just too old for combat, was the only groom left at Brougham, but he was already up and mucking out the boxes, for he still had six horses to do. The best half dozen hunters were still 'in, even though there was no hunting and no-one to ride them except Jenkins and a girl groom seconded from the village. The rest of the animals had been roughed off and turned away in a distant paddock. The young staff might have all gone to Flanders, but Lord Deverill's horses had not yet been volunteered.

'I in't done Buttons yet, your ladyship,' Jenkins apologized when he saw Artemis. 'I just in't 'ad the time.'

'It's all right,' Artemis replied. 'I'll do him. I like doing him.'

They barely talked while Jenkins started to groom a tall strong chestnut for his master and Artemis groomed her dark bay pony. They had both animals ready and saddled up in half an hour, which was as well, because five minutes later, on the stroke of half past seven, Lord Deverill himself arrived, accompanied by four couples of hounds.

'Thought we might have a bit of sport,' he announced generally. 'Hounds could do with a run.'

'Don't you go too bold now,' Jenkins muttered to Artemis as he checked her girths. 'Don't you go trying to do anything beyond you.'

'Let her ladyship do that, man!' Lord Deverill called as he swung himself effortlessly into the saddle. 'Otherwise if she kills herself it'll be your doing!'

'The catches be a bit tight on these little saddles, your lordship,' Jenkins replied, continuing to check the buckles. 'They're that tight they needs strong fingers.'

'Ready?' Lord Deverill asked his daughter, as if Jenkins had not even spoken.

'Yes, Papa,' Artemis said, as Buttons put in a good-natured buck.

'Your hands are too high,' her father said. 'You're riding. Not driving.' Then he kicked his horse forward and led on out of the yard.

It was a beautiful November morning, cold but clear. The hounds' and the horses' breath lay on the air, while a light frost still crisped the grass. Artemis put her heels down, straightened her back and softened her rein, so that by the time she caught her father up, she had Buttons perfectly controlled. Her father glanced down at her, but said nothing. Instead he kicked his horse on into a canter behind the hounds. Artemis followed suit and they headed away from the house up a long pull which led to a covert known as the King's Bushes.

As they rode, Artemis pushing Buttons on to keep pace with the free-striding chestnut, her father never spoke. Whenever she rode out with Jenkins, he always called to her what they were about to do, whether they were going to trot, or canter, jump or gallop. Her father said nothing. He just, on occasion, looked over to see how she was going, and then rode on. He didn't even nominate their first jump, which was a three-foot post and rails. He simply put his horse at it, then rode on. Fortunately Artemis had often jumped this particular fence with Jenkins, and Buttons sailed over it, which was as well since there was no other way forward. Next they met a small brook which Artemis and Buttons had also jumped previously, and which they flew again, and finally, before reaching the King's Bushes, they met a low but wide hedge. Buttons reached for it and it wasn't until they were flying it that Artemis saw the four-foot drop the other side. Ahead, her father's horse had pecked slightly on landing, throwing his rider up his neck. Buttons landed perfectly and came away from the jump so well that by the time her father had collected himself and his horse Artemis and Buttons were alongside them.

'Good,' Lord Deverill said as they drew up. 'Yes, that's the ticket.'

They waited a long time while the hounds drew the covert. Artemis's father smoked a cigarette and said nothing. Early on Buttons fidgeted, earning a look of disapproval from Lord Deverill. Artemis sat back, heels down, and he quickly settled.

Then the absolute quiet of the early morning was broken by the sound of hounds suddenly giving tongue.

'Right,' Lord Deverill said. 'Seems they've found.'

The hounds crashed out of the far side of the covert and swung away from Artemis and her father uphill. Ahead of them, Artemis got her first view of a fox in full flight, and found herself hesitating. Even from that distance, she could sense the feeling of panic as the animal flew across the open fields, its brush stuck out straight behind it. Then there was no time for further thought, as Buttons, excited by the baying of the hounds and the sound of Lord Deverill's hunting horn on which he was blowing a thrilling series of quick notes, took hold of his bit and flew. Artemis battled for control, but it was a fight soon lost, and from then on she was a passenger as her pony galloped in hot pursuit of horse, hound and fox.

Ahead, her father was riding alongside the hounds, at full stretch. But he was taking a cautious line, mindful of the child behind him. Instead of flying the hedges he went for gateways or gaps and Artemis, seeing what he was doing, managed to steer her bolting pony on the same course. They ran through field after field, with the hounds all the time slowly gaining on the fox. And then suddenly, just as Artemis felt Buttons was beginning to tire and that she was regaining control, as they topped a hill and began the run down the opposite side, a hedge loomed up in front of her, divided by a solid looking five-bar gate which was firmly closed.

She was still some way behind her father's horse, whom she saw her father checking as he realized there was no way through. The hounds, however, having wriggled under and through the gate, were still running, streaming away from them across the next field as the fox headed for the nearby covert. Artemis saw her father turn his horse towards her and raise a hand.

'Stop!' he shouted. 'Pull up, girl! There's no way through!'

Artemis sat back and pulled on her reins as hard as she could. But Buttons still had hold and if anything quickened as he galloped at the hedge. Artemis could hear her father still calling to her to turn her pony, but there was nothing she could do. The hedge was fast approaching, looking too big, far too big for Buttons to jump on his own. So instead of closing her eyes and praying, Artemis opened them wide and kicked on.

Buttons arched his back and leapt. Artemis threw the reins at his head so that nothing would check him. She didn't even look down. She just looked through her pony's ears at where she hoped he would land. Which he did, a good two feet clear of the gaping open ditch which lay on the blind side of the hedge.

Lord Deverill, having watched in silence, seeing his daughter was safe, popped his big horse over the gate and galloped on to the covert where hounds had checked, and so too finally had Buttons.

'I think the fox has gone to ground, Papa,' Artemis said breathlessly, pointing into the woods. 'In that hole over there.'

'Fair enough,' her father replied. 'We'll give him best.'

Picking up his hounds, Lord Deverill turned his horse and started to walk away from the covert, followed by Artemis. They left the field by a different route, going out through a hunting gate on the far side, before swinging back alongside the woods at the top of the park.

'Good pony you've got there, young lady,' Artemis's father said to her some time later, as they walked quietly on. 'That was a quick thing, you know. That was a dashed quick thing.'

And that was all that was said on the way home. Artemis's father broke the silence now and then by humming tunelessly to himself, but he never spoke another word, not even after they had ridden into the yard and handed their horses over to Jenkins.

And Artemis had never been happier in all her life.

It wasn't until they had climbed the stone steps leading up to the house that she learned the truth of the matter.

'That last hedge you jumped,' her father said, breaking another seemingly endless silence as he stopped and stared up at the facade of the great house. 'That was the hedge that accounted for your mother.'

Eleanor Mary Milligan, as she was hastily christened the same week her mother was buried, seemed to know from the moment she came into this world at number 1015 Westfield Avenue that in order to survive she must be good and quiet, and not be any trouble to her father or brothers. In fact she was such a quiet baby that sometimes when her father came home drunk on Friday nights he would fondly imagine she had joined her blessed mother in heaven.

'God love us,' he would mutter as he stumbled upstairs, 'and now wouldn't that be a thing? Wouldn't it only be right that she should go, too?'

Some nights he would stand by Eleanor's cot, convinced she had stopped breathing, and do nothing. He never tried to wake her, instead he would just stand and watch and pray that the angels had in fact gathered her and justice had been done. But then the baby would stir in its sleep and put up one tiny pink hand, perhaps seeking for something to hold on to. Patrick Milligan would sigh despairingly as if God had deserted him, before wandering drunkenly off to his own, now single, bed, where he lay cursing his miserable lot before falling into a deep and whisky sodden sleep.

Having lost her mother the moment she was born, the baby needed a nursemaid, so Patrick Milligan had hired the rat-faced Mrs MacDonagh who lived opposite. For the first month of her life Mrs MacDonagh had taken the baby into her own house, along with Eleanor's eighteen-month-old brother Patrick, and she had bottle fed the baby and kept an eye on her brother amidst the debris of her own life and the squalor of her enormous family. Once the feeding routine had been established, the baby and her brother were returned home at nights, since Mr MacDonagh, who worked with Eleanor's father as a building worker, had threatened to leave home if his wife got up once more in the middle of the night to feed a child which wasn't their own. So it was agreed that while Mrs MacDonagh would go on looking after the two youngest Milligans during the day, Dermot, Fergal and Mike, the eldest brothers, would take over as soon as they were back from school.

Not surprisingly, neither of the older boys appreciated their extra duties. With their mother gone they already had more than their fair share of shopping and cooking. Inevitably they took out their frustrations on Ellie and 'Patsy', as they had nick-named their youngest brother, leaving it to him to remember his sister's bottle when the others had left her crying, or to make endless attempts to keep her amused.

Mrs MacDonagh certainly had no love for children, even her own, and absolutely no time at all for young Ellie. And forced as she was by circumstances to bring her own dirty and vicious brood to work with her, she took a great pleasure in letting them loose on the two youngest Milligans, deliberately ignoring their torments and teases.

Patsy was a sickly child, growing very little in the first few years of his life. Weak and under-nourished, he barely survived a dose of diphtheria, which left him weaker than before, and an even softer target for the torments of his three hefty brothers.

The greatest laugh they enjoyed was pretending Patsy was a little girl. They would hide all his own clothes and, having forced him to wear his sister's, they would lock him out in the street to be chased and bullied by the neighbourhood gangs. When they were feeling particularly spiteful, they would blindfold the 'two sisters' as they were known and, as darkness fell, leave them in some unknown part of the neighbourhood to find their own way home. Little wonder that Ellie learned from an early age to defend Patsy in any way she could. Certainly, no day of their early childhood ever ended without one or both of them being beaten up by someone.

Their father made no attempt to intercede. On the contrary, he went out of his way to encourage his three eldest boys, the 'broth' as he called them, in their bullying.

'Tell us,' their father would ask the 'broth' nightly. 'And what have your sisters been doing today?'

The 'broth' would laugh, and while they were laughing would kick and pinch the two youngest under the table, and while Ellie and Patsy were rubbing their bruises, steal the food off their plates.

This constant persecution only served to throw Ellie and Patsy together. They came to the kind of unspoken understanding real twins enjoy. They soon learned not to talk when just a look would do, and even when separated, each seemed to know instinctively when the other was in trouble. This particularly infuriated Dermot, the pack leader, and sometimes he would knock Patsy about so badly that finally his father told him off, not for hitting the little boy, but because Patsy's subsequent sobs kept Patrick Milligan senior from his sleep.

When her fourth birthday dawned, Ellie secretly hoped that it might be a day just a little different from all the others. She had seen her three elder brothers enjoying their birthdays and being fussed over by their father, but neither her's nor Patsy's birthday had ever been celebrated. When she woke up that morning, with just a small hope in the corner of her heart, she found Patsy already awake, sitting upright in the old cot they still shared, his dark brown eyes shining with excitement from under his mop of brown hair.

'Happy birthday, Ellie,' he whispered, handing her a gift. 'That's for you.'

Ellie opened it. It was a birthday card, hand-made by her brother out of cardboard. He had painted a greeting on the front and inside had drawn a picture of an animal and signed his name.

'That's a dog,' he grinned. 'In case you didn't know.'

'Thank you, Patsy,' Ellie whispered back. 'I shall keep it for ever and ever.'

She tucked the precious card under her pillow and then got out of her cot to get dressed. Both she and Patsy still had to sleep in a cot because their father had not bothered as yet to buy them each a proper bed. They both got dressed, quickly and silently, and then tiptoed out of the bedroom and down the white painted wooden staircase. It was a Saturday, their father was sleeping in, as were their three elder brothers, so for once they had some time to play by themselves, which they did in the yard. They played hopscotch, their favourite, in the ever brightening sunshine, throwing a white pebble into the boxes they had marked out on the ground, and then trying to hop to where the pebble landed without touching any lines.

' 'Allo?' A voice called to them from above.

Both children stopped playing and looked up to see who had called them. It was their next door neighbour, the woman with the red hair. She was standing and smiling down at them from an upstairs window.

'Would you like some cookies maybe?' she asked. 'I 'ave made some. So if you like, come and I will let you in the kitchen.'

Patsy looked at Ellie to see what they should do. No-one had ever offered them cookies before, particularly not their strange-sounding neighbour, whom they hardly ever saw.

'It's all right!' the woman laughed, as if guessing their thoughts. 'I shall not eat you!' Then with a beckoning wave she disappeared from the window.

Encouraged by their neighbour's cheeriness, Ellie and her brother went round to the back of her house and shyly waited to be let in. After a moment the woman threw open the door.

'*Voilà!*' she said.

Neither Ellie nor Patsy knew where to look, because the woman was still in her dressing gown. So they both stared religiously at the ground pink-faced. Their father never opened their front door without first pulling on his coat, no matter what state he was in, and none of the boys were ever allowed to admit a visitor while they or anyone else was in a state of undress.

'Good 'eavens!' the woman laughed. 'Whatever is wrong? You have never seen a woman in her *peignoir* before?'

Ellie wasn't at all sure what a *peignoir* was, but if it was what the woman was wearing, no she most certainly had not. Nonetheless, she remained silent.

'Come, come,' their neighbour said, taking them both by the hand. 'Do not be shy.' And she led them inside her house and through to her kitchen. 'There,' she said, taking a jar from the sideboard and placing it on the table. 'Please. You 'ave just as many as you like.'

Patsy looked at Ellie and Ellie looked at Patsy, but neither moved. The woman waited with a smile on her face, then sighed and took a cookie out for herself, from which she then took a good bite.

'OK?' she asked. 'They are not *poison*!'

Then she laughed out loud and turned away to find her cigarettes. As she did both Ellie and Patsy stuck their hands into the jar together for the delicious looking cookies. By the time their neighbour had turned back, her cigarette lit and in a long ebony holder, both the children's mouths were full of her home-made produce.

'Ah, *bon*,' she said. 'Now, I must introduce myself. I am Madame Gautier. And you are Eleanor, or Ellie. And you, young man, you are Patsy – yes?'

The children nodded their agreement, their mouths too full of cookies to speak.

Madame Gautier watched them for a moment, drawing deeply on her cigarette. It was perfectly apparent the children were half-starved.

'You would like to eat them all, yes?'

'Oh, no, Madam,' Ellie said through her mouthful. 'No we couldn't.'

'Perhaps later, yes? We cannot 'ave them go stale, you know.' And as if to brook no further argument, Madame Gautier took a large paper bag and emptied the entire contents of the cookie jar into it.

'*Eh voilà*,' she said, twisting the bag up and over expertly, like a shop assistant. 'Now go and enjoy them in the sun. As you play your games. And Ellie – you 'ave a 'appy birthday, yes?'

Ellie looked back, astonished that this woman should know it was her birthday. She was about to enquire as to how she knew, but Madame was already chasing them out good humouredly.

'*Allez, allez!*' she laughed. '*Allez-vous en!*'

There was still no sign back home that anyone else was yet up, so Patsy put the paper bag down where they were playing and the two of them resumed their game. And whenever they stopped, they had a cookie. They were utterly delicious, quite unlike anything either of them had ever tasted before, light, crisp and lemony, with a fine dusting of sugar.

A shadow fell over them and neither of them had to look up to know who it was. They could both just feel his presence.

'What have we here?' their father asked, leaning down and picking up the paper bag. 'And what might these be pray?'

'They're some cookies, Da,' Patsy said tremulously.

'Yes,' Ellie added as fiercely as she could. 'They were given to me as a present. For my birthday.'

Her father stared down at her before taking hold of her arm and pulling her to her feet.

'Your birthday, did you say, child? Your birthday? How dare you, you miserable little spalpeen. Your birthday indeed.'

'Well so it is, Da,' Patsy ventured. 'It is. It's Ellie's fourth birthday today.'

'It is nothing of the sort!' his father roared back at him. 'Have neither of you a mind what day this is? Have you no mind at all! Tell me what day this is, Eleanor! You tell me or I'll beat it out of you!'

'It's my birthday, Da!' Ellie shouted up at him. 'And you're hurting me!'

'It's the anniversary of your mother's death, you little scut! That's what day it is! And that's what this day will always be! The day your blessed mother, may the Lord have mercy on her, was taken from me! There'll be no celebrating this day. Not now. Not ever!'

Then he seized the bag of cookies, and on his way back indoors, threw them where he considered they belonged, in the trash can with the rest of the garbage.

2

For Christmas the following year, the month after the Armistice, Artemis was given a new doll. She didn't much like dolls, and this one was no different. It was far too pretty, like most dolls, with huge blue eyes in a ridiculously beautiful china face, and the most exquisite clothes. Artemis much preferred things that were real, such as the injured squirrel she had rescued and nursed back to health, and her pet hen Jemima whose broken leg she and Rosie had mended, and who every now and then was allowed up to the nursery. Dolls were wet, and this doll, Artemis decided, with its great round eyes and silly little mouth, was without doubt the wettest doll of all.

Even so, she had to pretend to like it, particularly because it had been given to her by her father. Artemis could not remember him ever giving her anything ever before. But it was quite definitely from him, because that was what was on the gift tag. 'To Artemis, from Papa.'

She went over to where he was standing by the fire and thanked him.

'You must thank me too, Artemis,' said a voice from behind her. 'Because really it's from me as well.'

Artemis turned and looked at the owner of the voice, a beautiful woman in a blue dress, with bobbed blonde hair. Artemis frowned, trying to remember where she had seen her before, and then she remembered. She was the woman in the pale fur coat in the back of the car that day with her father.

'You see,' the woman was saying, bending towards Artemis and putting a long cold finger under Artemis's chin. 'I chose it for you, darling. Especially. It's meant to be from me as well.'

Artemis looked up at her father and found him staring down at her with a deep frown, as if to say, Artemis felt, that she should have known.

'I'm sorry,' Artemis told the woman, moving slightly away from her so that the finger could no longer reach her chin. 'But it didn't say on the card.'

'Oh, John – ' the woman sighed, turning to Artemis's father. 'John.'

It was a scold. Artemis knew that from the way the woman had sighed. Nanny often did that when she was cross with Artemis for leaving her clothes in a heap, or a dirty glass by her bedside. 'Oh Artemis,' she would sigh. 'Really.'

The woman with the bobbed blonde hair was bending down towards her again. 'It says Mama,' she smiled, her teeth slightly yellow against her over red lips. She also smelt of cigarettes. 'Listen.' She took hold of the doll and bent it slightly forward.

'Mama,' the doll croaked. 'Mama.'

'John?' the woman said, looking back at Artemis's father.

'Later,' Lord Deverill said. 'Not the time now, Bunny. Later.'

The woman stared at him for a moment, without expression, and then with a little smile handed the doll back to Artemis.

'Mama,' it said, as Artemis carried it across to where her other presents lay. 'Mama.'

There was a lot of whispering in the nursery at bathtime. Artemis sat absolutely still in her bath, trying to hear what Rosie and the other maids were saying, but all she could hear were their silly giggles. She asked Nanny what they had all been talking about as Nanny towelled her dry.

'Not for me to say, dear,' she replied. 'All I've heard is rumours.'

'What's a rumour, Nanny?' Artemis wondered aloud.

'A rumour is half a lie, darling. "They say so" is half a lie. That's what a rumour is.'

'Fact of the matter is,' her father told Artemis when he took her aside before lunch on Boxing Day, 'you're to have a new mother. Yes?'

'No,' said Artemis. 'I mean, how?'

Her father paused and stared at her. 'How, did you say?' he asked. 'You say how?'

'What about Mama?' Artemis said.

'What about her?'

'What will Mama say?'

Her father stared at her again, seeming even more baffled. 'Yes,' he said. 'Well I imagine she'll say good show. Point is, do you see, whatever your Mama might have said, point is, it's time you had a new one.' He walked away then and left Artemis trying to puzzle out what her father meant by putting her mother in the past tense.

She asked Nanny when they sat down to lunch. 'You said Mama had been gathered, didn't you Nanny?'

'That's right, child,' Nanny answered curtly, clearly not wishing to entertain morbid thoughts at such a festive time.

'You said Mama had crossed over somewhere,' Artemis continued, 'but we'd all meet again. But if we meet again now, and she finds I have another Mama –'

'Sssshhh, child,' Nanny said, between mouthfuls of goose. 'You won't all meet now. Not in this life.'

Artemis stared at the old woman's whiskery face. 'But Nanny you said –'

'No buts, thank you,' Nanny interrupted. 'Butts are for goats, not little girls.'

'You still haven't said how I can have two mothers, Nanny,' Artemis persisted, raising her voice and attracting the attention of a red-faced man at the main table.

'They can,' Nanny said firmly, 'if their fathers choose to remarry.'

'Gracious,' said the red-faced man, turning to talk across to their separate table. 'I had three mothers. All quite beastly, too.'

'I don't understand,' Artemis said.

'It's not for you to understand,' Nanny said, stifling a small hiccup.

'Your mother on the other hand –' the red-faced gentleman smiled at Artemis. 'Now your mother was a splendid creature. Finest huntswoman I've ever known. Loveliest creature ever to follow hounds.' He picked up his wine glass and drained it. 'I don't mind telling you,' he admitted. 'Cried me eyes out when she was killed. Terrible business. Cried my eyes out. Howled like a wolf.'

'Died?' Artemis said, staring first at the red-faced gentleman and then back at her nanny. 'But –' she began.

'Eat up, child,' Nanny commanded. 'You're lagging behind.'

'But, Nanny,' Artemis insisted. 'What does he mean? My mother isn't *dead*.'

'Of course she is, child,' her nanny replied impatiently. 'What on earth else do you think happened to her?'

Artemis lay in bed that night, and wondered in the black, black dark. Her mother was dead like the badger she had seen last week in the woods, with its hair all stiff, and its mouth curled open.

She had spent all afternoon trying to ask Nanny more, but Nanny had been in a funny mood, laughing one minute and crying the next, and not making any sense of anything she said. At last she managed to tax Rosie who looked at her astonished.

'But I don't understand, Lady Artemis! All this time? You mean all this time you thought your mother – no, I just don't understand. Whoever let you imagine such a thing?'

'If they had told me Mama was dead,' Artemis had told Rosie gravely, 'I would have understood, you see. But all this time, all this time I've thought – she was just gone.'

'Nanny Brougham told you, I was sure of that.'

'No. All Nanny kept saying was that we would all meet again,' Artemis insisted. 'And that I mustn't worry.'

'Well, now there's a thing,' Rosie had said, with a shake of her head. 'All this time, and there was you thinking.' She gave another shake of her head. 'Now there really is a thing.'

'And now I'm to have a new mama, and I don't really like her one bit.'

'She's very beautiful, Lady Artemis.'

'No, she's not Rosie. Really. She's horrid.'

Artemis hated her mama-to-be as much as she disliked the doll she'd given her. It took little time to decide that her new mama was just like the doll, with her big blue eyes, and her made up face and blonde hair.

She stared at the doll which Nanny had put on the shelf, and the doll stared back at her with cold blue eyes. Artemis reached up and took it down off the shelf. 'I hate you,' she told it, tipping it back to make her talk.

'Mama,' said the doll, 'mama.'

'And I am not going to be your mama!' She threw the doll with force back on to the shelf.

Perhaps it was the force, but the doll fell to its side, hit the wall, and then rolled off the shelf on to the floor. Its china face was smashed in, and one blue eye had disappeared. Artemis panicked. Looking round for somewhere to hide the wrecked toy she climbed on to a chair and put the doll on top of the nursery cupboard.

'Mama,' it called faintly. 'Mama.'

Much later, when she returned from her walk with Rosie, she found her mama-to-be inspecting the nursery floor with Nanny.

'Hello, my sweet,' she said, seeing Artemis. 'I've come to see where you live.'

Artemis said nothing, struggling to get out of her coat and gloves, hiding the panic she felt.

'Terribly gloomy up here, Nanny?' the new chatelaine announced. 'Really terribly gloomy, wouldn't you say?'

'Yes, your ladyship,' Nanny agreed. 'Although the decoration is really not my providence.'

'Province, no, I know, nor should it be. No, it's mine.' She turned to Artemis who knew what was coming before the question was asked. 'Where's your new doll, my sweet?' she demanded.

'I don't know, because I don't like her.'

'Great heavens, child,' Nanny said quickly. 'Where are your manners?' But she wasn't quick enough for the woman who was to be Artemis's new mother.

'And why don't you like her, my sweet?'

'I don't like the way she says Mama.'

'And where is she now?'

Artemis shrugged and pointed. 'Up there,' she said. 'On top of the cupboard.'

The next Lady Deverill nodded for Rosie to fetch the doll down, which the nursemaid did, while everyone else waited in the growing silence. Rosie handed the doll to her new employer, who when she saw the doll's broken face flashed a look of pure hatred at the child before her.

'How did this happen, my sweet?' she asked. 'I hope it was an accident.'

'Yes it was,' Artemis agreed quickly, remembering another accident. 'We were playing horses, and she fell off.'

A sudden noise from the cupboard followed by a distinct clucking distracted the next Lady Deverill's attention. 'And what is that, please?' she demanded.

'Mice, your ladyship,' Rosie put in. 'We do get a lot of mice up here, you see.'

'It sounded,' said their visitor, 'more like a chicken.' She opened the cupboard door, to reveal a big brown hen sitting on a pile of clean towels.

'That's Mima,' Artemis said, hurrying to collect her hen before any harm could befall her. 'I only put her in there for a minute.'

Where Jemima had sat, there now lay a large speckled brown egg. 'You see she broke her leg,' Artemis explained. 'And Rosie and I mended it.' She stroked the chicken who clucked delightedly, as Artemis's future stepmother stared in horror at the egg.

'I would hardly call that hygienic, would you, Nanny?' she asked. 'And I would hardly call this a way to run a nursery.'

'The chicken hardly ever comes up here, your ladyship,' Nanny stammered. 'In fact I can't remember when the last time was.'

'It's her Christmas treat,' Artemis explained. 'And there was a frost.'

'You.' The future Lady Deverill nodded at Rosie. 'Take that hen out of here, and then wash all those towels. And the chicken is not to come up here again, is that understood? Ever.'

No-one said anything. Rosie tried to take the hen from Artemis, but Artemis held on to her firmly.

Their visitor turned on her heel and went to the door where she turned back to hold the broken doll up to Artemis. 'As for this,' she said, 'I am taking this, my sweet, to show your father who, I feel sure, will not want to let such a thing go unnoticed.' She said the last word as two words. Un noticed. Very softly, almost sweetly. Unnoticed.

'These plates are cold,' said Patrick Milligan senior, looking up from his place and staring down the table at his five-year-old daughter, who at once scrambled to her feet.

'Sorry, Pa,' she said.

'Sit down,' he commanded, 'until I've finished talking. I have told you time and I have told you time again, but you will not learn. I will not have my food served on stone cold plates.'

'Sorry, Pa,' Ellie said again.

'All right,' her father conceded, but not referring to her apology. 'All right, so you're only a child, and so you find it's just one more thing. But you cannot have enough reminding. Your mother, may God rest her soul, your mother in all her born days never once served a hot meal on a cold plate. And if you're to try and fill her shoes, which I very much doubt you'll ever do, but if you're to be even half the woman that she was, may God have mercy on her, then you'll need all the reminding I can give you.'

From the silence that followed, Ellie gathered her father had finished with her, so she climbed down from her chair and hurried up to her father's place.

'Here,' she said, 'give me your plate, Pa. I can hot it on the hob.'

'Heat it, child,' her father sighed. 'Hot it indeed. You heat plates, not hot them. And you needn't bother, for it's too late. The soup's ruined.'

But he ate it all the same, Ellie noticed, as she hurried back to her chair. On her way past him, Dermot stuck a foot out and Ellie fell to the floor. The 'broth' sniggered.

'Be careful,' her father said, glaring up from his bowl. 'You want to watch where you put your feet.'

There was no way to keep the food as hot as their father liked. Ellie knew this well, although she was barely five and a half years old, because she and Patsy had talked endlessly about the problem as they sat up in their cot while their father and the 'broth' played cards below them in the living room. Between them they could think of no way to get the food Mrs MacDonagh had cooked that afternoon, and the plates she had left in the stove, from the kitchen to the table at dinner time without something getting cold.

'We need a trolley,' Patsy told her once. 'Like we saw in the magazine. If only we had a trolley. One on wheels.'

But to have a trolley they needed money, their father's money, and when Patsy suggested the idea to him, their father laughed and asked them where they expected him to find that sort of money.

And so something was always cold. Something was always not quite hot or right enough for their father, be it the plates, the pie, or the potatoes. Today it was the plates.

'It's such a simple thing, boys, wouldn't you say?' their father asked, opening the subject up. 'To keep things which are already hot warm at the very least.'

The 'broth' stared down the table at Ellie, and Ellie stared right back at them. She was already determined that nothing should ever frighten her.

'Now take this meatloaf, boys,' her father announced after a long silence, for no-one talked unless directly addressed by the head of the family. 'This meatloaf which that poor Mrs MacDonagh has cooked for us today, God help her. You, Dermot, and Fergal. You're both old enough to remember your mother's meatloaf. And wasn't it just the best meatloaf you had ever tasted?'

The two eldest of the 'broth' agreed with their father, nodding and grinning at him with their mouths full.

'Ah but poor Mrs MacDonagh, you see,' their father continued. 'Sure hasn't she enough on her plate without hearing complaints from the likes of us? Still, you'd have to say she can't cook a meatloaf. Not like your poor dead mother, me boys. May the Lord have mercy on her soul, and that's for sure.'

He looked down the table and held up his plate, as did the 'broth'. Ellie had barely started her own meal, but now she and Patsy had to get up, as was their required duty, to collect all the dirty crockery and bring in the pudding. It was a rice pudding.

'Dear God above us,' her father sighed. 'I sometimes think with the amount of this stuff we have to eat we'll all turn into rice puddings!' Nonetheless, he and the broth ate their pudding and then, pushing their chairs back, got up and left the two youngest to do the dishes.

Ellie stood on a chair at the sink to wash up, while Patsy waited patiently beside her on the floor, taking the plates carefully from her and drying them.

'Would you like to hear a story?' he asked his sister. 'The one you like? The one Madame tells you?'

'Yes please,' said Ellie. 'The one about the house.'

It was the favourite of both.

'Once upon a time,' Patsy began, 'in an old town, in an old street, there stood a very old 'ouse.' Patsy loved to imitate Madame.

Ellie laughed. 'Go on,' she said.

'Once upon a time,' her brother began again, 'in an old town, in an old street, there stood a very old 'ouse, such a grand 'ouse, the sort of 'ouse you do not find nowadays . . . '

Nanny stood on the bridge that spanned the ornamental lake and looked back at the beautiful house that had been her home for the last thirty years.

'Well, child,' she said to Artemis who was standing by her side dropping pebbles into the still water, 'I must say it's going to seem a little odd not living here any more.'

'Why are you going?' Artemis asked. 'You don't have to go.'

'Oh yes I do, dear,' Nanny answered grimly. 'I've been given my marching orders. The new broom is sweeping very clean.'

Artemis realized this was a reference to her new step-mother, but she preferred to try and keep dropping her gathered pebbles into the centre of the splash made by the last one she had dropped. Her nanny had other ideas and took her by the hand.

'Come along, child,' she ordered, 'and stop doing that.'

Together they walked slowly up towards the great house, Artemis lagging slightly behind to try and avoid conversation.

'I really don't know,' Nanny was saying ahead of her. 'If you ask me, it's just change for change's sake. First the nursery floor, then a new governess, then poor Rosie demoted to the kitchens – '

'Why was Rosie sent to the kitchens, Nanny?' Artemis asked. 'Was it because of Mima?'

'It most certainly was, child,' Nanny replied. 'Why else do you think? No, I really don't know, so I don't. It's just change for the sake of it.' She slowed down and looked up at the house now looming high above them. 'I must say,' she sighed. 'I did always think I'd end my days here, I must say.'

'Where are you going, Nanny?' Artemis asked. 'Can I come with you?'

The old woman looked round at the child and smiled, suddenly touched. 'Don't be silly, dear,' she said. 'You don't want to come with old Nanny.'

'Yes I do,' Artemis replied, having spotted her stepmother, sitting up on the stone balustrade, slowly swinging her shapely legs and smoking a cigarette. 'I hate this place.'

'Hullo you two!' the second Lady Deverill called down. 'No prizes for guessing what you two have been up to! Hatching more little plots, I'll be bound!'

Artemis and Nanny started to make their way across to the wing. The second Lady Deverill hopped off her perch and wandered down the steps after them.

'I'm having a small lunch party tomorrow!' she called, as she caught them up. 'And one of your godmothers is coming, my sweet.' She touched Artemis lightly on the shoulder as she said the last word, and throwing away her lipstick-stained cigarette butt, fell into step beside them. 'I think it would be fun if you were there, don't you Nanny?' Artemis's stepmother continued, having tapped Artemis again rather sharply on the shoulder as she said 'you'. 'Your godmother says she hasn't seen you in an age.'

'Which particular godmother is this, Lady Deverill?' Nanny asked. 'Her Grace the Duchess of Wells perhaps?'

'Lady Diana Lanchester,' Lady Deverill replied sharply, before bending down to make her face level with Artemis. 'A great friend of the first Lady Deverill's. Of sweety-pie's moth-er.' As always, she carefully split a word into two distinct parts, dropping her voice in a conspiratorial way, as if uttering a mild obscenity.

Then she stood back up. 'Have her downstairs and ready at a quarter past twelve, Nanny.' She smiled at her stepchild and then for the last time dug her long finger sharply in Artemis's shoulder, but Artemis didn't flinch.

' 'By-eeee!' her stepmother sing-songed gaily as she wandered off. 'Don't be lay-et!'

At twelve fourteen the following midday, Nanny left Artemis, dressed in her favourite old sailor dress and dark blue stockings, in the charge of Porter, the new butler, who then escorted the child into the drawing room.

'The Lady Artemis,' the butler announced gravely, but after a brief stare at the new arrival everyone resumed their conversations.

The new Lady Deverill was the centre of a group by the fireplace, smoking her habitual cigarette and laughing at something a handsome man by her side was saying. Artemis then saw her father standing by his favourite window, in the company of a tall dark-haired woman, whom Artemis found to be staring back at her. She saw the woman summon a footman and point at her, and the footman duly arrived to collect Artemis and take her over to her father and his friend.

Artemis followed the footman across the faded rug, behind the backs of the guests. She failed, however, to avoid her stepmother.

'Gracious me, sweetie!' she laughed rather too loudly, to attract the attention of her court. 'But what *has* Nanny put you in? What is that?' She laughed again, and Artemis stared back at her, blank-faced.

'It's my favourite dress,' she said. 'Stepmother.'

'Well, I think it's high time you stopped looking like something out of the last century, don't you, my sweet?' her stepmother said. 'We'll get Papa to buy you something a little bit more *à la mode*. Yes?'

46

Artemis just stared at her, then bobbing a curtsey, turned away and continued on her interrupted progress.

'Hullo,' the dark-haired woman said, introducing herself. 'I'm Diana Lanchester, one of your godmothers.'

'How do you do?' Artemis curtsied again, and then stared up at the beautiful and elegant woman.

'And I should pay absolutely no attention to your stepmother if I were you,' she laughed. 'I think you look like an absolute stunner, don't you, Bunjy?'

Her father grunted in reply, while Artemis frowned to herself, privately amazed that anyone should call her father, of all people, by a name as funny as Bunjy.

'I don't suppose you remember me,' her godmother said, taking another glass of champagne.

'No I don't,' Artemis said. 'Not a bit.'

'Why should you?' her godmother replied. 'I've been in America, which was the greatest fun. Much more fun than England,' she confided. 'Not nearly so darned stuffy. Tell you what, we'll go there together one day, I'll take you. You'll love it. It really is *fun*.'

'Some chap or other told me once,' Artemis's father suddenly said, 'that somebody or other discovered America before Columbus or whoever it was who did, but decided it was best to keep it under his hat.'

Diana laughed uproariously. 'Oh Bunjy you're wonderful!' she said. 'You always get things so wrong!'

Artemis frowned to herself once more, as in all her young life she had never heard her father say anything which was meant to be even remotely funny.

At lunch, she sat next to her godmother who told Artemis all about her late mother.

'We were the best of friends, you know,' she said. 'And your mother was the best horsewoman I have ever seen. Quite glorious out hunting. Always took her own line, kept her horses fresh, and never jumped anything unless it was absolutely necessary. But when we were young, she and I used to get up to the most dreadful pranks.'

Diana Lanchester began to tell Artemis about some of their escapades and soon had the child laughing quite helplessly, which earned a baleful glare down the table from the new Lady Deverill.

'Do eat up, sweetie,' she called to Artemis. 'And don't laugh with food in your mouth, please!'

Artemis was quite sure she had committed no such breach of nursery discipline, but even so was careful not to laugh out loud again.

'You know, when I was your age,' Diana whispered, 'at dos like this, your mother and I used to stick our food up the legs of our drawers.'

Artemis did her best not to burst out laughing once more, even though she had no food in her mouth.

'Your grandfather caught us once,' Diana Lanchester continued, 'during a rather grand lunch for a Russian prince. Of course we thought we were for it. But in fact he wasn't even cross. He agreed the food was so awful he asked us if we wouldn't mind hiding some of his.'

This time Artemis failed to control herself, and was forced to bury her laugh in her napkin.

'Diana —' her stepmother coo-ed down the table. 'If that child is sick from laughing I shall hold you responsible.'

'Quite right too, Katherine,' Diana Lanchester smiled back at her hostess. 'But I don't think she will be. This goddaughter of mine is a splendid laugher. In fact she's quite splendid altogether. So splendid that I declare my godchild is an absolute motto.'

'You'll never get higher praise than that,' said a man the other side of Artemis. 'If Diana thinks you're a motto, that's tops.'

'Another thing your mother and I did,' Diana went on, obviously enjoying defying her hostess, 'was to hang all the chamber pots outside the third floor windows, just as Queen Mary arrived for her stay. Luckily neither your grandmother nor Queen Mary saw them, but your grandfather did. But then he never missed a trick. Soon as the royal visitor had gone, he called us in and told us never to do such a thing again. Queen Mary had such an eye for antiques, you see, if she'd seen them, she'd have gone off with the lot. Royal privilege, did you know that? If they admire something, you darned well have to give it 'em!'

By now Artemis was quite helpless with laughter, and had to put her napkin to her face in case she made too much noise.

'What fun to hear Artemis laugh,' her stepmother's voice floated down the table. 'She's such a serious child. I didn't know she *had* a sense of humour.'

'That's probably because you never say anything amusing, Katherine, darling,' Diana replied.

The gentleman on the other side of Artemis laughed at that, but also into his napkin, adding 'bravo' in a low voice.

Diana was about to resume her conversation when once again her hostess cut in, addressing her stepdaughter with a glittery smile. 'Did you enjoy your lunch, my sweet?'

'Yes, thank you,' Artemis replied.

'Isn't she sweet?' Katherine Deverill asked her guests generally. 'But Artemis isn't just sweet, she's also a bit of a farmer. She keeps hens, isn't that clever? And that was one of her's we've just eaten. Wasn't it quite delicious? Well worth all the trouble she went to, I'd say, of mending the silly thing's leg.'

Artemis stared down the table at her stepmother, who was smiling brightly at her.

'It even had a name, that one, didn't it, what was it now?' she asked.

Artemis said nothing.

'Yes it did,' her stepmother went on. 'Let me see. What was it called? You know the one with the broken leg?'

'Jemima,' Artemis whispered, her eyes fixed on her lace table mat.

'Speak up, sweetie,' Katherine Deverill said, 'I can't hear you.'

'Jemima,' Artemis said firmly. 'Her name was Jemima.'

'Jemima, of course.' The whole table for some reason had fallen silent. 'And wasn't Jemima delicious, everyone?' Katherine Deverill smiled round at her guests.

'You have to feed them corn,' Artemis said to her godmother. 'That's what makes them taste so good. Rosie told me. You have to feed them lots of corn.'

Immediately there was a loud laugh of relief from the guests, who at once took it that the child had come to terms with her charges' ultimate fate.

'Well done,' her godmother said to her, looking at her pale face intently. 'You really are a motto. And don't worry if you can't eat your pud. I can stick it up the leg of my drawers.'

As soon as lunch was over, Nanny came and collected Artemis for her walk.

'I hope you ate up,' she said, sitting her on the stairs to change the child's shoes. 'I hope you didn't fiddle with your food.'

'No I didn't, I didn't ate up,' Artemis told her.

'Chicken, wasn't it?' Nanny said. 'Cook told me, chicken.'

Artemis said nothing, suddenly feeling sick and faint.

'We'll go down the back way,' Nanny told her, 'and out through the kitchen gardens.'

She took Artemis down a back flight of stairs and along a corridor which ran under one of the colonnades, and then through the kitchen wing, along another long corridor with rooms in which Artemis had never been.

Someone ran up the corridor behind them. 'Nanny?' the voice called. 'Wait!'

It was Rosie, red-faced from running, and from the heat of the kitchens.

'We haven't got long, Rosie,' Nanny said. 'So you'd better hurry please, or we'll be for it.'

Rosie took Artemis by the hand and led her down the corridor to a small room right at the end. She stopped outside the door.

'Listen, your ladyship,' she said. 'Listen.' Then she grinned at Nanny.

Artemis listened as she was told. She heard nothing at all.

'Stupid thing,' Rosie said, with another grin, then kicked the door.

Now Artemis heard something, something feathery shaking itself, and then clucking, in a low, solemn cluck. She turned to Rosie. 'Don't be silly, it can't be,' she gasped, her voice faltering.

'Don't be silly?' Rosie echoed with a laugh. 'You 'ave a look then.'

Artemis opened the door. There in a pool of sunlight which flooded the storeroom stood a fat brown chicken with one corkscrew leg. She rushed in and gathered her beloved hen to her, burying her face in its feathers, as the hen began to squawk with surprise and excitement.

'However did you *do* it, Rosie?'

'Changed it for another, didn't I?' Rosie told her proudly. 'Cook wasn't 'avin' any of that nonsense. She knew what her ladyship was up to, we all did, and we thought it was quite disgustin'.'

'That's quite enough of that, thank you, Rosie,' Nanny said firmly.

'So did you, Nanny,' Rosie protested. 'You said yourself it was a terrible thing to do.'

'Well, of course,' Nanny agreed. 'I mean serving up a one-legged chicken in front of all those guests. I never heard the like.'

'What a way of putting it, Nanny,' said Rosie, laughing in disbelief.

'I can't really thank you enough, Rosie,' Artemis told her.

'You don't 'ave to, Lady Artemis,' said Rosie, and she smiled. 'The look on your face is enough.'

Artemis looked at her and then, suddenly and quite accountably, burst into tears.

1923

3

It was Ellie Milligan's intention never to be caught crying in public again. Ever since that night when, with their father away inspecting a distant building site, they had been left alone in the house for the first time, and the 'broth' had decided to wreak mayhem.

From somewhere Fergal had got hold of a bottle of hooch, and the three eldest sat round the kitchen table getting their first taste of hard liquor, and smoking their way through a packet of Camel cigarettes, while Ellie and Patsy, locked into the room with them, were forced to watch. Ellie could sense there was going to be bad trouble, and it wasn't long in coming. Patsy was naturally selected as the target.

'Let's black him,' Fergal suddenly announced, when they had all but drunk their way through the bottle. 'Let's take all the little bastard's clothes off, and see how he looks as a nigger.'

'No!' Ellie shouted. 'No you leave Patsy alone! You leave him alone, do you hear!'

The 'broth' paid her no attention, but sat looking at their chosen victim, with crooked smiles on all their faces.

'He's got lips like a nigger,' Dermot said.

'*She's* got lips like a nigger,' Fergal corrected.

'No,' said Mike. 'She's got lips like a *negress*.'

Patsy was standing quite still, back against the sink, watching his bully-boy brothers with his big dark eyes, as they stared stupidly back at him. Fergal started to stand, pushing back his chair, and as he did so, Ellie made a bolt for the door.

Dermot got there before her. 'And where do you

think you're going, sis?' he asked. 'To fetch a police-man, maybe?'

'Go away!' Ellie yelled. 'Just leave me alone!'

She scrabbled at the door in one last and futile effort to unlock the door, but Dermot pulled her back.

'What shall we do with this little vixen, eh?' Dermot asked, twisting Ellie's arm up high behind her until, unable to bear the pain any longer, she started to cry.

'Don't you ever do anything else 'cept grizzle?' Mike asked, pulling her hair. 'All you and sister Patsy do is just *grizzle.*'

'Shut her under the stairs,' Fergal ordered.

'No!' screamed Ellie. 'No, not under the stairs, please no!'

'Shut her under the stairs.'

Mike and Dermot dragged her off, still crying and screaming, while Fergal held Patsy by both his elbows, which he had pulled behind Patsy's back. Dermot opened the half-sized door and Mike shoved Ellie into the pitch darkness.

'You can grizzle and yell 's'much as you like under there, sis,' Dermot said. ' 'Cos we're not lettin' you out till you learn to shut up.'

They bolted the door closed, top and bottom, and left Ellie crammed tight against all the junk that was stuffed into the tiny space. She banged her fists against the door, and yelled and screamed, but the 'broth' had gone back to the kitchen.

They left her in there, wedged among the wooden boxes and brooms, and bric-a-brac, barely able to move one way or the other, for the next two hours, while they stripped Patsy naked, covered him all over with shoe polish, and locked him out the front of the house for a while to see what it was like being a naked little 'nigger boy' in Westfield Drive.

That was the night Ellie vowed she would never cry in front of anyone again as she lay among the boxes. While Patsy silently and privately swore his revenge as he tried to scrub himself clean.

Now ten years old, Ellie was more or less expected to run the house day by day. She was rarely at school, kept away constantly by a variety of excuses dreamed up by her father and brothers who all decided that an education was of less use to Ellie than a clean and tidy home was to them. Even on Sundays she was expected to spend her day scrubbing, cleaning, cooking and tidying, once the family had attended Mass.

On this particular Sunday, Ellie had finished all her chores by mid-afternoon, and had the house to herself. The 'broth' were all out in the park, where they would remain until tea time, and Patsy was over with a boy called Ed, who had befriended Patsy at school. Ed was thin and undersized like Patsy, but he was fit and strong, because he boxed. And he was now teaching young Patsy, unbeknownst to his elder brothers, the rudiments of the noble art of self-defence.

Best of all, her father was six blocks away, playing poker at Harry Reilly's. That was his Sunday ritual: over to Harry's for cards as soon as lunch was eaten, and back at exactly a quarter after six, to read the Sunday papers and then sleep off the drink. Ellie understood nothing about prohibition. All she knew was that her father and his friends were never short of anything to drink.

Three o'clock exactly. The old wooden case-clock at the foot of the stairs where Ellie was standing chimed the hour, as if to tell her she had two hours to herself before the 'broth' returned, and three and a quarter hours before her father did likewise. Plenty of time to go quietly upstairs, take the key down from behind the faded watercolour of the lakes of Killarney, and slip it into the lock of her dead mother's bedroom. And to step into the shrine. For that's what her mother's room was, a reliquary for a woman gone, a monument to a long-dead wife. Nothing had been moved, and nothing had been changed, not since that fatal October day, when Ellie had been born and her mother had died. It was a room no-one ever came into, except the dead woman's husband, who visited it religiously every Sunday morning before Mass, locking himself in for an hour, while, Ellie guessed, he dusted and tidied the shrine he had created, and prayed for the soul of the one departed.

Every time Ellie crept into her dead mother's room, she knew she should not be there, and she would hesitate on the threshold of the airless room, while the skin on her scalp prickled with a guilty excitement. She hadn't meant to find the key. It wasn't as if she had searched for it, determined to see what lay behind the forever locked door. She had found it quite by accident, due to her diligence. If she had not learned to clean so thoroughly she would never have taken each and every picture off the wall to dust both the picture and the wall behind.

And there was the key, carefully jammed into the frame of the old watercolour. Ellie knew at once which door it must unlock, because the room at the end of the landing was the only room kept locked. But still, for week after week, she never dared see if she was right, because she was afraid of what she might find within.

For a long time she imagined she might open the door and see the body of her mother, stretched out in death on her bed, her arms folded across her chest, her eyes still open and staring at the ceiling. She knew that dead people could be kept in this state because the man who lived next door to Mrs MacDonagh worked in an undertakers, and Ellie had heard him talking about it to Mrs MacDonagh. So it was many weeks before Ellie dared try the key in the lock.

And when she did, she eased open the door, but not before she had shut her eyes. For an age she simply had not dared open them, until finally, unable to resist any longer, she opened and shut them again once and very quickly.

But there was nothing on the bed. Nobody and no body. Just a shiny pink counterpane, with a nightgown folded neatly in the middle of the bolster. Over the back of a chair in one corner lay a dress, neatly hanging, while on the seat of chair lay a small pile of immaculate underthings. The dressing table was laid out with hairbrushes, mirrors and small mother-of-pearl boxes, and on the table by the bed was a rosary, a missal and a photograph.

Arthur Leopold of County Cork had taken the picture, and the first time Ellie had tiptoed into the bedroom she had stood for a long time staring at the photograph, because it was the first time she had ever seen the likeness of her dead mother. She was beautiful, small of face but with big dark eyes, just like Patsy's, and very serious looking, just like Ellie herself. Ellie tried to imagine how her mother must have felt as she had left Ireland by boat, to sail the Atlantic and marry a man she had met only a handful of times. Looking even more closely at the photograph and the innocence in her mother's eyes, Ellie had decided that her mother must have felt very shy.

Today she closed the door quietly behind her, and tiptoed over to the polished wooden closet, as she always did, to look at her mother's dresses. She had learned when she had held the first costume up against her, that her mother had been small, hardly, it seemed, an inch or two taller than Ellie was now. On subsequent visits, as she had grown bolder, Ellie had started trying some of her mother's clothes on, first over her own dress, and then over just her underclothes. They were lovely clothes, beautifully made from fine materials, and if Ellie took a tuck with her hand at the back of the dresses, and turned the hems up a good six or nine inches, looking in the dressing mirror she could get more than a fair impression of how she might look once she too was a young woman.

At the back of the closet on a separate hook hung her mother's wedding gown. Ellie had often taken it down before, but had never dared try it on. But today, with more time at her disposal, she could no longer resist the adventure, and in a moment she was out of her own plain black Sunday dress, with its detachable white collar and cuffs, and into the sumptuous white silk which had clothed her dead mother once and for just a few short hours.

She found her mother's wedding shoes, and her headpiece and veil as well. And then when she was fully dressed, she shut the closet door over and stood looking at herself in the mirror which was on the other side. She stood dreaming, trying to imagine what it must be like to walk up the aisle to the side of a man who was waiting to marry you, and so enthralled was she with her imaginings that she never heard him. She never heard the front door close, nor his foot fall on the stairs, nor even the bedroom door slowly opening behind her.

And then suddenly she saw his image in the looking glass.

'And what's this?' her father said, almost too quietly. 'What have we here then?'

Ellie turned and looked at him, at a loss for any words. 'Pa,' was all she managed. 'I didn't hear you.'

'No,' said her father, 'I should imagine you didn't. And I should imagine from looking at you, you didn't imagine I'd be home so soon either.'

'I can explain,' Ellie said. 'Really I can.'

'Is that so?' her father asked. 'Is that really so. Well now. Well now I'd often wondered what you got up to when I left you here.'

'Pa – really – '

'And now I know, Eleanor. Now I know.'

He said nothing more for a while, leaving Ellie to stand waiting his instructions as he walked slowly round the room, as if to make sure nothing else had been violated.

'You know full well you're not allowed in here, Eleanor,' he said finally turning back to her. 'No-one's allowed in here, you know that perfectly well.'

'I know, Pa,' Ellie replied. 'I just didn't think – '

'You just didn't think,' her father interrupted. 'That's about the size of it.'

'I didn't think there was any harm,' Ellie finished.

Her father looked at her and nodded, which was a sure sign that he disagreed with what she had just said.

'If Harry hadn't been rushed off to the hospital with chest pains today,' he continued, 'then I'd still be at a loss to know what my only daughter gets up to when my back is turned.'

'I'll get out of these things,' Ellie volunteered in the ensuing silence. 'I was only dressing up.'

'Dressing up,' her father said thoughtfully. 'Dressing up.'

'Yes,' Ellie concurred. 'So I'll be out of these things in one minute.'

'No,' said her father suddenly. 'You'll do no such thing. You'll stay as you are and come downstairs with me.'

He took Ellie by her forearm, and marched her down the landing and the painted uncarpeted stairs into the living room, where he sat her in the big chair in the corner.

'You're to sit there, do you hear?' he instructed. 'And you're not to move until I tell you.'

'Why?' Ellie asked, puzzled by the quite unpredictable run of events. She had expected violence, she had thought her father would shout and roar at her, she was certain he would beat her. But he had done none of these things. Instead he had kept his temper, and not even threatened to raise his hand.

'Why am I to sit here, please?' Ellie repeated her question since her father had paid it no attention first time round.

'Because I want the boys to see how pretty you are,' her father told her. 'And to see if you remind them of anybody.'

It was over an hour before the eldest boys came home from the park, during which time Ellie was made to sit quite still and not move. After such a long wait, Ellie was so stiff and so fearful, that she was almost relieved to hear them, laughing and jeering at each other, and then greeting their father, whom they were surprised to see home.

'I've another surprise for you, me boys,' their father said. 'Next door in the living room.'

The 'broth' came through, followed closely by the tall figure of their father, who stood right behind his boys as they stood and stared at their sister.

'Stand up, Eleanor,' her father instructed. 'So they may see how you are.'

Ellie stood, all but swamped by her dead mother's wedding dress.

'Sure it's a little large,' her father said, 'but the impression's there all right. Wouldn't you say so, Fergal? Wouldn't you say there's enough of an impression there to remind you of someone? Of someone we all loved very dearly?'

'Yes, Pa,' Fergal answered, staring hard at Ellie. 'She looks the image of Mother.'

'I knew you'd see it, me boy,' his father smiled, putting an arm round his eldest's shoulder. 'Couldn't you be looking at herself? Isn't that all but a miniature of your poor dead mother, God rest her? All but a miniature. All but for her goodness and her grace.'

'I don't get it, Pa,' Dermot said. 'What's Ellie doing all dressed up in Mother's clothes?'

'Yes,' Mike added, 'what in heck's she doing, Pa?'

'She's thinking, my boys,' their father told them, 'she's thinking of taking the place of your mother, because she's thinking she's become every bit as pretty as her, God rest her soul indeed. And every bit as good.'

'She can never be as pretty as our mother,' Fergal said. 'She could never be half as pretty. Not even a quarter.'

'Ah well,' sighed his father. 'Sure you know young girls. Don't they just think the world of themselves?'

'She could never be as good as our mother neither,' Dermot growled, his eyes blazing with hate for his sister. 'Jeeze – if that wasn't mother's dress, I'd tear it right off her.'

'What in heck is she wearing it for anyway, Pa?' Fergal shouted, shaking off his father's half restraining hand and moving threateningly close to Ellie. 'What are you doing in Mother's wedding dress, eh? You little scut! You tell me now, or I'll pull every hair from your head!' Fergal already had hold of Ellie's long brown hair, and was jerking her head backwards.

'Come now, boy,' his father said, finally pulling his eldest son away, but not for a good half minute. 'You know that's no way to treat a *lady*.'

Ellie saw the mockery in her father's eyes, as she saw the hate. In all the eyes that were watching her, that's all she could see. Undiluted hate.

'Why do you hate me?' she asked them, still managing to keep the tears from her eyes. 'What have I ever done that makes you hate me like this?'

'Tell her, Fergal,' her father said tonelessly. 'Tell her what she did that makes us feel no love for her. You tell her, boy.'

Fergal walked slowly across to Ellie and put his face right up to her's. 'I'll tell you what you did, Eleanor Milligan,' he hissed. 'You killed our mother.'

'How could I have killed her, Madame?'

Ellie sat in the half-light of their neighbour's drawing room, the dark curtains pulled some of the way across the windows to keep out the sunlight. Madame Gautier did not like sunlight, as she had frequently informed her young visitor.

'You should ignore what he say, *chèrie*,' Madame replied. 'He is *sadiste*.'

'What is that, please?'

'What your father is, child. Now 'ave a bon-bon.'

Madame Gautier held the small silver tray of chocolates out for Ellie, who unable to resist, got up and helped herself to another one.

'Besides,' Madame added, when she herself had also taken a sweet, 'it is a complete nonsense.'

'What is, Madame?'

'To say you killed your mother.'

Madame rearranged her skirt as she sat back in her chair. The skirt was silk lined and made a lovely sound whenever Madame moved, which Madame still found intoxicating, even to this day, a day long after she had 'retired' from the theatre. Ellie also thrilled to hear it, for it sounded so glamorous, and put her in mind of some of the stories Madame had told her of her early days on the stage.

But today Ellie's mind was on other matters, such as what her brothers had meant by their accusation.

'I just don't understand, Madame,' Ellie confessed, 'I never even knew my mother.'

'I shall speak to that father of yours,' Madame sighed, raising a small glass half full of dark amber liquid to her lipsticked mouth. 'I shall go and tell 'im what a perfect swine he is.'

'Oh no, Madame,' Ellie frowned. 'You can't do that. He hates me coming here. He says you give me ideas. Ideas I really shouldn't have.'

'What nonsense.'

'I know. But if you went and *called*.'

'Yes, *chèrie*. I know.'

Madame put her glass down to put a cigarette in her holder. Ellie lit it for her with a match from a small silver box.

'*Merci, mon petit chou*,' said Madame.

'I still don't understand how I'm meant to have killed my mother,' Ellie frowned.

'You did not,' said Madame with a faint snort. ' 'Ow could you? You were a *bébé*. What 'appens is women 'ave *bébés* and sometimes they die. This is a fact of our life! But your mother she 'ad too many *bébés*. She did not want to, but the church – the church say she must, and so do your father. Your mother was too fine, *très*

64

petite, comme toi. She was not like an 'orse who can 'ave *bébés* every year! She was so small! So fine! And I say to your father, I say you will kill 'er! I say. As if with your own 'and!'

'I don't understand?' Ellie was becoming more and more confused.

'Your mother did not need to be always *enceinte, n'est ce pas?* There are little what do we say? little preventions. There are these ways. And they are *très necessaire*, if we women are not to die like this.'

'How, Madame?' Ellie asked, still entirely baffled. 'If women are not to die how?'

'Look,' Madame sighed hugely. 'There is no need for anyone to die like this. And most certainly not your mother, and not you. If your father 'e 'ad listened to the nurse and called for the doctor and not for the priest – puh!' Madame shrugged and pouted her lips. 'But your father –' she leaned forward and whispered at Ellie. 'Your father did not want to pay for the doctor, while the priest 'e comes free! If 'e 'ad called the doctor then I say that no-one dies!'

'So why does my father say I killed her?'

'*Ah bon,*' Madame said, putting out her cigarette. 'I tell you why. If you are 'aving a *bébé,* and there is danger, the church say you must die, and the 'usband keep the *bébé.* Not 'is wife – but the *bébé!* This is good for the men, yes? But not so good for the children who *soudainment* they 'ave no mother! And it is not at all good for the mothers who *soudainment* are dead! It is a rule of the church, the mother must die. And who make the rules? The men of course!' Madame lit another cigarette and blew a long curl of blue smoke upwards from the side of her mouth.

'So the church killed my mother?' Ellie asked, cautiously. Madame nodded. '*Oui,*' she said. '*Vraiment.*'

'Then I shall never go to church again,' Ellie vowed.

Madame looked at her through a veil of smoke which she fanned away with a jewelled hand. 'No, no,' she said. 'I think so. I think you do.'

'No, Madame,' Ellie insisted. 'I won't ever go to church again. Not ever.'

'You will go to church, and there's an end of it, do you hear me?'

'Yes, Father.'

'Well?'

Ellie said nothing, deciding to stare down at the polished wood floor instead.

'If you do not go to church, child, you will be in the most deadly and mortal sin.'

'Yes, Father.'

'And when you die, you will be as nothing. You will be as worthless as a piece of dirt on the sole of my shoe. You will be consigned straight to hell, where you will roast in eternal agony, never again to know any peace, and never to look upon the face of God. Is that what you really want, child?'

'No, Father,' Ellie replied, without looking up. 'I just don't want ever to go to church again.'

'But why ever not, my child?'

By now the priest was becoming exasperated with the child who in turn was becoming ever more stubborn by the minute. It was a boiling hot morning, he had three other appointments before lunch, and his head ached dully from the excess of Jack Daniels he had drunk the night before with the child's father, who had been beside himself with rage when he had arrived at the Presbytery.

'She shut herself in her bedroom all day, Tom!' Pat Milligan had ranted. 'I'll not brook such disobedience! How dare she! I'll not have any child of mine disobeying not only me, but turning her back on God's own holy ordinance!'

'She's a little girl, Pat,' the priest had tried to reassure him. 'Sure children get all sorts of crazy ideas, all sorts of ideas so they do.'

He had then put the bottle of whisky out on the table, in the hope that after a couple of shots, Pat Milligan's rage would abate, and they could talk instead about the Red Sox's chances in next week's match against the New York Giants.

But Pat Milligan was in no mood to be mollified. 'You're to come and see the child tomorrow, Tom,' he ordered. 'And you're to scare the living daylights out of her, do you hear? I want her back at Mass next Sunday, and if you can't persuade her, then this belt of mine'll have to do the talking!'

The priest took his handkerchief out and wiped the beads of sweat from his brow. It seemed there was nothing he could do to persuade the child to cease her disobedience, nothing he could say which would frighten her sufficiently for her to come to her senses. She just sat there, mostly in silence, staring down at the floor, with her hands clasped tightly between her knees.

'You know what will happen to you, child, if you continue to disobey your father,' he said wearily, 'and if you continue to fly in the face of God's will.'

'Nothing that hasn't happened before, Father,' Ellie replied, almost as wearily, but still refusing to look up.

'Why, child?' the priest said, deciding on another approach, one of pained bewilderment. 'You've always been such a good little girl. Such an obedient and faithful member of the flock. So I find this, well, this rebellion of yours, for that's what it is, isn't it? Some kind of rebellion now. It just doesn't make any sense. Unless of course it's something you've done.' The priest leaned forward, in his best confessional manner. 'Something you yourself have done and which you're afraid to confess.'

'No, Father,' Ellie replied, trying to manoeuvre herself away from the smell of stale whisky and nicotine. 'It's nothing that I have done.'

'Ah,' said the priest. 'Then it's something someone has done to you, yes?'

'Yes,' Ellie agreed.

'And who might this wicked person be?' the priest asked.

'You,' said Ellie, finally looking at him straight in his watery red eyes. 'You and my father.'

The priest frowned and pulled at his collar to try and gain some respite from the suffocating heat. Then he tried smiling back at the serious-faced child, for this must surely be a tease. Because he couldn't for the life of him imagine what he personally could have done to her. That brute of a father, certainly. But himself? Never.

'Come on now, child,' he said. 'You'll have to do better than that. What in heaven's name has this poor old priest ever done to you, eh?'

'You killed my mother,' Ellie told him. 'Instead of calling the doctor, my father called you, and you and the church killed her.'

The priest frowned and sighed, and then tried reasoning with the child, but only half-heartedly, his enthusiasm for this particular subject having long gone, so often had he had to cover this ground. Finally, and seeing he was getting nowhere, overcome by an incipient lethargy induced by the excesses of the previous night and exacerbated by the heat, the priest slowly rose to his feet and picked up his hat.

'Then there's nothing more I can say to you, child,' he sighed, wiping his sweating brow with his hand. 'There is nothing I can do or say to save you from the wrath of God, or indeed from the wrath of your own father, poor man.'

But for all Patrick Milligan's wrath, and for all the constant beatings he administered to Ellie with his thick leather belt, he was unable to break her will. Ellie never returned to her parish church. Even when her father beat Patsy for no reason other than to force his daughter to change her mind, Ellie stood firm, as privately Patsy had made her swear to do.

'It's no good, Father,' Ellie had said. 'You can beat me till I die, I don't care. Because I would rather die than ever again go to church.'

Finally her father stopped belting her every weekend.

'Very well,' he said, 'but just remember what you are. You are doomed. You and your brother. You both are doomed to the bottomless pits of hell. You're no longer worthy, either of you, of the sight of God.'

Ellie listened, but said nothing, thinking that if indeed there was a God, and if he was anything like her father, then hell and its bottomless pits would be infinitely preferable to so-called heaven.

'You really should be riding a horse,' Artemis's stepmother said to her one morning as they waited for the hounds to move off. 'You're getting far too tall for that pony.'

Artemis knew this to be true, but was more than a little reluctant to part with Paintbox. Bought as a second pony after she had grown out of Buttons, he had proved himself such a marvellous jumper and such a resolute galloper, Artemis couldn't possibly imagine life without him.

'Oh, I know what you're thinking, Artemis,' her stepmother continued. 'I was just the same at your age. You couldn't possibly part with him, there'll never be another animal like him, and when your pony goes, there goes your childhood. Well that's true, up to a point, but these things have to be faced. And the point is you've suddenly grown rather tall and stringy, and as a consequence you look quite ridiculous on that thing.'

'Paintbox can still carry me all day,' Artemis replied. 'He's terribly strong.'

'That's not the point, Artemis,' her stepmother said. 'It's time you moved on to horses. I shall have a word with your father about it. I know he'll agree. He thinks you've become quite the little horsewoman.'

The hounds moved off and her stepmother followed, leaving Artemis to consider her father's compliment. It was the first he had ever paid her. Normally when she had gone well, it had been her horse which had received the praise. 'Pony went well today,' he might say as they dismounted. 'Certainly jumps.' Or after a fast thing, 'That pony certainly keeps you out of trouble, yes? Certainly knows a thing or two, that chap.' But nothing was ever said to the rider.

And yet now, it seemed, he considered her to be a horsewoman. Artemis was completely bewildered. For her stepmother to tell her meant that she and her father must sometimes talk about her, and that her father had undoubtedly on at least one occasion said that he thought Artemis had some ability. And if that was the case, then the idea for Artemis to move up to a horse must surely have sprung from him. Because her stepmother would never have made such a suggestion. Normally all she did was belittle Artemis's riding skills whenever she could.

As she moved off with the other mounted followers, Artemis determined that if her father thought it was time for her to stop riding ponies and learn to hunt on a horse, then so be it. She would make the transition.

'Isn't he a little tall?' Artemis asked, as she stood admiring her fifteenth birthday present, a stunning looking dark brown thoroughbred gelding which Jenkins had been instructed to lead up outside the house as a surprise. Artemis wasn't afraid of riding tall horses, only anxious in case she might still be too short in the leg to get the best out of them. 'He must be at least sixteen hands.'

'He is sixteen hands exactly,' her stepmother informed her. 'And you won't be over-horsed, not since you are going to ride him side-saddle.'

'But – ' Artemis started, appalled at the notion of not being able to ride such a racey looking creature astride.

'No buts, Artemis. It's your father's idea, not mine.' And then the second Lady Deverill turned to Artemis and smiled a small, closed smile. 'I think,' she added, 'that your father wants to be as proud of you as he was of your *moth-er*. So. Happy birthday, my sweet. And as an extra treat, Annellie Clyde is coming to stay for a week to teach you the rudiments.'

And that was that. Artemis's father was away for a week's sport in Leicestershire, and apparently it was expected of Artemis that she should be ready and able to go out and ride her new horse side-saddle alongside her father on his return.

Fortunately Annellie Clyde was an inspired teacher and Artemis, besides being a very talented rider was also an extremely quick learner, so much so that the principles of riding side-saddle were learned by the end of day two, although without the help of Artemis's new horse, Hullabaloo, who had proved himself to be somewhat too fidgety and edgy to be included in the preliminary tuition. But by the morning of the fifth day, rider and horse became a team, and by that afternoon Artemis and her teacher went for a stiff ten-mile hack. On the morning of the sixth day, Hullabaloo and Artemis jumped a line of good hedges in perfect harmony, and by the end of the first week Annellie Clyde considered her pupil ready for her first full day out.

'Whose mad fool idea was this anyway?' Diana Lanchester demanded of her godchild when she saw her mounted on her new horse. 'It would be hardly sensible on a quiet day, but you know how they run here.'

The hunt was met at Parks' Lodge from where, at this time of year provided the scent was good, it was inevitably a red letter day.

'It's all right, Godmother,' Artemis assured her, doing her best to stop Hullabaloo from fidgeting. 'We'll keep at the back.'

'Keep at the back?' her godmother snorted in disbelief. 'On that thing? He looks as if he's about to come under starter's orders at Epsom! You'll get off, if you've any sense!'

'But he's lovely, Godmother!' Artemis protested. 'And he's got the most amazing jump!'

At that moment Hullabaloo suddenly spun and lashed out, nearly catching the horse behind. Artemis sat him well, and quickly brought him back under control.

'Has he seen hounds?' Diana Lanchester demanded. 'He doesn't look as if he's ever seen hounds before! Where in heaven's name did you get him?'

'My father bought him for me,' Artemis replied. 'For my birthday.'

'Nonsense!' her godmother called, as Hullabaloo began to spin again. 'Your father would never be such a damn fool!'

'He did, Godmother!' Artemis called after her, 'I promise!' But her godmother was gone, making her way through the throng of horses to Lord Deverill's side.

Artemis reined her horse back again, but he was becoming more and more strung-up and excited by the minute.

'You do look a picture,' said a voice behind her. 'Someone said they thought for a moment you were your mother.' The second Lady Deverill, also riding side-saddle and turned out in a quite immaculate habit, pulled up alongside Artemis on a bay Artemis hadn't seen before.

'I wish they'd move off,' Artemis confessed, 'before Hullabaloo causes a real hullabaloo.'

'He looks frightfully well,' said her stepmother. 'You really do both look quite the thing.' Then she suddenly dropped her voice and leant slightly forward. 'Your Papa will be *terr-ibly* pleased.'

But Artemis was hardly attending. She was too busy watching her godmother, who had reached her father's side and was having an animated conversation with him, albeit a somewhat one-sided one. Artemis saw her father turn right round in his saddle and stare back to where she was, while her godmother was still haranguing him. Then, just as Diana Lanchester detached herself and began heading back in Artemis's direction, one of the huntsmen blew for hounds to move off, and the day began.

Diana Lanchester didn't catch up with Artemis and her stepmother until Lord Deverill and his huntsmen cast their hounds into a field of kale for the first draw.

'Beautiful morning,' the second Lady Deverill said. 'Perfect scenting weather.'

'I'm not in the slightest bit interested,' Diana Lanchester retorted. 'All I'm interested in is where you found that damn' horse.'

'Mine you mean?' Artemis's stepmother enquired ingenuously. 'This is a new chap. Came from Buffie Stanford's.'

'The horse Artemis is riding, Katherine. Where did it come from?'

'He's lovely, isn't he, Diana? I rather fancied him for myself.'

'Where did he come from?' Diana Lanchester repeated. 'Has he seen hounds?'

'He was passed on to us by a friend, darling,' the second Lady Deverill replied. 'With a known history. But I'm terribly sorry, you see, because he just isn't for sale.'

'I don't want to buy the damn' animal!' Diana Lanchester said, raising her voice, and earning looks of disapproval from the gentlemen nearby. 'All I want to know is what you think you're playing at!'

'Playing at?' Artemis's stepmother laughed. '*Playing* at? Why should I be playing at something, Diana darling?'

'Telling Artemis her father had bought the animal!' Diana Lanchester replied. 'John may be mad, but he'd never buy a horse as hot as that as a first horse for his daughter!'

By now the disapproving looks Diana Lanchester had been earning had turned to ones of open curiosity as those around became intrigued by the confrontation.

'You bought it, didn't you, Katherine?' Diana Lanchester demanded. 'But where from? And why?'

'Darling, if you will persist in raising your voice while the hounds are drawing, sweetie,' the second Lady Deverill sighed, 'John will only send you home.'

'He should send his daughter home, damn it.'

For a moment Artemis thought her godmother was

going to strike her stepmother with her hunting whip, which she was now holding half-raised. But in fact the whip was for Artemis's benefit, and not her stepmother's.

'But if he won't, I will. Artemis,' she said, hooking the end of her whip round Artemis's forearm, 'take that animal back to the stables at once.'

'But Godmother – ' Artemis began to protest.

'This instance, do you hear?' her godmother interrupted.

But it was already too late, because just as Diana Lanchester was issuing her orders, there was a crash of hound music as they found in the kale, and they were away, the fox streaming out of the vegetation and through a large hedge which led to the adjoining field. Artemis's horse whipped round twice, plunged and bucked, and then with Artemis, much to its apparent displeasure, still well on board, took off after the leading group.

The first hedge seemed to pass miles below Artemis as Hullabaloo landed a good ten or twelve feet the other side. Artemis, who had never sat such a prodigious leap on a horse, let alone one taken side-saddle, leaned well back and sat the jump well. Through her reins she felt the horse cock his jaw in the hope he could take hold completely, but having sat enough 'bolts' on both Buttons and Paintbox, Artemis was wise to this, and she quickly shortened up her reins and then relaxed them, confusing the horse quite deliberately. The manoeuvre worked, and by the time the second hedge loomed in front of her, Artemis had some semblance of control.

She knew this hedge well, having jumped it both ways innumerable times. There was a ditch the other side of it, which should present no problems provided they met it on the right stride. Hullabaloo had ideas of his own and put in a short one. Artemis responded by sitting and kicking on hard, which drove the horse at the bottom of the fence so that he would have to take off or run into the obstacle head-on. He took off.

They landed well over the ditch and as Artemis gathered him up, she looked ahead and saw that hounds, her father and his huntsmen were all swinging right and heading towards a line of big hedges in the Vale. Normally Artemis would have responded by kicking on and flying the raspers behind the leading group, for to her way of thinking there was no feeling like it in the world. But today, realizing the problems she might have in controlling her mount let alone in staying on should it prop at a hedge or peck on landing, she decided discretion was the better part of valour and shortening her left rein swung Hullabaloo away in the other direction to take what was known as the Funks' Run, which ran round a long ridge of elms, across the brook at its narrowest point, and then over a good two miles of open ground, with only one reasonable sized open ditch and hedge to be jumped at the bottom of the dip before a long run uphill which led back to the last of the Vale hedges. Artemis had sometimes taken this run when out with her cowardly cousins, although she would always jump the open ditch and hedge while her cousins were fumbling with the gate.

It wasn't until she turned away from the elms that Artemis realized she was not alone. She took a look over her shoulder and saw a horse and rider behind her and at full stretch, but with the sun in her eyes, Artemis couldn't distinguish who it was.

But whoever it was, they were determined to catch Artemis, for when Artemis stole another look she saw the horse behind was really stretching out. This was just what Artemis didn't want, some thruster charging up behind Hullabaloo whom she had just got settled, and trying to make a race of it, particularly with the big hedge fast approaching at the bottom of the dip. So she checked Hullabaloo, and, to her surprise, the horse came back to her, perhaps having now learned to trust his new jockey.

Even so, Artemis had no time to relax or to shout at

whoever it was still charging up beside her to slow down because the hill was beginning to flatten out into the dip and they were fast approaching the big open ditch.

Which was when the other horse got to Hullabaloo's quarters, a big, handsome bay, his bit covered in a white froth, his nostrils wide and red, and his eye set fast on the forthcoming obstacle.

His weight was suddenly on Hullabaloo's flank. Artemis was being purposefully ridden off, across the corner of the hedge towards the closed gate. She dare not look round at who was busily trying to kill her, but shout and scream she could and she did. It made no difference. The big bay three quarterbred was being driven hard into Artemis's lightly framed thoroughbred, and Artemis could feel the distress signals through her hands and seat as the horse shortened its stride in a desperate attempt to find a way out. Which it quite failed to do.

Faced with either crashing into the heavy gatepost or jumping the dark gaping ditch off far too short a stride, Hullabaloo tried to put in an extra stride and met the obstacle entirely wrong. A second later he lay dead on the far side of the hedge, his neck snapped in two, with his young rider lying prostrate in the grass beside him.

The second Lady Deverill, having pulled her horse off Hullabaloo at the last minute, leaving herself just enough time to put him right at the ditch and hedge, didn't even bother to stop and admire her handiwork before riding on up the hill to rejoin the hunt and tell her husband that there seemed to have been a rather fearful accident.

4

Ellie Milligan was scrubbing the back step when there was a knock on the front door. Wiping her hands on her apron, she went to see who was calling so early in the day. It was their neighbour Madame Gautier, dressed in a pale yellow linen coat and dress, with a matching cloche hat.

'I am taking you out,' she announced. 'So 'urry now and change, please.'

'I can't, Madame,' Ellie replied. 'I have all the housework to do, and the shopping.'

'Nonsense,' said Madame. 'Your father is away until the end of the week I know, with the three eldest. So you 'ave no reason to refuse. Now 'urry. I 'ave a cab waiting.'

Madame sat down in Ellie's father's chair, by the unlit fire, and took out a cigarette from her purse, while Ellie stood uncertainly by.

'I cannot wait all the morning,' Madame said, lighting her cigarette. 'You have until the end of this smoke.'

Ellie ran upstairs, threw off her old blouse and skirt and her much darned stockings, and got hurriedly dressed in her Sunday best, yet another variation on the plain black dress with detachable collar and cuffs she had been wearing for as long as she could remember. Then, having quickly brushed her hair, she rushed back downstairs just as Madame was throwing her finished cigarette in the fire.

'Uhhh,' Madame said disapprovingly, as she appraised Ellie. 'This is something I should 'ave done a very long time ago. *Alors. On va.*'

Ellie was now eighteen years old, and in all those years

she had never travelled in a taxi-cab, nor had she ever been into the heart of Boston. She had spent all her formative years within the confines of the outlying suburb of Westfield, where there were few if any shops for ladies. Where she lived, there seemed to be nothing but barbers' shops and grocery stores, drab haberdasheries, hardware stores and endless pawnshops. There were no stores like the ones she could now see flashing past the cab window, fine jewellers and milliners, bookshops and department stores, their windows displaying a variety of goods Ellie had only ever seen in the pictures of second-hand magazines.

'Thank you!' Madame called to the cab driver. 'Stop 'ere if you please!'

The cab drew up outside an enormous emporium in the very heart of the town, and Ellie alighted while Madame paid off the cab. The store was called O'Hara's, of which Ellie had often heard, mostly from Madame, and of which she had, of course, seen photographs in the newspaper advertisements. But nothing had prepared her for the monumental size and sheer glamour of the building. It seemed it was not a shop, or a store, but a palace, full of the stuff of dreams, stocked with fancies and sheer imaginings, desires and private caprices. Ellie felt an elemental thrill as she stepped through the great swing doors, as if she was entering an ancient cathedral rather than a modern monument to commercial enterprise.

'Ready-made,' said Madame, as she guided Ellie towards the elevator. 'I think this is our first port of call, yes? I would 'ave preferred couture, of course. But alas, as you say, we are not madé with money.'

The first dress which was tried on her would have suited Ellie somewhat more than fine. To her it was quite perfect, a light red costume made of silk, which seemed to cling to her like a second skin.

' 'Opeless,' said Madame. 'I do not know what I am thinking. Go please – and take that off at once. Then come with me.'

Back in her drab black dress, Ellie was escorted smartly out of the ready-made department and back into the elevator.

'Have I done something wrong, Madame?' Ellie finally asked, afraid the dream was already over.

'No, no, *chèrie*,' Madame sighed reassuringly. 'No I am the foolish one. You need underclothes! You cannot wear today's dress over such things as you 'ave on!' Madame laughed, ignoring the stares of the elevator's other occupants, and Ellie's quite visible embarrassment. 'You poor child! You cannot feel like a woman in such 'orrible bloomaires!'

Ellie recovered her composure and understood perfectly well what Madame meant once she had tried on her first set of crêpe de Chine camiknickers.

'*Voilà!*' said Madame from her chair in the corner of the well-curtained booth. 'Perfect. You have such a *good* figure!'

Ellie had never really given her shape much thought up until that moment. She was always in such a hurry, jumping out of bed and straight into her workaday clothes, that she had failed to take notice of the fact that she was growing into a very shapely young woman. But now as she stood looking at herself in a full length looking glass, she could see that she had indeed what the magazines described as the perfect figure, firm round breasts, a narrow flat waist, good hips, a small posterior, and long slender legs which were greatly enhanced by the silk stockings the assistant had carefully rolled on to them.

'We will take that, please,' Madame ordered. 'And the chemise and knickaires also, in triple *ninon* I show you in the display case.'

Ellie was ordered to keep her new lingerie on under her old black dress as they made their way back downstairs to the ready-made department. Here Madame rejected the dress Ellie had previously tried on, in favour of a pale blue two piece, with a scalloped and belted waist, a calf-length pleated skirt, a large but neat bow to one side of the neckline, and two very small bows on the elbows of the wrist-length sleeves.

'*Très chic,*' Madame announced. '*Très très chic.* Except for your feet. And your 'ead.'

Shoes were no problem, and Ellie was soon fitted with a pair of navy blue leather shoes, with gently curving two inch heels. The question of her hair, however, brought about a confrontation, Madame arguing that Ellie's long hair, even caught up as it was in a chignon, was completely out of fashion, and quite ruined the look Madame was trying to create.

'Besides, *chèrie,*' she argued, 'with such 'air you cannot wear an 'at! The cloche is still the fashion, whether we like it or no, and with your 'air as it is! What can you wear? Nothing!'

'My father will murder me, Madame!' Ellie pleaded, as Madame marched her off to the *coiffeuse* two floors up. 'The one thing my father likes about me, or rather about the only thing he isn't directly rude about, is my hair!'

'Your father 'e can go smoke,' Madame retorted, sitting Ellie down in a chair. 'You are a beautiful young woman, not some old-fashioned Irish 'ousemaid! Now please!' Madame instructed the hairdresser who was now in attendance. 'We will 'ave all this off, yes? And waved. But 'ere – the shingle – 'ere we will 'ave a curl. No shaving you understand, but cut into a soft curl just 'ere. *Comme ça.*'

Madame indicated the preferred style from a set of drawings in a folder and Ellie, attached as she was to her mane of dark hair, was forced to agree how chic the chosen style was. Particularly when Madame bought her a matching pale blue cloche, cut quite high at the back, and with a deep brim on the right side, which practically obscured her right eye.

'I 'ear,' Madame laughed as Ellie examined herself in a mirror hand-held by the assistant, 'that in London these new 'ats are lethal! Because the way the English drive, on the wrong side, with the brim – ' and to illustrate her point, Madame put a hand up to her right eye, 'with the brim *comme ça* they cannot see the oncoming traffic!'

'Such is happily not the case in Boston,' the assistant said, making a final and quite unnecessary adjustment to Ellie's new hat.

'No, no,' Madame agreed happily. 'Nor *en* Paris. Where *naturellement* the fashion 'e start. As always.'

'But why is it important for me to be fashionable?' Ellie asked as they climbed once more into the elevator. 'Please don't think I'm ungrateful, Madame, because I'm not. But I don't quite understand the purpose of this outing.'

'Ah, the more we understand,' Madame replied, 'the less then our pleasures.'

'But when am I going to wear these clothes, Madame? It's not as if I ever go out.'

'No no, *ma choupette*. It is as if you 'ave never gone out, yes. But this does not mean you not ever go out. Today for an instance, yes? Today you are out! Today you are out to lunch!'

There was a young woman waiting for Ellie and Madame as they stepped out of the elevator, which now only they occupied, on the very top floor. Ellie wondered to herself what new department she was being taken to now.

'Madame Gautier?' the young woman enquired. 'Mr O'Hara is waiting for you.'

Mr O'Hara? Ellie wondered with a shock. The Mr O'Hara? The name above the building?

'Madame – ?' she began.

'Quiet, *chèrie*,' Madame interrupted. 'Just straighten your dress, and do not say anything too foolish.'

A young man in an immaculate dark blue suit took over from the young woman who had met them at the elevator and led them into a vast room, furnished with antiques. Ellie understood this to be an office, because there were young men in dark blue suits and white shirts, and young women stenographers in dark blue dresses with white collars sitting at mahogany desks carefully checking perfectly arranged papers, or moving silently across the deeply carpeted floor to file immaculate folders away in mahogany bureaus. Every so often, as the young man led them across the room, a telephone would ring, but quietly, its bell having been adjusted to suit the tone of the office, and someone would answer the muted telephone in a lowered voice. No-one stared at Ellie as if she had no right to be there. If anyone caught her curious eye, they just smiled politely back and got on with their business.

Ahead of her, the young man opened one of a pair of tall deeply polished rosewood doors. 'Your visitors, sir,' he announced before stepping aside. 'Madame Gautier and Miss Milligan.'

Madame swept in while Ellie hesitated, afraid that any moment she might wake up from a dream. She looked to the young man as if for reassurance, and he smiled back and nodded for Ellie to go on in, which she did without, much to her surprise, suddenly finding herself sitting upright at home in bed, clutching her thin bedding around her and wondering how her mind could imagine such things.

'Miss Milligan,' a man said somewhere in the haze in front of her. 'This is indeed a pleasure.'

Ellie saw him now, perfectly clearly, an elderly man, short, bespectacled, immaculately dressed and judging from the hand he was extending to Ellie, beautifully manicured. His face was open and pleasant, with a skin as pink as a child's.

'I'm very pleased to make your acquaintance, Miss Milligan,' the man continued. 'I'm William O'Hara. But my friends all know me as Buck.'

Ellie shook his hand, which was small, soft and un-calloused, so unlike her father's, which was large, hard and leathery. She looked round the room, unable to believe her surroundings. Again, she had only ever seen pictures of rooms like this in magazines, in the homes of film stars: enormous chambers furnished as this one was with deep wing chairs and buttoned leather chesterfields, warmed by a huge log fire blazing in the grate, and with every wall hung with various and ornately framed oil paintings.

One particular painting caught her eye, and Ellie found herself staring back at it, time and again as Mr O'Hara and Madame began to chat. It was of a harbour on a rough and windy day, which some small sailing ships were trying to enter with, it appeared to Ellie, no little difficulty, while behind them a steamer was cutting through the seas at great speed.

'I find that an astonishing painting, don't you?'

Mr O'Hara was now at Ellie's side, having arrived unnoticed, so deeply was Ellie involved.

'Yes,' said Ellie. 'It's the most astonishing painting I have ever seen.'

'It is indeed, and I have to say it's my own personal favourite. It's by an English painter, William Turner, he painted it in 1822. And what I like about it – no.' Her host stopped and nodded courteously to Ellie. 'No I'd prefer it if you told me what you like about it.'

Ellie stared at the painting some more, before she started to explain. 'I love the movement of the sea,' Ellie said. 'These waves whipped by the wind. And all the reflections in the water, and all these deep shadows. I can almost feel the spray, and taste the salt in the air.'

'I do so agree,' said Mr O'Hara. 'But what does the painting tell you?'

'I don't know.' Ellie puckered her brow and stood a little back from the canvas. 'I sort of get the impression that these little boats, the sail boats, they're in trouble, because the wind appears to be blowing away from the harbour, so if they're trying to get in, they're not going to make it.'

'They're not, are they? Not unless they wait for the tide, or row in.'

'But the steamer, you see. Here.' Ellie pointed. 'Behind

this boat here, which is also in difficulty, the steamer is obviously having no trouble, and is going to make harbour easily, at least that's how it appears. Judging from the excitement going on on the jetty.' Ellie pointed again, indicating the figures on the pier, people waving and running, accompanied by a startled dog.

'And these poor fellows,' Mr O'Hara added, 'they're in real bad trouble I'd say, wouldn't you?' He indicated the fishing boat in the foreground, where the fishermen were struggling with a mass of unfurled canvas. 'If they don't make sense of that lot soon, they're either going to go under, or at the very least collide with another boat.'

'If I was any of those people,' Ellie concluded, 'I'd want to be one on the steamer, wouldn't you, Mr O'Hara?'

'I most certainly would, Miss Milligan,' her host agreed. 'And I think that's what the painter was saying. I think he was celebrating the coming of steam power, and showing the people of his time how much safer they were going to be on the seas, don't you?'

'I'm afraid I hadn't yet made that conclusion, Mr O'Hara,' Ellie replied.

'Perhaps not, young lady,' O'Hara smiled. 'But I'm certain you soon *would* have done.'

They lunched next door in a wood panelled dining room, hung with more fine paintings.

'Is this where you live, Mr O'Hara?' Ellie asked.

'I'm afraid so,' her host replied. 'Yes, most of the time. But I'd far rather be at home.'

Madame Gautier looked up and caught Ellie's eye just for a moment, and the glance seemed to say, See? See what the world can hold? And then Madame Gautier picked up her Waterford glass and took a sip of her wine.

'You always have such exquisite wines, Buck,' she said. 'As well as the most perfect food.'

'You only deserve the best, Madame,' Mr O'Hara replied. 'I'm forever telling you that.' And he smiled at her, but his eyes left Ellie's face for only one moment.

*   *   *

'*Bon*,' Madame said on the cab ride home. 'You did so very well, *chèrie*.'

Ellie said nothing. She just sat and stared blankly as the world outside her changed from one of elegance and opulence to one of uniformity and poverty. She said nothing because she did not know what to say. One minute she had been on her hands and knees scrubbing and the next she was being wined and dined by the owner of the largest store in town. And he had never stopped talking to her. He wanted to know what she thought about everything, because as he told her he found everything she had to say so interesting.

Ellie was in fact surprisingly erudite, due, Patsy used to tease her, to her missing so much school. Because she had spent so much of her teenage by herself, she had found plenty of time to read the newspapers and the books Patsy would bring home from school, or take out for her from the school library. But she had never realized quite how much knowledge she had assimilated until today, until she had been forced into conversation for the first time ever with a total stranger. And obviously she had done more than hold her own.

'Yes indeed,' Madame sighed, lighting a fresh cigarette and blowing the smoke out of the side of her mouth, 'yes, you did very well indeed.'

'Why?' Ellie suddenly asked her companion. 'You see I just don't understand, Madame. Why did you take me there?'

Madame adjusted the cigarette in her holder, and then took another deep draw on it before answering. 'In life, *choupette*,' she said, 'the most difficult thing is *la choix*.'

'I don't understand, Madame,' Ellie frowned.

'To make a choice, *chèrie*. No – *the* choice,' Madame explained. 'And so often it is better for someone other to make the choosing.'

'Are you saying I have a choice, Madame?'

'We all have a choice, *choupette*, *d'accord*. Either we grab 'im by the beard — '

'Who, Madame?'

'The mountain lion, *chèrie*! Either we grab 'is beard, and teetaire on the brink! Yes? Of the cliff! Or we die from boredom. Old, and depressed. And with nothing in our *journaux* except the jottings of regret. You want to be an unpaid 'ousemaid for the rest of your life? Or for the rest of what matter of your life? Your youth? Yes? No, no, of course not, *choupette*! No the only thing to regret is what we do not do, which is what happen! We regret the part we 'ave left, rather than rejoice over the part we 'ave preferred!'

Madame then settled back in her seat and fell into a deep sleep for the rest of the journey, full of good food and wine, and liqueurs, while Ellie stared back out of the window and tried to make some sense of all that had just been said, and all that had just happened.

Patsy was horrified when he saw his sister's hair.

'Now you look like everyone else!' he complained. 'You look like every other shop girl!'

'No I do not, Patsy!' Ellie retorted. 'No shop girl could afford this style! This style is the very height of fashion!'

'You bet,' Patsy said. 'And where are you planning to show it off? At Sunday lunch? When Pa gets home?'

Ignoring her brother's last remark, simply because Ellie had not yet worked out an answer to that particular problem, Ellie started to clear away their supper things into the kitchen. Patsy followed her out, bringing some dishes.

'He'll kill you,' Patsy said. 'He'll murder you.'

'I'm over eighteen, Patsy,' Ellie replied, 'and I can wear my hair as I want.'

Even so, Ellie made sure she was upstairs and well out of the way when her father returned on Saturday. She didn't know what she was waiting for, a miracle perhaps, because one thing she did know, and that was that Patsy was right. It didn't matter how old she was, or what her personal wishes were, when her father saw what she had done to her hair he would undoubtedly try to murder her.

She heard her father come into the house and call out for her, and she called back that she would be down in a moment, as soon as she was dressed.

And then the miracle Ellie was still praying for happened. There was a ring at the front door. Her father called twice for her to come down and answer it, but Ellie pretended not to hear. After a moment, she crept out of her room and looked round the corner of the landing, down the stairs. Outside the front door, which was open, she could see her father standing talking to someone in the porch. At first Ellie was not sure who it was, as her father totally obscured her view. And then when he moved and Ellie could see who the caller was, she didn't believe her eyes.

It was Madame Gautier.

Her father turned, to look suddenly up the stairs, as if he could sense Ellie hidden there, listening. So Ellie darted back to her room, and shut herself in, her heart pounding. It seemed an age before she heard the front door close again, and then another age before her father finally summoned her. This time, since there was no reason for further prevarication, Ellie straightened her dress and went downstairs.

'And what time may we expect supper, Eleanor?' her father asked, standing by the front window with his back to her.

'It's ready and cooked, Pa,' Ellie replied. 'But what about the others?'

'Your brothers won't be back until tomorrow,' her father replied, still staring out on to the street. 'They stayed on for the game.'

He said nothing more to her. He just stood there looking out, his large leathery hands clasped tight behind his back, while Ellie wondered what on earth it could have been that Madame Gautier had said to him.

'Patsy?' Ellie called up the stairs, still wondering at her good fortune. 'Supper!'

Nothing was said over supper either, not one word. Not only that but Patrick Milligan ate his meal without a word of complaint about either the temperature of the plates or the quality of the food. He simply cleared his plate, drank his tea, and then got up and went out of the house.

It was left to her brothers to pass comment at lunch the following day.

'Jeeze – who do you think you are?' Dermot sneered. 'Jean Harlow?'

'Jean Harlow's blonde,' Mike said. 'No she looks more like one of those cheap broads in the chorus.'

'Shut it,' Patsy said.

'Hey, hey!' Dermot put down his knife and fork and stared at his kid brother. 'Any of you guys hear what I just heard?'

'Yeah,' said Fergal. 'I thought I heard a worm turning.'

'Me too,' Mike agreed. 'Anyway, like I was saying. I don't know about you fellahs, but I don't like having a sister that looks like a tramp.'

'Shut it, Mike,' Patsy said again. 'I mean it.'

Ellie looked down the table at her father, expecting an intervention. Normally at table he nipped any argument in the bud, at least until he had finished eating. But today he just carried on eating his pot roast with his head down, paying no attention at all to his argumentative brood.

'I don't think I heard you right, Patricia,' Mike said, looking Patsy in the eye.

'You heard me right enough,' replied Patsy.

'I think Sis's new style would look good on Miss Patsy, fellahs, don't you?' Dermot asked. 'I think she'd look very pretty.'

'Prettier maybe than her trampy sister here,' Fergal added.

'I can't take you all,' Patsy said. 'So who's it to be?'

'Patsy – ' Ellie started.

'Just keep out of it, Ellie,' Patsy said. 'OK?'

'That's right, tramp,' Mike agreed. 'Keep your slummy nose out of it.'

'OK, Mike,' said Patsy, rising. 'In the yard.'

Dermot and Fergal gave a great whoop and rose with Mike and Patsy. Ellie looked once more down the table to her father, silently praying he would put an end to it, and prevent what was sure to be a bloodbath. But he was still to all intents and purposes uninterested. For he just pushed his plate aside, wiped his mouth on the back of his hand, and getting up from the table once again went out of the house without saying a word.

In the yard, the protagonists were preparing for battle. Patsy had his jacket and tie off, and was carefully rolling up his sleeves. Although he was now nearly twenty, he was still considerably smaller than even Mike, who was nearest him in age. He was also still considerably lighter, although as he rolled his sleeves right up to the top of his arms, Ellie for the first time was aware of the amount of muscle he seemed to have gained.

His brothers certainly were not as they formed a conspiratorial circle round Mike in the other corner of the yard, which all at once had become a boxing ring. Dermot looked round briefly at Patsy and Ellie and then said something to his two brothers which made all three of them laugh.

'You don't have to do this, Patsy,' Ellie told her brother. 'You don't have to do this for me.'

'I'm not doing it just for you, Ellie,' Patsy said, spitting into his hands. 'Don't you worry, I'm doing it for both of us.'

Ellie squeezed her brother's arm, then turned to go. She could never bear to watch her brothers fight, least of all when one of them decided to give Patsy a pasting.

'No – don't go,' Patsy said. 'I'd like you to stay.'

'I couldn't,' Ellie replied. 'I'm sorry.'

'You'll be sorrier if you go,' Patsy suddenly grinned. 'For there'll be no second shots.'

'Look out!' Ellie cried, as she saw Mike hurling himself at the unprepared Patsy.

Patsy turned in plenty of time, nimbly, quick on his feet as a buck hare. Then he jinked and side-stepped, and Mike crashed clumsily past him straight into the fence.

'Now will you stay?' Patsy asked. 'You'll be missing something otherwise.'

'You're mad,' Ellie told him.

'I've been mad for too long,' Patsy replied, moving out into the centre of the yard. 'And I'll stay mad till this is settled!'

Ellie stayed.

It was no contest. From the moment Mike put up his fists, the fight was over. He moved in against his young brother, slowly this time, determined not to be made a fool of twice. Patsy jinked away from him, on his toes, his hands held low, leaving his face completely exposed.

'On the button!' Dermot yelled. 'Let's see the bastard bleed!'

Mike moved in even closer, and this time it seemed he caught Patsy flat-footed. Certainly Mike had all the time in the world to launch a right hook, but Patsy also must have had all the time in the world to see it, for he simply swayed back on his heels and the punch missed by over a foot.

Still Patsy didn't put up his hands, inviting his opponent to take another swing. He even moved in, thrusting his bobbing head well within range. Mike met his brother's eyes and saw they were like steel.

'Come on, cissy,' Mike hissed, 'put up a fight. Make a show of it, come on – before I knock the shite out of you.'

'OK,' said Patsy, and hit him with a perfect straight left. Mike didn't even see it coming. One minute Patsy's hands had been by his side, the next moment Mike's nose was split and the blood was gushing down his face and flooding the back of his throat.

'Jesus!' Mike cried, 'you bastard! You sneaky bastard!'

'You said you wanted a fight,' Patsy replied, circling round his enraged brother. 'If you didn't want me to hit you, you should have kept your mouth shut.' He jabbed Mike again, suddenly, right under his nose. 'That mouth,' he said. 'My – it's that big – ' Patsy hit him again. 'I can hardly miss it.' And he hit him again.

'What in hell are you doing, kid!' Dermot shouted from Mike's makeshift corner. 'You gone to sleep or something!'

Patsy backed off and dropped his hands again, but not his mental guard. He kept moving all the time, on his toes with his weight perfectly balanced, just as he'd been taught, down at the gymnasium, every Saturday and every Wednesday for the past five years, times when everyone thought he was busy doing something else. The occasional black eye he had collected early on, when he was still at school, he had attributed to the fights he was always having in the playground, or on the street coming home. And no-one had ever suspected a thing. Because no-one was in the least bit interested.

Least of all his brothers, who were now watching with ever increasing dismay as Mike, the 'broth's' best fighter, was having the rings run round him by the family runt.

'Wake up, you dozy bastard!' Fergal yelled at Mike. 'Pick him off with your right!'

But Mike was hurting too much already from the blow that had split his nose; he'd never been hit that hard. And then the three straight jabs in the mouth – Mike could feel several loose front teeth, one of which seemed embedded in his swollen upper lip.

'OK, Patsy,' he mumbled as his young brother weaved round him. 'OK so you got lucky. So let's call it a day – OK?'

'No,' said Patsy. 'It's not OK, Mike. Not yet I'm afraid.'

Then again from nowhere came a punch, like iron, straight into Mike's solar plexus, knocking the breath from him so completely Mike thought he was going to die. He doubled over, unable to help himself, only to be immediately uprighted by another punch which rocked him back on his heels. He stood there, his face awash with blood, his swollen mouth hanging open, but still conscious, still awake enough to see his younger brother's eyes as they fixed his own and lined him up for the *coup de grâce*. Which came mercifully swiftly, in the shape of another devastatingly accurate straight left, and then a perfect right uppercut which hardly seemed to travel more than a foot, but which was delivered with such a force that it lifted Mike up on to his toes, before toppling him backwards in a heap at his elder brothers' feet.

Eight punches. That's all it had taken. A straight left, three jabs, a right, another right, a straight left, and a right uppercut.

'Christ,' said Dermot. 'Jesus Christ.'

'Jesus Christ Almighty,' said Fergal.

Patsy turned to them, unmarked except for where he had been stained by his brother's blood. 'OK,' he said. 'Who's next?'

'You didn't learn to fight like that in the playground,' Ellie said as she bathed Patsy's knuckles in onion water.

'You're right,' her brother grinned, and told her about the gymnasium. 'I haven't lost a fight in three years,' he said.

'Look,' said Ellie, wiping her hands dry. 'If you were that fancy, we'd have heard about you.'

'No you wouldn't,' Patsy replied. 'I fight under the name of Charlie Farrell. No-one knows I'm a Milligan. And no-one in the family follows boxing. Least not amateur boxing.'

'So why didn't you stand up to them before?'

Patsy shrugged. 'Once I'd learned to fight, it stopped bothering me. The only thing that gets me steamed up is when they have a go at you. And I guess today – I guess they just went a little too far.'

Ellie leaned up and kissed her brother on the cheek, then she put both hands on his biceps. 'I didn't even notice these,' she said. 'I should at least have noticed you'd got stronger.'

'How?' her brother smiled. 'We don't share a room any more. We haven't shared a room for ten years. And I haven't put on much weight. I've just gotten strong.'

'I wonder what Pa will have to say?' Ellie smiled.

Nothing, was the answer. At least not to Ellie. But that Saturday for the first time in his life, he invited his youngest son Patsy to attend the ball-game along with himself and his other three sons.

'You must not be surprised if 'e choose to ignore you, *choupette*,' said Madame when Ellie next visited her. 'You know they say the Irish, they ignore what they cannot hit or drink.' Madame laughed and poured them both some more tea.

'I think maybe the reason he isn't speaking to me,' Ellie ventured, 'is something you might have said to him.'

'Me?' Madame protested, the picture of innocence.

'When you called last Saturday.'

'He nevaire told you that. That I called.'

'I saw you. From the landing. Why did you, Madame? And what did you say to him?'

Madame drank her tea and put the fine china cup carefully back on the saucer which she was holding in her other hand. 'That, I think, is a matter between your father and myself,' she replied finally.

'Pardon me, but – '

'No,' Madame rebuked her sharply. 'Nevaire such a vulgarism! I keep reminding you! Nevaire "pardon me". "Excuse me." "Excuse me".'

'Excuse me,' Ellie stood corrected. 'But I thought – I thought my father and you weren't on speaking terms.'

'Yes?' Madame said, giving a small but definitely supercilious sniff. 'That is not the truth. The truth is I am not speaking to your father.'

Ellie was baffled. At home Madame, if referred to at all, had always been the person who had been derided. She had been called a despicable woman, a scarlet creature, a hussy, a jessy, and on the occasions when her father had taken drink, much worse. His contempt for her had been occasioned, as Ellie understood it, by her father's disdain for Madame's previous occupation as an actress, since, as he said, he had always held the theatre to be nothing but a den of iniquity.

So why was it and how come that Madame was claiming that the opposite was true and that it was her father who was the person out of favour?

Madame must know, of course, but Madame was not telling.

'If you search for truth, *choupette*,' was all she would allow, 'you will find nothing but contradictions.'

What Madame did tell Ellie, however, was that Mr O'Hara was very keen to renew their acquaintance, which he had found all too brief. If it was agreeable with Ellie, he would be delighted to escort her to dinner and the opera on Saturday.

'What about my father?' was Ellie's first enquiry.

'Your father,' Madame replied, 'is not included in the invitation.'

'You know perfectly well what I mean,' Ellie said, ignoring Madame's tease. 'What shall I tell him?'

'Tell him you are going to dine at Auguste's before being taken to see *La Traviata*,' Madame instructed, 'by one of the richest and most influential men in Boston.'

'Why you?' was her father's first question, echoing Ellie's own bewilderment. 'My God – he has the whole of Boston to choose from!'

'I think he's just being nice,' Ellie offered rather feebly. 'He's a very sweet gentleman.'

'Trade knows no gentlemen,' her father replied loftily, as if he himself was an important landowner instead of just the foreman of a modest building firm. 'Money doesn't automatically confer breeding.'

'So what shall I tell him, Pa?' Ellie asked. 'Shall I tell him no?'

'You will tell him nothing, Eleanor,' her father replied sternly. 'Not until you have told me how you met him.'

Ellie told him the truth. She had no alternative. There was no point in trying to invent a story, because under these circumstances no made-up story could begin to sound even remotely plausible. Besides, Ellie never told stories. Ellie had always believed in the truth.

'I knew it!' her father roared in response. 'I knew that Jezebel would have a hand in it!'

'Madame simply took me out shopping and to have lunch,' Ellie countered. 'What could she possibly be having a hand in? Please may I go? Please?'

'I want to know what is behind this first,' he snapped, 'because for the life of me I cannot understand why a man in his position should want to take up with the likes of you. So I intend to find out exactly what is going on first, before I even consider giving my consent.'

Ellie groaned as she watched her father stride to the door, intent, it appeared, on confronting Madame. But then he stopped, with his hand still on the door handle, and hesitated for what seemed an age. And with good reason. For Patrick Milligan knew what Madame's answer would be. It would be the same answer she gave him when she forbade him to chastise Ellie on account of her newly-styled hair. If that was what he wanted, she would no doubt tell him again, if he wished to forbid the outing, then perhaps it was time for Madame herself to break her long silence.

'You can't possibly go,' Ellie heard her father say finally, still with his back to her, and her heart sank.

'Why not, Pa?' she pleaded. 'Why on earth not?'

'Because, girl,' he said, 'you have nothing to wear.'

'Madame said she'd lend me something,' Ellie said, hardly able to believe her ears. 'She said she could alter something of her's – '

'No!' her father thundered. 'I'll not have any daughter

of mine going out second-best! And certainly not in that hussy's cast-offs!'

He turned to Ellie, and reaching into his back pocket, withdrew a roll of bills. 'Here,' he said. 'Go out and buy yourself something pretty.' Then he turned and went out, leaving Ellie to stare speechlessly at the most money she had ever seen in her life.

And so began a friendship that before Ellie knew it had become a courtship. William O'Hara, whom Ellie quite properly never called anything but Mr O'Hara, and who equally properly never called Ellie anything but Miss Milligan, escorted Ellie to the opera, to concerts, to Boston's fine art galleries, and to the theatre. With the money her father had given her, Ellie, with the necessary help of Madame Gautier, had chosen and bought for herself her very first evening gown, a simply stunning and practically backless dress fashioned out of moire in the new fashionable colour of rose-opaline. The night Ellie first wore the gown to the opera, her three eldest brothers all wolf-whistled her to the door and Patsy, his eyes like saucers, gave her a corsage of orchids and escorted her to the limousine which had come to collect her.

But of course one evening gown and one day dress soon proved to be a woefully insufficient wardrobe for someone who was being escorted around Boston as much as Ellie now was.

'Please don't take this as an impertinence, Miss Milligan,' Mr O'Hara said to her early on in their relationship, 'but a girl as pretty as you, and one as elegant, should really have the clothes to enhance her beauty. Now I know what you're going to say,' he continued, holding up one expensively gloved hand to forestall Ellie's objections, 'that clothes are expensive and that you do not have the means. But I would consider it a great honour and privilege if you would allow me to help you overcome this disadvantage by making you a gift of whatever you may need.'

Ellie had of course tried to refuse, but Mr O'Hara would not hear of it. So Ellie conceded, and went one day with Madame to Mr O'Hara's emporium and bought two more day dresses, another pair of shoes, and, very reluctantly, another gown for the evening.

Mr O'Hara smiled when Ellie showed him her selections upstairs in his private office, and sent them straight back downstairs to their various departments.

'That was not at all what I had in mind for you,' he said, pouring the three of them glasses of champagne. 'Forgive me, but if I may say so, you have far too modest an opinion of yourself.'

'This is what I am telling 'er always,' Madame sighed. 'But this girl she is too 'umble. And too *stubborn*.'

'Perhaps after lunch, Madame,' Mr O'Hara suggested, 'you and I might be able to persuade Miss Milligan otherwise.'

'I am sure we can, Buck,' Madame concurred, dropping her voice mock-conspiratorially. 'Particularly if you give 'er some more champagne.'

Even if Ellie had been quite and utterly sober, she would have still found the clothes which were paraded after lunch for her sole benefit in one of the salons reserved for such occasions quite irresistible. As it was, with two glasses of champagne inside her, and as the mannequins displayed the latest fashions from Paris and London, she felt she was once more in heaven, even more so two hours or so later as Mr O'Hara's chief assistants wrapped up the final choices: dresses, gowns and lingerie made of georgette, and flowered taffetas, moires, silks and satins, subtle lamés, artificial marocain and crêpe de Chine, in colours of white or pastel blue, cerise, pearl-grey, oyster and of course rose-opaline.

'If I could perhaps have your address for delivery please, Miss Milligan,' the chief assistant requested.

Madame gave the woman her own address. 'Knowing your father, cherie,' she whispered to Ellie, 'perhaps it is a little more tactful.'

But even if Patrick Milligan had known the size of 'Buck' O'Hara's munificence, he would not have raised any objections. Patrick Milligan knew a good thing when he saw it, as he told his 'broth', and their sister's relationship with one of Boston's most successful citizens was all of that.

'What we must hope and pray for, me boys,' he said one night as they dined alone on salad and cold meat, Ellie being out at a concert, 'is for a state of some permanence. Now I know it's a lot to expect, what with your sister still only nineteen, and the old "Buck" being every year of sixty five, so they tells me, but May and September's always been a heady mix, and the old fool seems besotted.'

'Ellie'll not marry Mr O'Hara,' said Patsy defiantly. 'She's too much good sense. She'd never throw herself away on some dirty old man.'

'And sure why do you think she'd be "throwing herself away", Pat? Eh?' asked his father. 'How can you "throw yourself away" down a gold mine?'

The 'broth' laughed, but Patsy remained intransigent.

'Ellie's not that sort, Pa, that's why,' Patsy answered. 'Ellie's no gold-digger.'

'Well, as I said,' Patrick Milligan said carefully, 'it's a lot to expect, but suppose – .' The head of the family rested his knife and fork on their heels and looked down the table. 'Suppose they was to get wed, just suppose now – .' Patrick Milligan was careful to keep it hypothetical, mindful of the dark look on Patsy's face. 'Because to be fair, Pat, your sister has her own life to lead, and we must all respect that. You've all of you, there's no denying it, you've all too often taken advantage of Eleanor, and so it's only right and proper now you should respect the fact she has a life of her own.'

'You'll have to excuse me, Pa,' Patsy said rising, 'but I've business to do. I still have a lot of premiums to collect.'

'You're excused, me boy,' his father said. 'You're excused.'

Patsy went, using his work for the insurance company as a pretext, for in truth he could take no more of the hypocrisy.

'As I was saying,' Patrick Milligan continued, once his youngest was out of the house, 'if the best came to the best, and your sister married the old codger, we could be in clover. Sure people like O'Hara, they always need men. They need people to look after their interests. To protect them. Particularly in these hard times. If you see what I mean.'

The 'broth' was beginning to see what their father meant. What he meant was they might be able to come off the building sites, and fall into a featherbed job, one in which they could wear nice suits and drive fancy cars, in return for looking after one very rich old man's 'interests'.

'Let me put it another way, boys,' their father said, sitting back and wiping his mouth on his hand. 'And this is just supposing. Just suppose the old codger does get serious. Suppose he does want to make the relationship permanent. I mean, one can always make conditions. When it comes to giving your consent to a girl who's not yet reached her majority, sure a father's every right to make one or two conditions, now wouldn't you say?'

The 'broth' all grinned and nodded. Yes, they all said. Yes indeed they would.

William O'Hara proposed to Ellie on the anniversary of their first date. Ellie was rendered speechless. There had never been a hint of any romance between them, although their friendship had deepened with each meeting. Ellie provoked and stimulated Mr O'Hara with her inquisitive and questioning mind, and entertained him with her ever truthful and utterly pragmatic approach, while the kindness, respect and affection that he had accorded Ellie had enabled her to grow quickly and painlessly from a gauche teenager into a poised young woman.

But one who had given no thought to love.

'I can see I've surprised you,' Mr O'Hara apologized over dinner. 'That was not my intention.'

They had been to see *La Bohème*, at which Mr O'Hara had cried quite openly, and which Ellie had sat through dry-eyed, but with a breaking heart.

Taking time to recover, the first course of their dinner had been eaten practically in silence.

'I should have given you more time,' Mr O'Hara continued. 'Or perhaps I should not have asked you at all.'

'No!' said Ellie, almost too emphatically, afraid that even though she did not know her own mind, he might withdraw his offer. And Ellie did not wish to lose Mr O'Hara, at least not as a friend. 'You did surprise me,' Ellie confessed, truthful as ever. 'But then that's my fault. I have obviously been taking you for granted.'

'If you have been taking me for granted,' Mr O'Hara argued, 'then that is *my* fault. I should have been more entertaining company.'

'Nobody could be better company than you, Mr O'Hara.'

'Nor anyone better than you, Miss Milligan.'

The waiter served them their next course, and neither of them spoke until he was gone.

'I can't think why someone such as yourself should want to marry me,' Ellie said eventually.

'That is the very first foolish thing I have ever heard you say, young lady,' Mr O'Hara replied with a smile.

Ellie looked down. 'What I meant was – ' she explained quietly, 'is that you can't marry me. I'm – I'm from the wrong side of the tracks.'

Mr O'Hara stared at her then laughed. 'So am I, Miss Milligan!' he said. 'Why heavens – so am I! Except I am much more so than you! Why, my family came from a two bit shack. Right by the railroad. Every time the express went by, we had to hold the windows in. I had no schooling. I was an errand boy, a boot black, a bellhop, a messenger boy – all before I was nine years old! Then I went to work in a five and ten, and gradually worked my way up until I was managing a general store. Age twenty

I was. Manager of a store. But still on the wrong side of town.' He paused to take a sip of wine as he recollected the distant years. 'And even though most would have been quite happy to get where I had got at that age, I believe that a man is nothing unless he believes he has greater possibilities. Which I did. So I borrowed some money and bought a store of my own, a tiny place, a cigar store, but in the right part of town, and in the right part of the right part of town. On a corner. If ever you're thinking of buying a store, Miss Milligan, buy one on a corner. That way you get two fronts for the price of one.'

Ellie laughed and then smiled at her companion.

'So don't you worry about being from the wrong side of the tracks, Miss Milligan,' he reassured her. 'In fact we probably wouldn't be such friends if you weren't. And please don't worry either about the fact that you don't love me.'

Now Ellie really was knocked off balance. If she was going to decline Mr O'Hara's proposal, it was going to be for that very reason. 'But I don't,' she said.

'Why should you?' he asked.

'Because when people get married,' Ellie tried explaining, 'it's better if they love each other.'

Mr O'Hara smiled. 'I don't wish to disillusion you, Miss Milligan,' he said. 'Nor do I wish to sound like a cynical old man. But frankly when people marry it's often a far better thing if they don't love each other. Oscar Wilde said it, you know. Something along the lines that a man can be happy with any woman as long as he doesn't love her.'

'Does the same apply to a woman with any man, Mr O'Hara?'

'I'm quite sure it does, Miss Milligan. At least in this case I am quite sure it would apply. You see, the reason I want to marry you is a very simple one. When, after an evening such as this, you go home, and I go home, I miss you. I miss your wonderful company. If I stay in my apartment, or if I go home to my house, I am lonely. I'm not lonely because I am bored, please understand. I have never minded being by myself, and I consider those who do to be selfish. No, I am lonely for you, Eleanor. For the sunshine you have brought to a place where I thought the sun would never shine any more. And I would like to keep that light shining, until the day I die, you see. Because it's a long time since I felt like this, as good as I do now. As good as you make me feel. And I think in return for what you have given me, I should marry you. And you will never want again. Not for the rest of your life.'

'You did not say no!' Madame rose from her chair, appalled by the notion, her cigarette holder clenched between her teeth. 'Tell me you did not say no, Eleanor!'

Ellie stared out at the full moon above the yard, above the wrong part of town. Unable to sleep and seeing Madame's bedroom light still on, she had thrown a pebble against the glass and called her down.

'Why did you introduce me to him, Madame?' Ellie asked. 'It can't just have been a whim.'

'That is not important, Eleanor,' Madame replied sharply. 'What I do, I do.'

'And that's no reply, Madame.' Ellie turned and looked at her friend and her neighbour. 'Do you find girls for him, is that it?'

'I should slap your face for that.'

'I shouldn't blame you if you did. So go on.'

They stared at each other, a foot apart, eye into eye, the battered urchin from next door now a beautiful young woman in a gown by Patou, and the beautiful young woman from Paris now a battered old woman in much-mended *peignoir*.

'I find girls for people, yes,' Madame confessed, 'but not for 'im. Monsieur O'Hara, I find him company. But most of the girls I find, they are so stupid. And they take from him. Take, take. That is all they do.'

'I've taken from him,' Ellie said. 'What's the difference?'

'The difference is, *chèrie*,' Madame replied, 'you 'ave given more, much more than you take. And anyway, you do not take! Monsieur O'Hara, he give these things to you! You 'ave nevaire asked for *anything*! Once! These other girls – they take 'is 'and, they squeeze 'is cheek, they pat 'is 'ead, like 'e was a *bébé*! And then they say – I want a new pair of shoes, Buck sweetie. Can I 'ave a new gown, some silk pyjamas, some French lingerie, a fur coat! You 'ave nevaire ask 'im for anything! Not even a pair of gloves!'

The moon was now hidden by clouds as Ellie turned and looked back out of the window. Madame came to her side, and slipped her arm through Ellie's.

'Listen,' she said. 'I did this for you. More than for 'im. I knew 'e would like you, because you are a wonderful girl, and 'e is a wonderful man. But this time, I do this for you. Think. And take this thought with you to bed. Marry 'im. Marry Monsieur O'Hara. He will want nothing from you but your company.' Ellie looked round. 'Nothing at all,' Madame continued. ' 'E will not want to make love with you, I promise. That is, if you wish it, that will be part of the arrangement. I know this. I 'ave 'is word. And Monsieur O'Hara, 'e is a man of his word. So marry 'im, Eleanor. And cross the tracks. And live like a princess. Like I always say you will, evaire since I first tell you stories, eh? I say you will live one day like a duchess, because this is what you deserve. And then when 'e die, everything, but everything, it will be your's.'

The clouds passed from the face of the moon, which now threw a clear cold light on the two adjoining yards. Ellie stared out, and saw no future there. What she saw was all past.

1931

5

On her twenty-first birthday, Artemis Deverill was called into the offices of Grafton, Grafton and Grafton and handed a letter personally by Arthur Grafton, the senior partner and the eldest of the three named brothers. The front of the envelope was formally addressed: To Lady Artemis Deverill, daughter of John, the 4th Earl of Deverill and Lady Mary Deverill (deceased) and grand-daughter of George, 7th Duke of Brougham (d.1906), with an underlined instruction in the top right-hand corner which instructed that the letter be handed to the addressee on the occasion of her reaching her majority. The back was sealed, significantly, not with the Deverill crest of lion sejant, but with her mother's family crest, the Brougham crest, of a falcon, rampant regardant.

Arthur Grafton left Artemis alone to open and to read the letter. She broke the seal and took from the envel-ope several pages of expensive straw-coloured writing paper, again headed by the Brougham, not the Deverill, family crest.

But what made Artemis stop to put a hand to her throat and catch her breath as she unfolded the letter was that it was written in a hand almost identical to her own, her mother's hand.

'My dearest Artemis,' the letter began. Artemis had to put the letter down on the deeply polished mahogany table in front of her and stop reading, for all at once she could see her mother so clearly, that last morning of her life, in her silk top hat and perfect black habit, so beautiful on her big grey horse. She could see her bending down to kiss her goodbye, she could feel the softness of her mother's skin, and she swore she could even smell the bitter-sweet tang of her scent. And then she saw a sight she couldn't remember ever seeing before, her mother in a pale white and gold evening gown, with the corridor light catching the brilliance of the jewels at her neck and in her hair, as she quietly closed the nursery door.

She picked up the letter and began reading it again.

My dearest Artemis,

How I wish I could be with you today on this your most important birthday. But if this letter has to be given to you to read, then I shan't be, and there you are. But nothing will stop me from wishing you a happy birthday, darling, and wherever I am, I am thinking of you and sending you my love always.

I can see you as I write, just below me on the lawns, walking some very brave steps with Nanny holding your hand. I wonder what you look like now? Now you are twenty one. I'm trying to look forward to imagine it, and I think I can see you, still blonde I'm sure, very slender, and breaking hearts with those large cornflower blue eyes of yours. I do so hope and pray that I live to see you grown, but I'm afraid if what they say is true, then there's very little chance.

Anyway if what they say is true, my darling, you'll know by now. You'll have known for some time, so I might as well write it down. Doctor Mandeville told me this morning that there's something wrong with my heart and if I don't 'slow down' (slow down!) I shan't live for very much longer. The trouble is by 'slowing down' Doctor Mandeville means giving everything up, everything strenuous that is, and spending most of my time in bed, and quite honestly I really couldn't bear that! I really couldn't bear being stuck in bed unable to ride or to enjoy all the wonderful things life has to offer.

No-one will blame you if after reading this you think what a selfish old thing your mother is. But even if you do, I know it won't be long before you understand. In fact if you're anything like me you'll understand straight away. Quite honestly, if I did give up everything and take to my bed for however long is left to me, I actually would much rather *be* dead.

Now, the other point of this letter is to tell you something you probably know already, and that is, on this your twenty-first birthday, you inherit Brougham. I'm leaving it to you, just as it was left to me, but for different reasons. My father left me Brougham because he had no sons. I'm leaving you Brougham because I want you to have it, and not anyone else. I'm not going to tell you why in this letter because it's too painful. It's pretty hard just writing you this without going into *all* the whys and wherefores. All I can say is by the time you get to read this letter, you'll probably know why I haven't left it to your father. I don't altogether blame your father. Your father is a fine man, but a little weak, I'm afraid. The person I blame – well, again, by the time you've read this, that's something else you'll most probably know.

So the house is your's, dearest child, and whatever you do, try not to let anyone take it away from you. Most of all, don't let any man marry you for it! As Nanny would say – 'keep it under your hat'! Live your life here, where your family's always been. I'm quite sure you'll be happy here, that you'll love it, because it really is a magical place. And above all I hope and pray you'll find someone wonderful with whom to share it. Someone who deserves you.

I'm going to stop now, so that I can come out and enjoy the last of the sunshine with you. You're still just below me on the lawn, you and Nanny, and you're playing with your big red and yellow ball, surrounded by the dogs. One day, please God, you will be sitting out there, a beautiful young woman, in the company of some perfectly divine young man, perhaps with your own child playing beside you.

So goodbye, darling, and a happy, *happy* birthday. I do so wish I could be there with you to see you today, but if I can't, be certain of one thing, darling, and that is I love you.

Your ever loving
Mama.

Artemis put the letter down in front of her and stared at it. *The person I blame – well, again, by the time you've read this, that's something else you'll most probably know.* Of course she knew who that person was. There was only one person it could possibly be. But surely not all that time ago?

And then she remembered, a memory from infancy, long before she saw her sitting in furs in the back of her father's car, she remembered being in her nanny's arms, being carried into the great drawing room of Brougham, and seeing two people getting up hurriedly from a sofa. She could see them, there they were, her father and a tall, slender blonde. Her father and Katherine.

She spread the pages of the letter out with both hands and studied her mother's handwriting. It was a beautiful hand, strong, and confident, and flowing. There was nothing in it, nowhere in the letter, which suggested even remotely something might be wrong, something wrong emotionally let alone physically. Yet she had just been told she was soon going to die. And five months later she was in fact dead. But not from a weakened heart as her doctors had so confidently predicted, but from an accident in the hunting field.

From an accident, in the hunting field.

For a moment Artemis looked up from the letter and stared ahead of her, trying to sort her thoughts out.

Then she folded up her late mother's letter, placed it carefully in its envelope, and went off to have lunch with her godmother at Claridges.

'Your father and your wretched stepmother were lovers before your father met your mother,' Diana said. 'For a god-awful moment everyone thought he was going to be a complete ass and marry Katherine then. But thankfully he met your mother, fell wildly in love with her, and lord, what man in his right mind wouldn't have? And that, one thought, was that.'

'But it wasn't,' Artemis replied, not asking a question, but stating a fact. 'I mean obviously.'

'No,' Diana sighed. 'Somehow Katherine got herself back in at Brougham, and once in, she stayed. I'm afraid she made your mother's life a misery. That last year.'

'Yes? And Papa?'

'Your father was enthralled. I don't honestly think he knew quite what he was doing. He can be most frightfully weak.'

A waiter arrived to refill their wine glasses, while another removed their plates. Diana lit a cigarette.

'I suppose,' Artemis ventured, picking up Diana's discarded matchstick and toying with it, 'once Mama's heart condition had been, you know, diagnosed, I suppose she thought it wouldn't be long before she'd be living at Brougham full time.'

'She being Katherine, I take it?'

'Absolutely. But then supposing Mama *hadn't* had a dicky heart? Or been killed out hunting. Papa would never have divorced her. He doesn't think much of divorce.'

'I don't imagine for a minute he'd have done anything, darling,' Diana replied. 'Your father might be a touch odd sometimes, but no, he's certainly no Dr Crippen.'

Artemis broke the match in two and dropped it in the ash tray. '*He* might not have done anything,' she said.

'Meaning she would have,' Diana replied, picking up the nuance.

'Meaning I wonder if she knew Mama had left me Brougham?' Artemis asked, looking Diana suddenly in the eyes.

'I should imagine so,' Diana replied, having given the matter thought. 'Knowing Katherine, I should imagine the matter had been given a great deal of air.' She frowned. 'What are you getting at?'

'It doesn't matter,' Artemis said, as their pudding was set before them. 'I was just wondering.'

She was wondering about her accident, and even now she still could remember very little about it. All Artemis knew was that when everyone had been asked, no-one it seemed could remember anyone else behind her on the Funk's Run. Hounds had just hit the line, the hunt was on, and everyone, so she was told, was understandably distracted.

Everyone except the person who had ridden after her in pursuit.

Because of the concussion she suffered from her fall, try as she might, Artemis couldn't even remember arriving at the meet that morning. All she could ever recall was going to bed the night before her accident. But now, having read her late mother's letter, and having learned of her father's and stepmother's previous relationship, something more was coming back to her. And the image was so powerful she found herself catching her breath, and clutching the edge of the table.

She was riding at a hedge. She could see it in her mind's eye quite clearly. It was the hedge and ditch at the bottom of the hill. And the horse that had been behind her was now up alongside, so close she could see its rider.

'It's her,' Artemis said, startling Diana who had been in the middle of recounting a social anecdote.

'Who, darling?' Diana asked. 'What on earth are you talking about?'

'I can see her,' Artemis replied. 'She has a veil, and a top hat, and she's very slender. On a big bay horse.'

And big bay horse with a blaze, a very distinctive blaze, like a big splash of white paint, right down its face.

'Of course,' Artemis announced to Diana. 'The horse that rode me off that morning was a hireling ridden by the second Lady Deverill, by Katherine.'

'Was there some unsettled business, Lady Deverill?' Mr Arthur Grafton asked once he had settled himself back behind his partner's desk. 'Something you don't perhaps understand about the terms of your legacy?'

'I want you to confirm I am now the rightful and legal owner of Brougham, please,' Artemis said. 'I doubt this letter will be enough.'

'It's in your late mother's will,' Arthur Grafton replied. 'She added the necessary codicil.'

'Exactly,' Artemis said. 'Then when the will was read, it would have been — I mean everyone would have known.'

Arthur Grafton took a small snuff box from his pocket and opened it. 'Of course,' he agreed. 'Everyone within the immediate family.'

'Yes,' Artemis said. 'That's rather what I thought. Thank you.' She leaned forward, just as her lawyer had placed some snuff on the back of his hand. 'In that case, Mr Grafton,' she instructed, 'please inform my father and my stepmother they have precisely four weeks in which to vacate my house.'

Arthur Grafton was so taken aback he inhaled the snuff too deeply and started to cough. 'I beg your pardon, Lady Artemis?' he said in between gasps. 'Perhaps I didn't hear you right.'

'My father and my stepmother are to be out of Brougham,' Artemis repeated, 'in four weeks exactly. To the hour.'

'Might I ask why, Lady Artemis?' Mr Grafton said, raising his bushy grey eyebrows.

'If you would just make sure my instructions are carried out,' Artemis returned, picking up her gloves and purse.

'I feel sure your father will enquire as to your reasons, Lady Artemis,' Mr Grafton insisted, rising as she rose.

'I'm absolutely certain he will, Mr Grafton,' Artemis replied. 'Which is why I wish you to give him none.'

She picked up her silver-topped cane and wished him good day.

Artemis turned and made her way slowly to the door which Mr Grafton hurried to open for her. She walked past him and out into the outer office without another word or look. The lawyer watched her go, an arrestingly beautiful girl, albeit to his mind a somewhat eccentric one, dressed as she was in an old silver-buttoned jacket, the kind of shirt favoured by the Romantic poets in the eighteenth century, a crimson hat with a turned up brim, a long twill riding skirt, and pale brown leather ankle boots. But how sad, the lawyer thought, as he watched her take her final leave of his offices, that someone as beautiful as the young Lady Artemis Deverill should have suffered from such a hideous riding accident, one which had left one of her long slender legs so much shorter than the other.

At the same time as Lady Artemis Deverill learned of her inheritance, it was decided between Eleanor Milligan and Madame Gautier that before the engagement could become formal, William O'Hara first had to ask his intended's father, Patrick Milligan, for his daughter's hand in marriage.

They met at Mr O'Hara's club to dine and discuss the matter. Patrick Milligan was a long way out of his social depth, but he was not a man to be cowed by such occasions, nor intimidated by the formal surroundings.

In fact in his rented white tie and tails he presented a most impressive and formidable aspect, a fine upright figure of a man, as opposed to the rather over-fed and under-exercised bodies of most of his fellow diners. Even his table manners were above reproach, thanks to Ellie's painstaking coaching.

'You are not to comb your moustaches with your fork, Pa,' she had instructed. 'Nor wipe your mouth on the back of your hand. You'll have a linen table napkin for that purpose, so for heaven's sake use it. And don't, whatever you do, tuck it in your collar — lay it on your lap. And use the cutlery on the outside of the place setting first, working your way inwards.'

'All right, all right,' her father had sighed. 'I can manage. I'm not a total gombeen, you know.'

'You will be if you don't listen, believe me,' Ellie had retorted.

'And how would you know all these things anyway? Sure you're no better than I am, whatever you say.'

'I know these things, Pa,' Ellie had said, 'because I have watched people. I watched Mr O'Hara from the first time I sat down at his table, and I have watched people ever since. So if you find yourself at a loss, like not knowing which knife to use, or which glass to drink from, or whatever, just watch what the others are doing. Which means you just keep your eye on Mr O'Hara.'

Her father had kept up his grumbling until he left the house to keep his appointment, but even so he had taken his daughter's advices to heart. Patrick Milligan had no intention of making a social nonsense. There was far too much at stake.

For his part, William O'Hara was charmed by his guest. Having never met Ellie's father, he had expected, from what Madame had indicated, to be entertaining a loud-mouthed roughneck. But instead he found himself in the company of a good-humoured and handsome man, with an Irish eye for life's absurdities and an apparently limitless fund of anecdotes. As a consequence, they had a most enjoyable dinner.

Afterwards they sat in the library, drinking the club's finest Napoleon brandy, still yarning and story-telling. In typically male fashion, the main item on the agenda, namely the proposed marriage of Ellie to the host, had not yet been broached.

'Now before we become altogether forgetful, Pat,' Mr O'Hara said, as their second large cognac was carefully placed in front of them, 'I think perhaps we should get the formalities out of our way.'

'Fire ahead, Buck,' Patrick Milligan replied, 'you just fire ahead. All I have to say is there's no need to go down on your knees.'

'Even so,' Buck O'Hara laughed, 'this has more than a hint of absurdity about it. For heaven's sake I'm practically old enough to be *your* father, and yet here I am, asking for the hand of your daughter.'

'What's age got to do with it, Buck?' Pat Milligan asked, inhaling the heady fumes of his cognac. 'You know what they say back home, no man is truly old until his mother stops worrying about him.'

'I'll make your daughter a good husband, Pat. I can promise you that.'

'And sure don't I know that, Buck. No man could make a better one. That's not what I'm concerned about.'

'You have an objection then?' O'Hara looked at Pat Milligan in surprise.

'No, no, Buck,' his guest replied. 'An objection? Never. Just a concern. Namely for meself. For sure what am I to do? What's a man to do, a poor old widower, when he loses his daughter? I tell you, Buck, you're lucky. You have no idea of what a little saint you're getting. Of course I know she's me daughter, so I know I've a bias, but God love her hasn't she been like a little wife to me? It hardly bears thinking about, Buck. What me life'll be without her.'

'You'd have had to face this some day, Pat,' O'Hara told him. 'A man with a daughter as fair as your's.'

'Ah sure and don't I know that, Buck? But then isn't truth the one that wounds deepest? All I've done is put off the moment, and there's never an advantage to be had there. Grasp the nettle, Buck. A man has to grasp the nettle of life.'

'Perhaps a housekeeper will provide an answer.'

'And how's a man like me to afford a housekeeper, Buck? With all due respect. I could never afford a housekeeper.'

'I can see you're a proud man, Pat.'

'I am, Buck. I'm that indeed.'

'I knew that from the moment you walked in here.' O'Hara paused and tapped the end of his cigar into a silver ashtray. 'Even so,' he then continued, 'under the circumstances perhaps you'd allow me to make a small settlement.'

'Never!' Ellie's father announced, in tones of hurt pride. 'I'd hear of no such thing! Isn't it bad enough that my daughter brings nothing to her wedding? As a fellow Irishman you understand that well enough, to be sure! For a father to allow his daughter to go to her marriage unbestowed? Oh, no, never! I would never take a penny as compensation! I'd rather end me days in the poor house!' Patrick Milligan shook his head, as if to end the conversation, while his host nodded in understanding, although never once taking his eyes off his visitor.

He had expected a bit of bartering, particularly since the Milligans hailed from County Cork, and O'Hara, coming from Dublin stock, knew well enough that as far as doing business went, the people from Cork took all the beating. But he had not anticipated a point blank refusal. In fact if he had been a gambling man he would have bet good money that Patrick Milligan would not have gone home that night empty handed.

But such seemed to be his intention, as O'Hara's prospective father-in-law would hear not another word on the subject. Instead the two men rekindled their good spirits over some more cognac before deciding to call it a night.

'Can I have my driver drop you home, Pat?' O'Hara asked as his Cadillac drew up in front of the club. 'It's no trouble.'

The liveried chauffeur opened the rear door of the limousine and stood back to allow his employer and his guest to climb into the back.

'This is very kind of you, Buck,' Pat Milligan said, settling in the seat beside O'Hara. 'Thank you.'

'Good. As long as you wouldn't mind if Sam dropped me off first?' O'Hara asked. 'It's been a grand evening, but I am a little tired.'

'Why not at all,' Pat Milligan replied. 'You'd hardly want to be driving all the way out to Westfield and back.' He looked around him, at the custom-built interior of the car. 'My, but this is a fine motor car, Buck,' he said.

'I have the V16 model as well,' O'Hara told him, 'which is undoubtedly the best model Mr Leland has ever produced. But I was advised, given the prevalent economic climate, to do my motoring in something a little more discreet.'

'Where I live, Buck,' Pat Milligan laughed, 'believe me, this'd still cause a right old stir!'

The car set off for O'Hara's apartment, with both passengers in fine fettle. Twelve hours later every newspaper carried the story of their journey, The Boston Herald running it as their headline.

KIDNAP ATTEMPT FOILED ON BOSTON MILLIONAIRE STORE BOSS SAFE AFTER 'NAPPERS BUNGLE

Two armed gunmen late last night made an attempt to shanghai one of Boston's richest citizens, multi-millionaire William John 'Buck' O'Hara, owner of O'Hara's, the city's top departmental store. Only the presence of mind of his passenger, a Mr Patrick

Milligan from Westfield, Boston, and his chauffeur, Samuel Clayton, who has been in Mr O'Hara's employ for fifteen years, saved the millionaire businessman from certain abduction.

Mr O'Hara and Mr Milligan were being chauffered home after dining at Boston's exclusive Colony Club when two masked gunmen forced their way inside O'Hara's limousine as it stopped outside his apartment. At gunpoint they then made the chauffeur drive to deserted wasteland north of the city limits, where it appears the intention was to shoot Milligan and the chauffeur. But at the critical moment it seems one of the executioners' gun jammed, and in the ensuing struggle, Milligan overpowered the gunman and seizing his revolver, courageously returned to the hijacked limousine to try and rescue his companion.

However, sensing the game was up, the second kidnapper panicked and fled, leaving the chloroformed O'Hara in the back of his Cadillac. Unfortunately the gunman who had been knocked down but left momentarily untended also managed to escape in the ensuing mêlée.

Police are searching for the two well-built young men, but because of lack of any further physical detail they hold out little chance of an early arrest.

Patrick Milligan went to visit O'Hara that evening. O'Hara was hardly conscious and very weak. According to the doctor in attendance, O'Hara had been badly shaken by the incident, and needed careful watching.

'We're lucky he's still with us, Mr Milligan,' the doctor confided to Ellie's father, as they left O'Hara to sleep. 'I'm surprised the incident didn't kill him.'

'But why should it have, Doc?' Patrick Milligan enquired in astonishment. 'It wasn't as if the poor man was rough-housed.'

'No,' the doctor agreed, 'but then had he been, there is absolutely no doubt he certainly would be dead. Mr O'Hara has high blood pressure, and he suffers quite regularly now from angina.'

'I had no idea,' Patrick Milligan replied, a deep frown on his brow. 'No idea at all.'

'Why should you?' the doctor asked. 'Everything is kept well under control and Mr O'Hara is in no danger as long as he is not exposed to, well, how shall I put it, unnecessary anxieties? Sudden stress, or shock? The chloroform was practically enough to do the trick, you know.'

'The chloroform?' Patrick Milligan exclaimed. 'And what harm could a bit of chloroform do, Doc, except put a man to sleep?'

'Anaesthetics aren't as simple as that I'm afraid, Mr Milligan.' The doctor poured them both a shot of O'Hara's best whisky before settling down in a leather chair by the fire. 'If Mr O'Hara had been in hospital to have an operation, he wouldn't have been allowed anything to eat or drink for at least four hours prior to surgery. But Mr O'Hara had just had a very large meal, and quite a lot to drink, I gather. Being anaesthetized on top of that lot, he could very easily have vomited, inhaled the fluid into his lungs and died.'

'Never,' Patrick Milligan replied, taking a deep draught of his whisky. 'I've never heard of such a thing.'

'Mr Milligan,' the doctor sighed, 'believe me, anaesthetics aren't playthings. And these fellows, these gangsters, kidnappers, what you will – what do they know about dosage? I tell you, they could have killed their victim not just by administering the chloroform when they did, but by the very amount they administered! They used enough to put four people to sleep! Oh yes, it's lucky they didn't have a corpse on their hands.'

Lucky? Patrick Milligan thought to himself. Lucky? Dear God, their guardian angel must have been passing overhead.

'I'll not be able to repay you,' Buck O'Hara said as he and Patrick Milligan sat in front of the fire, drinking to their mutual survival a fortnight later.

'Sure what did I do?' Pat Milligan asked, 'besides be in the right place at the right time?'

O'Hara smiled and drained his well-watered whisky. In the last week he had at last started to get some strength back, but the incident had considerably weakened him, and he was still finding even the smallest of tasks required a great deal of effort.

'Apparently it's the anaesthetic, Pat,' he explained, pulling the rug up over his knees. 'Apparently it takes much longer than you think to leave your system.'

'You'll be as right as rain in another few days, Buck,' Pat Milligan replied, draining his own glass. 'Ah sure we come from a strong people.'

'We do, Pat,' Buck agreed. 'None stronger.'

'Even so,' Pat Milligan said, rising to replenish their drinks. 'Even so.'

'Yes?' Buck enquired. 'I have the feeling you want to tell me something.'

Patrick Milligan returned with the two drinks. He set Buck O'Hara's down by his chair, and then went and stood for a moment to gaze into the fire. 'The thing is, Buck,' he said finally, 'and you can shoot me down here. But the thing is I don't think it's right. I don't think it's right for a man of your substance to walk around the city, how shall I put it? To walk around the streets unprotected. Not in this day and age.'

'It was an isolated incident,' Buck replied. 'A couple of kids probably, with some damn fool notion.'

'That's nonsense, Buck,' Pat Milligan retorted, 'and you know it. No man as wealthy as you can take that sort of risk! Didn't you read about that banker in Chicago? Only last week? They're holding him for a $1 million ransom! He walked out of his house to get in his car, and they snatched him there and then! In front of his wife and kids! I mean what sort of world are we all living in?'

'I have a large staff, Pat,' Buck replied. 'I have a driver, a butler, a staff here and at my country house. I'm hardly alone for one moment.'

'They wouldn't be able to do a thing, Buck,' Patrick Milligan replied. 'They'd be less than useless, believe me, if the real boyos wanted you bad enough.'

For a while they sat and drank their whisky in silence, while Buck O'Hara considered the danger.

'So who would I get?' Buck finally asked. 'I'd need people I could trust.'

'I have three good lads,' Pat Milligan replied. 'They're honest and strong.'

'Of course you have,' Buck agreed. 'And then there's yourself.'

'I suppose if you couldn't trust us, Buck,' Patrick Milligan sighed, 'who could you trust?'

'Grand,' Buck O'Hara smiled, extending his hand. 'That's a deal then.'

Dermot and Fergal were both at home playing brag when their father returned that night.

'When I was a boy,' he told them, as he sat down to celebrate with a bottle and three glasses, 'I spent many a long day fishing. But I've never waited so long as this for an old trout to take the bait.' He looked at his two eldest boys, and smiled at them, and they all grinned back.

'But jeeze, lads,' he sighed, 'it was a near run thing. You nearly killed the old boy with the chloroform, you eejits.'

Everything had gone.

'I can't see how you can have allowed it,' Artemis had said.

'There was nothing, regretfully,' one of the lawyers had replied, 'absolutely nothing we could do about it.'

'I simply don't believe it. My mother's instructions were crystal clear. Brougham was left to me.'

'Brougham was indeed left to you, Lady Artemis,' Mr Henry Grafton had agreed. 'The house and estate were left to you in their entirety.'

'Precisely,' Artemis had said. 'My point precisely.'

'Brougham was left to you, Lady Artemis, but not its contents,' Mr George Grafton interpolated, carefully, as if their client had not fully understood his brother's meaning the first time round. 'That was the loophole, do you see? The house, and the entire estate, yes, these were correctly bequeathed. But alas, and doubtless due to nothing more than just some careless legal wording in your late mother's will, your father and stepmother have been able to claim the contents.'

'Careless legal wording?' Artemis had enquired. 'Whose?'

'Not our's, I am happy to say, Lady Artemis,' Mr Arthur Grafton had volunteered. 'Grafton, Grafton and Grafton were not called upon to draw up your late mother's will.'

'I believe,' Mr Henry Grafton had added somewhat smugly, 'that your mother called upon the services of a small local solicitor.'

And so now as a result of some 'careless legal wording', everything that was Brougham was gone.

Artemis made her way slowly across the great marbled hall, staring at the empty niches where once had stood the perfectly sculpted statues of Bacchus and Diana, Venus and Apollo, and on into the saloon, where the late afternoon sunshine filtered down through the glass skylight at the top of the magnificently coffered ceiling on to the now empty room. All the fine Regency chairs and sofas were gone, as were the paintings hung high on the walls above the doorways. The urns and their plinths were gone, and so too the superb and delicate candelabra.

'They've even taken the doorhandles, Porter,' Artemis said to the butler, who was standing to her right, just behind her shoulder. 'Look.'

'Indeed, milady,' he replied, pointing. 'And the locks.'

They had taken all the portraits which had lined the great staircase, too. The tap of Artemis's stick echoed across the marbled floors as she made her way to the stairwell where she stood staring up at where the great paintings had hung. Gone, too, was the vast and famous chandelier which had hung in the hall and shone down on so many titled and famous faces, gone from the dining room the great eighteenth-century dining table, capable of seating sixty guests, yet made up in only three leaves, with its gold and silver centrepiece of three prancing horses crowned with garlands, and the gold plate presented to Artemis's great-grandfather to commemorate the signing of the Treaty of Vienna. The set of Coronation chairs, they were gone. Taken too the portrait of the Honourable Miss Deverill painted in 1795, the portrait by Romney of The Countess of Brighton, and the exquisite painting of Lady Mary Deverill in her riding habit executed on commission by Sargent.

They had taken everything, Artemis slowly realized. She had thought, when the lawyer had informed her of the loophole, that the removal would not be a wholesale one, rather that her father and stepmother would simply have taken a few of the things they liked and wanted, rather than strip the house bare of its entire contents.

But they had. They had taken everything.

The replica of the York Gold Cup, won by Heroic, her great-great-grandfather's most famous horse, the intricately designed gold wine coolers made by Paul Stirr in 1825, the Charles I Loving Cup, the James II candlesticks, every glass, every decanter, every salt cellar and pepperpot, every knife, spoon and fork, they had removed them all.

One picture remained in the drawing room, the portrait painted by Joseph Manning of Capers, her mother's favourite horse.

'I'm not surprised she left that,' Artemis said to Porter. 'I'm just surprised she left it undamaged.'

Otherwise there was not a thing left in the once magnificently furnished room.

'I mean,' Artemis said, almost under her breath, 'it looks as though the Barbarians have been in.'

Limping round the room, she stared at the marks on the walls where the pictures had hung, and the indentations on the floor where the priceless furniture had stood, and tried to remember what had been precisely where.

It was easy to remember where the large pieces had stood. Here for instance had been a Regency marble and colonnaded side-piece, which invariably bore a vast bowl full of her stepmother's favourite flowers. And there was where a fine eighteenth-century inlaid table had stood, undecorated by ornaments, to the side of one of the enormous gold and damask sofas, designed and constructed especially for the 4th Duke of Brougham. Here had been one of a pair of Queen Anne card tables, and there the other one, each set with two Hepplewhite arm chairs. And on the wood floor had lain a vast Persian rug, so huge it had taken twenty men to lay it, and which an eccentric female ancestor in a fit of pique and to annoy her husband had made her maids paint green.

There was absolutely nothing left in the drawing room now, except the great fireplace and the frescoes on the ceiling both of which had obviously proved irremovable, but for different reasons.

Upstairs, all the doors which had been forever closed to her during her childhood now stood open, revealing a succession of empty rooms. Ahead of Artemis, as she progressed slowly through the deserted chambers, ran Doodle and Scrap, her two terriers, barking excitedly and running round in circles, as if they also knew they were invading territory which had previously been forbidden to them. The excitement finally proved too much for Scrap, who chose to relieve himself against a pile of stained and moth-eaten cushions.

'I think that's fair comment, don't you, Porter?' Artemis said. 'After all, what Lady Deverill has left is really only fit for dogs, wouldn't you say? And how in heaven's name did they get the Charles I bed out of here?'

They had entered the State bedroom, where Queen Mary had stayed only a short time before.

'It was built for the bedroom, Porter,' Artemis continued, 'as you probably know. It couldn't have been removed through either doorway.'

'No, milady,' Porter replied. 'The estate carpenter was requested to dismantle what he could of it.'

'What he could of it, Porter?' Artemis asked, in astonishment.

'Yes, milady,' Porter said. 'I have to say there were portions which had to be sawn. Mr Dibbs did not take kindly to so doing. Even though Lady Deverill assured him those particular portions could be reassembled with adhesive.'

'Adhesive,' Artemis sighed, taking her weight on her stick in order to rest her bad leg. Such had been her stepmother's grim determination to remove everything that she had been quite prepared to cannibalize and thus ruin things which were really nothing if not irreplaceable.

Every piece of furniture was gone, and every painting.

Artemis stared at the walls of the State bedroom, at the rectangles and squares of brighter red where the pictures had hung and where as a result the original colour had been preserved over the centuries.

'Aren't the original colours bright, Porter?' she said. 'Look.' She pointed with her stick. 'One would never dream of painting walls that colour nowadays.'

'No, milady,' Porter agreed, 'I don't suppose one would.'

In another room, Artemis opened a door almost concealed in a wall and peered in to what had been a dressing room.

'They certainly made a first class job of it, Porter,' she said as she re-emerged. 'They even took the coat hangers.'

'Apparently their instructions were to remove everything, milady,' the butler replied. 'Even the lavender bags on the linen cupboard shelves.'

'Imagine,' said Artemis, reclosing the door in the wall.

'There's nothing left anywhere, milady,' Porter said sadly, unable to contain his emotions any longer. 'Everything was stripped. It was like locusts, milady. Like one would imagine a plague of locusts. One minute this place was as it always was –' He looked round him as they stood at the top of the main staircase and fell silent. Then he drew a deep breath and continued. 'One minute it was like as it always had been, milady, and the next minute all the years, the centuries, had all gone. We all took it hard, as you can imagine. But none so hard as poor Jenkins.'

'What about Jenkins?' Artemis asked almost harshly, for in all the time she had spent wandering forlornly through the great house, she had never once given a thought to the stables, because she had assumed they fell outside her stepmother's province.

'You didn't know, milady?' Porter asked, in obvious surprise. 'You mean they didn't tell you?'

Artemis didn't even bother to enquire as to what they had failed to tell her. She just knew the news had to be bad, worse than anything which had happened so far. She couldn't run, but she could hurry, which she did, and as best as she could. Porter followed on behind, watching her as she hobbled across the marbled floors, stabbing her stick down impatiently with every step in an effort to gain more speed. He wished he could pick her up and carry her, so touching was her haste, but he knew that even if he could there would be little point because the damage was irreparable.

'Stay here, Porter,' Artemis ordered as they reached the front doors. 'Thank you for your help, but there's no point in you coming over to the yard.'

'No, milady,' the butler said, closing the great doors behind her. No, there was no point at all. Because there was nothing he could do. There was nothing anyone could do.

'Jenkins!' Artemis called, as she hobbled with great difficulty across the cobble stones. 'Jenkins! It's me! Lady Artemis! Jenkins!'

He appeared behind her, from one of the many open and empty stables Artemis had passed, and when she turned and saw him, at first she couldn't believe it was him. Jenkins had always been so upright, and square shouldered, clean shaven and ruddy cheeked. Now before her stood an old man, a man with a stoop, with stubble on his chin, and when Artemis got near him, the smell of drink on his breath.

'Jenkins?' she said quietly.

'Milady.' Jenkins took off his cap, and ran a dirty hand through his thin grey hair. 'I'm sorry, milady,' he muttered. 'But no-one 'as told me you was comin'.'

Even had Jenkins looked her in the eye, which he did not, Artemis would have known something was dreadfully wrong, simply by the fact that he had been wearing his old cap back to front. Jenkins only ever did that when there was trouble, in times of crisis, like when a mare was late foaling and he suspected twins, or if a horse was badly lame the morning after a hard day's hunting, or worst of all, when he was waiting for the veterinary to come and put one of his old friends out of their misery.

'They've all gone, Lady Artemis,' he told her, before she even had to ask what was amiss. 'Every blessed animal.'

'What do you mean, Jenkins!' Artemis said, now hurrying from stable to stable in search of her beloved horses. 'Gone? What in God's name do you mean?'

'They took 'em all, milady,' Jenkins explained, catching Artemis up as she entered the stable building which housed all the loose boxes. 'They took all our 'orses. Ragtime, The Poacher, Ladyjane, Joxer, Clem, Sutton Lad, Principal Boy, the yearlings, even old Jenny, who's no use to anyone with those feet of her'n. Took 'em all so they did, every blessed one. An' I'll not vouch they'll be keepin' 'em all neither, milady. Not Lady Deverill. She don't 'ave no time for some of 'em. Most of all Ragtime. She can't stand that 'orse at no costs, she can't, 'cos 'e's smarter 'an 'er. But 'e's never given 'er a bad day out, not the once.'

Artemis was listening to every word he said, although she didn't look at him once. Her eyes were too busy searching, in case he was mistaken, in case they had missed some. But all the loose boxes were empty, and when Artemis hurried through to the tack room, she found every peg was bare. There wasn't a saddle or a bridle to be seen anywhere.

There were some they might have missed, Artemis suddenly thought, in fact some they almost certainly would have missed, she assured herself, as she turned and hurried from the immaculate wood panelled tack room and out into the paddocks behind.

'Get your motorbike, Jenkins!' Artemis called to Jenkins as he followed on slowly behind her. 'I want you to take me over to Drover's!'

'There's no point, milady,' Jenkins answered.

'Of course there is, Jenkins!' Artemis replied. 'I want to see the ponies!'

Jenkins didn't answer. Instead an ominous silence settled on the late afternoon air.

'Jenkins?' Artemis turned, and saw that Jenkins was still standing by the door of the tack room, staring down at the ground. 'Jenkins?'

'They're gone as well, milady,' he replied. 'Both of 'em.'

'Gone?' Artemis said. 'Gone – but gone where, Jenkins? They can't have gone! Buttons and Paintbox? They're both old! I mean nobody'd want them!'

'No, milady,' Jenkins answered quite miserably, twisting his cap in his hands and still staring at the ground.

'No, Jenkins,' Artemis finally said. 'It's not true.'

'I'm afraid it is, milady,' Jenkins answered. 'Her ladyship sent 'em both to George.'

'No, Jenkins, no,' Artemis found herself repeating. 'No, no, not George. I don't believe it's true.'

George was the local meat man. Often, when Artemis had been out hacking in the park as a little girl, and long before she had heard his van approach, the pony she was riding, be it Buttons, or Paintbox, would suddenly snatch up its bit, or shy and run away from the estate wall, or simply bolt in the opposite direction to the oncoming vehicle. Because they could smell the fear of other animals long before Artemis could even hear the sound of an engine, and they would run as fast as their legs would carry them away from the butcher. Other times Artemis might be lying out in the long grass by the paddocks when George's van passed by, and she would see the young animals stop grazing and prick their ears to listen to the plaintive whinnies from the animals captive in the back of George's van. The horses in the paddocks would call back, as more desperate cries would be heard from the back of the van, before it disappeared finally out of earshot. It would be a long while before the horses in the paddock returned to their grazing, particularly the older ones, who would stand staring into the distance rather than resume their eating.

And now her beloved Buttons and Paintbox had been sold off for meat, taken off in the hated van to be butchered.

Artemis walked back into the tack room, and in the cupboard in the corner where any tack which was either no longer required, or that needed mending was put, looked for and found a pony size bridle. It was clean, and the beautifully hand sewn name on the browband, a present one Christmas to Artemis from her absent godmother, was still there for all to see. 'Buttons', it said.

'How much did she get for them, Jenkins?' Artemis asked.

'No more 'n five pounds for both I imagine, your ladyship,' the groom replied.

Five pounds. For Buttons and Paintbox.

She had taken everything. The gold, the silver, the paintings, the glassware, the china, the books, the furniture, the rugs and the horses. She was welcome to everything, if only she would give back the horses.

Artemis limped back alone to the house, clasping in her free hand the tiny bridle, back across the park with its lake, and woods, ornamental gardens and rolling pastures, up the great flight of stone steps and into the dark and empty house.

'For as long as you can afford its *upkeep*, Lady Artemis,' Mr Henry Grafton said as tactfully as he could, 'Brougham is yours.'

'Its upkeep,' Artemis repeated, more as a statement than as a question.

'Estates such as Brougham need astute management,' Mr Arthur Grafton added. 'Otherwise they perish, the victims of profligacy.'

'Fortunately your grandfather – ' Mr George Grafton began.

'Your grandfather fortunately had been somewhat less profligate than others we might mention,' Mr Henry Grafton continued, 'and so when your mother died – '

'When your mother died, precisely so,' Mr Arthur Grafton interrupted, 'the death duties were able to be met without an undue strain being placed on the family resources.'

'It did, however, mean selling North Park Square,' Mr Henry Grafton reminded his brother.

'Indeed it did,' Mr George Grafton agreed. 'It also involved selling – '

'It also involved selling Cumberland Avenue, precisely so,' Mr Arthur Grafton concluded. 'But alas North Park Square and Cumberland Avenue were the last of the family's London holdings.'

'Do we have any other "holdings"?' Artemis enquired.

'There are some shops somewhere in the north of England,' Mr Henry Grafton admitted.

'There are some shops in the north of England somewhere,' his brother Arthur agreed.

'A little bit of fishing in Aberdeen,' Mr Henry Grafton added with a small sigh.

'And there's a shoot somewhere,' Mr George Grafton volunteered.

'There is a shoot in Yorkshire,' Mr Arthur Grafton concurred. 'But very little else.'

'How much will it require to run Brougham?' Artemis asked.

The three brothers all looked at each other, and to a man all cleared their throats. The senior brother, Mr Arthur Grafton, then picked up a buff folder and turning it the right way around for her, placed it on the desk in front of Artemis. Artemis examined it in silence, and for a long time.

'It's no good, I'm afraid,' she said finally. 'I don't understand one word of this.'

Mr Arthur Grafton picked up a wooden ruler and still from his side of the desk ran it down a column. 'These are rents,' he explained. 'And these, and these, and these. These – that is what the various farms yield, when they do yield, and these are what they lose, when they lose.'

'Which at the moment is usually the case,' Mr Henry Grafton added with a grim smile.

'Which indeed is usually the case,' Mr George Grafton agreed. 'Indeed.'

'These figures here –' Mr Arthur Grafton continued, 'these are wages, these are wages, and these and these and these –'

'Please,' said Artemis. 'In nursery language. If I am to live at Brougham –'

'Were you to live at Brougham,' Mr Henry Grafton began.

'Were you to live at Brougham,' Mr Arthur Grafton

interrupted, 'you would need to generate an income of at least this amount.' He tapped a figure on the last page of the accounts with his ruler, and then sat back.

Artemis stared at the amount, which was so unreal to her it seemed magical. 'And where am I expected to find such monies?' she enquired.

The question was initially met with silence, and then another series of looks exchanged between the three brothers.

'George?' Mr Arthur Grafton said. Poor George, Artemis thought, looking at the youngest of the brothers, poor soul, he would get the dirty work.

'Under happier circumstances, Lady Artemis,' he said, having first mopped his brow with a handkerchief, 'let us say the sale of a few treasures . . .'

Artemis just stared at him, astounded by such a suggestion.

'Perfectly proper procedure, Lady Artemis,' Mr Arthur Grafton explained, reading his client's expression correctly. 'Happens all the time.'

'But of course under these more unfortunate circumstances,' poor Mr George Grafton was continuing.

'Under the circumstances my brother George is of course quite right, Lady Artemis,' Mr Henry Grafton chipped in. 'There are no treasures remaining.'

'There are the farms,' Artemis suddenly remembered. 'What about all the farms? They must be worth something.'

'The bank has a charge on all the farmland, Lady Artemis,' Mr Arthur Grafton explained.

'So how am I expected to raise these monies?' Artemis demanded to know, as if she had been directly insulted.

'You have a lot of trees,' Mr Arthur Grafton suggested. 'You could expect a fair sum if you sold all the timber on the estate.'

'During the war, Lady Artemis,' Mr George Grafton informed her, 'your father was offered £120,000 by the government for all the timber on Brougham. Had he accepted the offer –' George continued, oblivious to the stares of his brothers, 'that would have balanced the books nicely. But he refused. "I should say not," he said apparently. "Sell the woodland? I should say not. What's a man fighting for?" '

'Of course,' Artemis agreed, similarly unable to imagine a deforested Brougham, 'and quite right too.' She looked at the astronomical sum at the bottom of the relevant page once more, before looking back up at her lawyers. 'If I did manage to raise these monies,' she asked, 'how much would I have to live on?'

Mr Arthur Grafton looked at the upside figures and then removed his spectacles in order to wipe them. 'That is a minimum requirement, Lady Artemis,' he explained. 'Given that you are able to generate this income, you yourself could not expect to take more than say one thousand two hundred pounds per annum from the estate.'

'Really?' Artemis asked, curiously, turning back through the folder to another page which she began to scan thoroughly. 'One thousand two hundred, you say. And yet – ' she stopped, her finger by some figures, 'I see I am expected to pay my land agent two thousand nine hundred per annum, and my lawyers, your firm, Mr Grafton, I have to pay the three of you seven and a half thousand pounds. Per annum.' Artemis closed the folder with a finality that suggested she wanted to have nothing more to do with it. Then she looked across the desk challengingly at the three lawyers, as if to await their suggestion.

'George?' Mr Arthur Grafton sighed once more, but this time with deep resignation.

'If you cannot generate this income, Lady Artemis,' he said quietly, and apologetically, 'I am very much afraid you only have one course left open to you. And that is to sell.'

It was what she had been dreading to hear, but knew full well that she must. She had known it the day when she found all the horses and her beloved ponies gone, and had walked back into the vast and empty, and already dusty house. She had known there was no way she could support such a place, refurnish it, heat it, staff it and maintain it, unless there was also a large bequest to go along with the inheritance of the great house.

'I have no alternative?' she asked.

'You have an alternative,' Mr Henry Grafton admitted, looking round to his elder brother.

'You could sue your father and stepmother,' Mr Arthur Grafton announced.

'I'm sorry,' Artemis replied. 'But that is quite out of the question.'

'In that case, Lady Artemis,' Mr Arthur Grafton continued, 'you may well have to sell.'

'In which case, Mr Grafton,' Artemis replied, 'you have my instructions to do so.'

'You are aware, Lady Artemis,' Mr Henry Grafton enquired, 'that these large country houses are no longer – shall we say – inviolable?'

'Meaning?' Artemis asked in return.

'Not everybody wants them, Lady Artemis,' Mr Henry Grafton replied. 'Not any more.'

'Not once they've bled them dry, you mean, Mr Grafton.'

Artemis rose, picked up her gloves, handbag and walking stick, and limped over to the door. Before she finally departed, she turned round and looked at them all, from under the turned up brim of her hat.

'Please inform me of the valuation,' she said, 'and *when* Brougham is sold. But I have absolutely no interest in to *whom*.'

It was now only a month until they were to be married. And Patsy still couldn't understand.

'You don't have to, Patsy,' Ellie retorted. 'Because as I keep telling you, it's none of your business.'

'You're my sister, dammit!' Patsy replied.

'So what! That doesn't give you the right to tell me who I should or shouldn't marry!' Ellie exclaimed angrily, and hurried out of her bedroom and downstairs. Patsy followed her, arguing all the while. Ever since Ellie's engagement had been made official, Ellie and he had hardly exchanged one civil word.

'I think it's disgusting!' her brother shouted at her down the stairs.

'I know you do!' Ellie shouted back. 'And I couldn't care!'

Patsy ran down the stairs, taking the last four in one leap, and throwing himself between his sister and the front door. 'Ellie for the last time think what you're doing!' he implored his sister. 'A girl like you – c'mon! You could marry anybody!'

'You said it, Patsy,' Ellie answered. 'I could marry anybody. And that's just who I would marry if I stayed round here, Anybody. Not somebody – a nobody! And have to spend the rest of my life like I spent the first part! On my hands and knees scrubbing floors and up to my elbows washing up! Thanks Patsy, but no. This way I get out of here. I get out of this no-hope part of town. This way I get some sort of a life.'

'What sort of a life?' her brother challenged. 'As a rich man's floozie? That's a life? What sort of life are you looking at? Everyone else thinks O'Hara's a dirty old man! And that you're just an adventuress! That you're marrying him for his money!'

'Well they're right,' Ellie said coolly, looking up at her brother now she'd finished buttoning her gloves. 'I am marrying for money. And so would you, Patsy, if you got the chance.'

'I'd rather shoot myself!'

'Of course you would,' Ellie agreed. 'Rather than be given the chance to chuck up your rotten underpaid job with that two bit insurance company, and move out of this miserable dump – '

'This is not a miserable dump!' Patsy yelled at her. 'This is our goddam home!'

'You mean this is your goddam home!' Ellie replied

hotly. 'A home I made for you! Well I'm not going to spend the rest of my life doing it! Making a home for you lot, OK? Somewhere for all of you men to come back and collapse all over the place with your feet up, and moan about how hard life is! While I've spent the day clearing up the mess you've all made! And shopping for your food! And changing your bedding! And cooking for you! And washing your filthy clothes! I'm not going to be the one to turn away the chance of a lifetime!' Ellie checked her hat in the mirror and then prepared to leave.

'You'll regret this, Ellie,' Patsy warned her, 'believe me, but you will.'

'Why?' Ellie asked. 'What's there to regret? Nothing. Not a thing.' But then she smiled and put a hand to her brother's cheek. 'I'll miss you though. That I will do,' she said. 'I'll miss you like crazy. Now I must hurry — or I'll be late for my wedding fitting.'

Ellie kissed her youngest brother on the cheek and gave him one last look, before hurrying out to the waiting Cadillac.

Artemis liked Boston. She had liked New York, liked its urgency, its energy, its informality. It was all such a different world from the one in which she had been living, from the polite sobriety of Brougham and its environs, and she found it heady and intoxicating. Diana Lanchester whose idea it had been to invite Artemis to cross the Atlantic with her once she had heard the news about Brougham, affected a boredom with the city, pretending to find it brash and vulgar, which Artemis didn't believe for a minute, particularly once she had watched Diana at work in business and at play socially.

'I can't imagine why you don't live here all the time,' Artemis told her. 'You're right. It makes England seem so stuffy.'

Diana had laughed and said if she lived in New York all the time, she'd be dead in a year, so fast was the pace.

'I don't believe that for a moment, Diana. Everybody here seems so much more alive, you couldn't die, they wouldn't let you.'

'Well if you like it that much, darling, one day when you've got oodles of boodle again *you* can come back and live here.'

'Actually I don't think I'd mind that much,' said Artemis after giving it some thought. 'In fact I think I'd rather enjoy it.'

'Wait till you've been to Boston, darling,' Diana warned her. 'Boston will soon change your mind.'

But the very opposite was true. The more Artemis saw of America, the more she fell in love with it. She ignored the countryside as they rail-roaded through it, preferring to read, because, as she explained to her godmother, all she'd ever seen as she was growing up was countryside. When they reached their destinations, which so far besides New York had included trips to Cleveland, Pittsburg, Baltimore, Washington, New Haven and finally now Boston, Artemis came alive.

'You know you're behaving just like a tourist, darling,' her godmother teased her. 'It's as if you've never seen a city.'

'I haven't really, if you think about it. Not besides London.'

In Boston, Diana's day was one long business appointment, which left Artemis even more time than usual to explore the museums and art galleries, the shops and the places of interest. She found it a beautiful city, formal and spacious, old fashioned yet energized.

'I'm going to shop for some clothes tomorrow,' she told her godmother one evening over dinner. 'I suddenly realized if we're to dine with your cousins, I haven't anything really very formal to wear.'

'You'll certainly need something formal, darling,' Diana drawled. 'Because the Rossdale-Douglasses are nothing if not very formal. There's a very good department store you could try, on Main Street. O'Hagan's, I think it's called. No – O'Hara's, that's it. They have some quite nice things.'

'You mean they have things I can afford,' Artemis corrected her.

'We have to walk before we can run, darling,' Diana replied. 'And you have a lot to learn about money. Such as not spending that which you don't have.'

'I don't think I'll ever be good with money,' Artemis said. 'I find it so confusing.'

'You're going to have to get good at it, darling,' Diana warned her. 'Things are changing P.D.Q., especially for them such as us. So you're going to have to learn all about the filthy stuff, or else you'll go to the wall, like a lot of one's forebears.'

'It would be so much easier, don't you think?' Artemis asked, 'if the bank could just hand it out to one. Like Nanny did with the biscuits. Then one wouldn't have to worry about it.'

'That's something we can learn from the Yanks, darling,' Diana said. 'They don't mind talking about money, and they're *very* good at making it work.'

But deep down inside, Artemis didn't really believe she could ever be like that. It wasn't a snobbish thing, she didn't find discussing money a vulgarity, it just deeply embarrassed her. And never more so than when she heard how little her beloved Brougham had fetched at a private sale.

'Any idea who bought it?' Diana had asked her on the voyage over.

'None whatsoever,' Artemis replied. 'I'm not interested.'

'But you know what it fetched.'

'Not much.'

'And you're not really interested in that either.'

'Not really. What's the point?'

'None, really.'

Diana had smiled and poured them both another gin.

'I can't say I much enjoyed saying goodbye to Jenks,' Artemis said after she had taken a sip of her drink.

'And I wouldn't have missed not walking round the stables for the last time. But there you are. No-one made me do it.'

'You're beginning to sound more and more like your mother,' said Diana, adding, 'God bless her.'

'Can you manage all right, lady?' the cab driver asked as he leaned back and opened Artemis's door without moving from his driving seat.

'Yes, thank you, driver,' Artemis replied, pulling herself to the edge of the seat.

'Listen,' the driver said, 'there's no need for that! Hey – Mac!' The driver gave a shrill whistle to one of the store doormen, who at once came hurrying across.

'No really –' Artemis began to protest.

'OK, Mac –' the driver continued, ignoring Artemis's protest. 'Give this lady a hand, would ya? And see her into the store. You just take care of her, right? She's from England.'

The doorman helped Artemis carefully out of the cab and held her elbow while the driver handed him her stick.

'My aunt has a stick,' he grinned. 'And she's just like you. Stubborn as a mule. You take care of yourself now. You hear me?'

Artemis turned to smile her thanks to him, but he was gone, away back into the busy traffic. The doorman was intending to take her elbow all the way to the swing doors, but Artemis removed her elbow from his hand and made her own way into the store.

It was bright and busy, and smart. That was another thing which so impressed Artemis wherever she shopped. The girls were smart, and so were the shops.

'Can I help you, madam?' a floorwalker asked. 'Is there something you're looking for in particular?'

'I want to see something for the evening,' Artemis replied. 'Something for this evening.'

'Of course, madam,' the floorwalker said, leading the

way, but at Artemis's pace. 'I'll have someone take you up to model gowns. Helen?'

A tall redheaded girl, with an hour-glass figure and perfect teeth escorted Artemis up to the required department and didn't leave her until she had found the right assistant.

'There,' she said before she departed. 'Jodie here will look after you really well, madam. I hope you find something nice.'

The salesgirl showed Artemis to a comfortable armchair, and Artemis sank gratefully into its soft upholstery.

'I'll bring over a selection, and if you tell me which ones you like, madam, I can have a girl show them on for you.'

'If I buy something,' Artemis warned her, 'I should need to have it altered.'

'That would be no problem, madam,' the girl replied.

'I'd need it by this evening.'

'That would be no problem at all.'

She brought Artemis such a clever selection of gowns, that Artemis found it almost impossible to choose just one.

'Perhaps when you see them on, madam,' the girl said, signalling for a model. 'Though I feel this one, in the very fashionable shade of rose-opaline, I think this will look quite wonderful on you.'

While she waited for the model, Artemis pretended to flick through a magazine, while all the time watching the comings and the goings in the busy department. Everyone, she noticed, was accorded the same personal treatment, and Artemis could only suppose whoever owned and ran the store had to be someone of the highest sensibility.

And then she saw the girl in the wedding dress, and abandoned all pretence at reading her magazine. She had never seen a vision like it, nor a girl so beautiful. She had come out of a room down the end of the department, in a luminescent white silk wedding gown, with two girls behind carrying the train. She looked so young and so pure that everyone nearby stopped what they were doing and turned to see her. Some gasped, others looked as though they were going to applaud. Artemis just stared.

The girl was willowy and perfectly shaped, and her dark brown hair was caught back in a beautifully sculpted pearl and silk headdress. The dress itself seemed alive, so luculent was the silk, and when the young girl moved, she seemed to shimmer. But above all, and what Artemis noticed most even above the beauty of the dress and whole effect of serenity, were the girl's large dark eyes, set in a beautiful milk-white face.

'That is the future Mrs O'Hara,' the salesgirl said, who was staring, too. 'Isn't she quite beautiful?'

'Yes,' Artemis replied. 'Very.'

'She is going to make a very beautiful bride,' the salesgirl continued.

'Yes, she is,' Artemis agreed, without a trace of envy. 'Extremely.'

'She has the most wonderful trousseau,' the salesgirl confided. 'As far as Mr O'Hara is concerned, nothing is too good for Miss Milligan. Everything is hand embroidered with her initials, and everything is of the finest materials, silks, satins, crêpe de Chine, cashmeres. We all think it's just like a fairy-tale. Because Miss Milligan is *so* beautiful. And Mr O'Hara – well, we all just love him. He is such a sweet gentleman.'

'Mr O'Hara,' Artemis said. 'Isn't this store called O'Hara's?'

'Yes, madam,' the salesgirl replied. 'Miss Milligan is marrying Mr O'Hara, our proprietor. Look, that's him there.'

The girl picked up the newspaper which was lying beside Artemis on the sofa and indicated a photograph. It was of the beautiful doe-eyed girl dancing with a kindly faced gentleman who was, it appeared, old enough to be her grandfather. Artemis stared at it and nodded.

'Really?' she said. 'Well.' Her eyes widened slightly, but that was all Artemis said.

When she was small, Nanny had been in the habit of reading out details of such marriages and liaisons from her Sunday paper, and expressing her disgust for any great difference in age with a snort of disapproval. 'Disgusting,' she would say. 'Some girls will do anything for money.'

Artemis turned away from the vision in front of her and concentrated instead on the first of the models who had appeared wearing one of the earmarked gowns.

'Thank you,' Artemis said, once the girl had shown the gown off. 'I like that one very much.'

She liked all of them, but finally selected a figure-hugging pastel blue silk with a deeply scooped out back.

'If you wouldn't mind,' Artemis said, holding out one hand to the salesgirl so that she might be helped to her feet. 'I should like to go and try this one on now.'

'Of course, madam,' the girl replied. 'This way, please.'

Artemis followed the girl across the floor to where the fitting rooms were to be found, keeping her gaze to the front of her. It was always better, she had found, not to look at other people too closely, that way they were spared any embarrassment they might feel looking at her, and so she passed the future Mrs O'Hara.

'I have something for you, Ellie,' Buck said when they had finished dinner. 'Or rather I thought I had,' he added, after searching his pockets. 'It's my age. I guess I must have left it behind in the apartment. Would you mind stopping by so as I can give it to you on your way home?'

Ellie hesitated for a moment before accepting Buck O'Hara's invitation to accompany him to his apartment. It had always been an unspoken agreement between them that after their evenings out, Ellie would be driven straight back to Westfield after Buck had been dropped off home by his chauffeur.

'I'm sure it could wait until tomorrow,' Ellie said, finishing her coffee. 'Until we have lunch.'

'Of course it could,' Buck agreed, 'but I don't want it to. I feel I have to give this to you tonight. Don't ask me why. I don't know why. I guess it's something in the stars.'

'Of course,' said Ellie. 'I understand. I often get those sort of compulsive feelings myself.'

'Yes,' Buck said thoughtfully as they rose from the table. 'Yes, I guess that's exactly what I feel this is. I guess this is something compulsive.'

When the Cadillac pulled up by the private entrance to the store and Buck got out to open the door, as she followed him Ellie noticed yet again the plain brown sedan that was now parking about ten yards down the street.

'They really are necessary, are they?' Ellie asked once more as they entered the building. 'I mean are they going to follow us around everywhere when we're married?'

'Don't worry,' Buck smiled as they got in the elevator, 'we won't take 'em with us to Europe.'

'Who are they, anyway?' Ellie asked. 'I've never seen them get out of their car.'

'And hopefully you won't have to,' Buck reassured her, but even so he still did not reveal his bodyguards' identity. Patrick Milligan had not considered that to be a good idea.

'There's a lot to be said, as they say, for anonymity,' Patrick Milligan had laughed. 'Particularly by those who don't know you.'

'It's not such a bad idea, Eleanor,' Buck told her as they got out of the elevator. 'We don't want you ever to be in a position where you might be required to pay out a lot of good money for this old hasbeen.'

Ellie smiled, and while Buck was searching for the gift he had left behind him, sat down at the boudoir grand and started to play.

Buck came out of his bedroom carrying a small box in his hand. He placed it on the piano in front of Ellie.

'I left it on the dresser,' he said. 'No – don't stop playing. You play so well. Open that when you've finished.'

He stood by the piano and watched with an aching heart as Ellie played. She was so beautiful, with her dark eyes and pale skin, her pretty little mouth and just perfect figure. He died to tell her how wonderful he thought she was, how sweet, and funny, loving and concerned, and most of all he died to tell her quite how much he loved her. But he didn't, because he couldn't. He couldn't tell her he loved her, because if he did she would run away and he would lose her.

So he just watched her instead. He watched her play the piano, while his heart seemed to break in his chest, and he said nothing, except to congratulate her.

'I don't believe you never had a lesson,' he said. 'It just isn't fair.'

'I really should go home now, Buck,' she replied, smiling back at his smile. 'Don't you think I should go home?'

'After you've played "I Can't Give You Anything But Love",' Buck said. 'I love that song, and I love the way you play it.'

'So,' Ellie agreed. 'I'll play it once, but then I must go home.'

'No you must not,' Buck said quietly, and Ellie fell silent, afraid for a moment lest Buck was about to try and break their agreement. 'I'm afraid you're not going home, Ellie, you're not going anywhere. Not until you've opened this.' He pushed the small dark-red box across the top of the piano, nearer to Ellie.

'Would you like me to open it now?' Ellie asked.

'If you would,' Buck replied. 'Sure.'

The box was of wood, covered in velvet, the stuff of Ellie's dreams. Inside, the lid was lined with a dark blue satin that was almost black, the other half containing a cushion, again made of velvet, the crevice of which held a diamond ring.

All Ellie could do was frown. She frowned at the ring as

if it shouldn't be there, then she frowned in bewilderment up at Buck for being the person who put it there, and then she frowned back at the blinky and quivery and glimmerous stone.

'Put it on, Ellie,' Buck said. 'Why don't you?'

'But what's it for, Buck?' Ellie asked.

'It's for you, Ellie.'

'You've already given me an engagement ring, Buck.'

'I know I have. This one's for eternity.'

Ellie put it on the third finger of her left hand and stared at it some more. It blinked back at her, alive with light, like a star plucked from the night sky.

'Good,' Buck smiled. 'Now play me the song.'

Ellie played the introduction.

'And I'll sing it,' Buck added. 'If you don't mind.'

He really must have once been a fine lyric tenor, Ellie thought again, as she listened to Buck sing. His voice was still very pure, but no longer quite so strong, but that was only noticeable towards the end of the held notes. And his pitch was still perfect, his manner of singing affectionate and wry.

Dream awhile —
Scheme awhile — you're sure to find —
Happiness — and I guess —
All those things you've always pined for —

Buck hadn't been looking at her, he'd been standing with one hand clasped to one lapel, the other deep in a jacket pocket, facing away from her, as if singing to a roomful of people. But now at the end of the line he turned as they both paused fractionally, and looked at her with the light of love in his eyes. And Ellie couldn't help but smile back at him, and at the sweetness of his face.

Then they continued the song.

Gee I like to see you looking swell, baby
Big diamond rings that Woolworths wouldn't sell,
baby!

Ellie laughed at Buck's adaptation of the lyrics, while the ring on her finger flashed with light.

And as Buck looked again at the young girl at the piano, the ache in his heart was very real.

But till that lucky day you know full well, baby –

But then what had been just an ache in his heart turned to a pain in his chest, an agonizing, brutal pain that shot down his left arm and up into his throat. A second later he fell to the floor, his eyes wide open, his song unfinished.

'You killed him.'

Ellie paid no attention, sitting quite still and staring ahead of her.

'You killed him, you hussy. And if you didn't, you did the very next best thing.'

She had been on her feet the moment he fell, as he crashed against the piano, his collar grasped by both his hands. But by the time she knelt at his side it seemed the life had already gone from him.

'No impropriety indeed.'

'There was no impropriety, I keep telling you that.'

'Impropriety or no – you've ruined us all.'

Patrick Milligan sighed and poured himself some more whisky, while Ellie gritted her teeth and looked out into space.

The doctor had thought the same. 'The best way to go, I suppose,' he had said, as he closed up his bag. 'I have to say when I go, this is the way I'd want it. A night on the town with a pretty girl – no no.' And then a telling pause. 'It has to be the best way to go. That'll do fine by me, any day, any night. Particularly any night.'

'He was just singing, that's all,' Ellie had explained to him, as she tried to explain to everyone. 'I was playing the piano for him, and he was singing. He was just singing this song!'

'Which song would that be now?' her father had asked, sarcastically. ' "The Last Rose of Summer" maybe?'

'Does it matter which song! It doesn't matter which song! He's dead!'

'Yes he is so — and you killed him, you hussy. You couldn't wait until you were decently married —'

'What do you think you're *saying*! He was just singing! Just standing there singing! He died while he was singing!'

'I never heard the likes of it. I never heard of a man dying from singing.'

'Well Buck did!' Ellie cried. 'That's exactly how Buck died!' She sank to the sofa and put her head in her hands.

Her father straightened his shoulders and sniffed. 'And as for there being no impropriety,' he went on, 'I should never have listened to that old goat next door. Ach, I know you were both fully dressed — but what of it! That's not to say that earlier on in the night there'd not been any *impropriety*. Can you imagine what people are saying? Sure the whole town's full of it! Did you hear tell of old Milligan's hussy of a daughter? And that dirty old Buck O'Hara? Ah sure the whole of Boston's talking about nothing else.'

It had been there and now it was gone. One moment she had a future and now she was back in her past. Yesterday there had been a tomorrow, today there was just today. Buck O'Hara was dead, and gone was the hope Ellie'd had for a life. And yet —

'Died on the nest, that's what they're saying. You know that, don't you? They're saying, if you're listening, if you're even remotely interested, that Buck O'Hara died on the nest!'

And yet there was still a light under the door which had seemed once more to be shut tight on Ellie. They had been going to sail to Europe for their honeymoon. First-class, adjoining cabins and a private lounge.

'Have you no shame?' her father demanded, coming round to stand in front of his daughter, blocking out her daydream.

She looked up at him, weary of his bullying, tired of his brutality. 'No,' she said. 'I have no shame. Why should I? The only shame I have is the shame I feel for you.'

She knew he'd hit her, but she didn't care. She didn't even feel it, not the pain anyway. She was only aware of the trickle of warm blood running out from one side of her nose.

'You've ruined us all!' he roared. 'You little slut! You jezebel!'

'And why should you be ruined?' Ellie calmly asked, taking a handkerchief from her purse to hold to her nose. 'You couldn't be ruined by Buck's death. Not unless you were up to something.'

'We weren't up to anything, do you hear? We'd just got ourselves gainfully employed, you might say. Mighty gainfully employed. And now you've put your spoke in our wheels and crashed the cart all right.'

'You were working for Buck?' Ellie asked, with a sudden thought, as she remembered the parked sedan full of big men. 'You and the "broth"?'

'We were working for O'Hara, that's right. I'd got us all a very good job. The sort of job a man can work up from. Until he makes it one hell of a good job.'

'How did you do it?' Ellie asked curiously. 'Buck might have been a rich man but he was no soft touch.'

'A rich man like him needed *protecting*! A man like that, with his money, walking round the streets like he was anybody! He needed protecting, we gave it to him, your brothers and I.'

'The only thing Buck needed protection from, Pa, was from people like you,' Ellie replied, before she rose and walked out of the house.

6

'Your tickets and passport are in the desk, darling!' Diana called to Artemis from her bedroom as they dressed for Artemis's final evening in Boston. 'Don't forget!'

'I wish I wasn't going,' Artemis called back, half turning to examine the back of her new gown in the mirror. 'I'm sure it's going to be frightfully dull after America.'

'Ireland is never dull,' her godmother announced, coming into the drawing room of their suite. 'The one thing you are guaranteed to get going to Ireland is a good time. And the one thing you must always remember is never to believe one blind word anyone says.'

The tickets and the passports were in the desk. Buck had showed them to her, before they had gone out for the last time, and sure enough, there they still were, stowed neatly inside the lavishly illustrated brochure for the S.S. *Baltimore*. Ellie took the entire package out of the drawer and slipped it into her purse.

'Did you find what you were looking for, Miss Milligan?' her late fiancé's private secretary asked her as he escorted her from the deserted offices, just as he had escorted her into them over a year before when taking her to meet his employer for the first time.

'Yes thank you, Richard,' Ellie replied, and then hesitated. 'But you won't say anything about this to anyone, will you, Richard?' She looked beseechingly at the young man, knowing that in reality her secret was safe. Richard had been quite hopelessly in love with her since their very first encounter, a fact he kept well concealed from his employer, but which he was not quite so good at hiding from Ellie.

'Why!' Madame used to laugh on the way down in the elevator, 'It is wonderful! I nevaire see such cow eyes! He follow you round like a little dog!'

'I won't tell a soul, Miss Milligan,' Richard replied gravely. 'You have my word.'

'If anybody does find out,' Ellie continued, 'they might say something to somebody else – and in no time at all it could get back to my father. And since I'm not yet twenty-one, you see ... And he wouldn't just stop me leaving, Richard. Believe me. He'd take his belt to me. Like he always has.' Ellie was ashamed of what she had said, even though it was the truth. She was ashamed both of the truth and of having to use it to buy his silence.

'No-one, I promise you, Miss Milligan, will ever know a thing.'

'You won't ever know what this means,' Ellie told him as they waited for Buck's private elevator to arrive.

Richard cleared his throat. 'Are you going to be away for long?' he asked as casually as he could.

'No, and yes, in a way. That is, I just want time to think, Richard, you know, sort myself out?'

Richard smiled at her as the lift doors closed. It was the sort of smile that tried to say nothing and said everything, and looking up at him Ellie knew at once that she had been right to lie. It would be a long time until she saw him again. Or America.

'Why don't you come with me, Patsy?' Ellie asked him in a low voice, but her brother shook his head.

They were sitting in their local drugstore, in front of two as yet untouched milkshakes.

'I've enough money to get us both over there. If I don't encash Buck's ticket –'

'No, Ellie, I've told you. It's out of the question.'

'There really will be no problem once we get to Ireland.'

'No, Ellie,' Patsy repeated, firmly. 'I really can't. It's all set. Dad and the boys are all going to be at the game that night. The Red Sox are playing the Dodgers –'

'Why *not*?' Ellie hissed. 'One good reason.'

'And they'll be leaving home real early,' Patsy continued.

'I said,' Ellie persisted, 'I want just one good reason, and I mean why don't you come with me? There's nothing, Patsy, *nothing*, to keep you here.'

Patsy pulled his milkshake towards him and stared at it. 'There is. I met a girl.'

'You met a girl?' Ellie frowned.

Patsy grinned. 'If you really want to know, Ellie, she's called Helen, and I met her three months ago, when I dropped you off one morning at O'Hara's. She works there. She's a floorwalker. And the dishiest little walker that ever trod across Mr O'Hara's shop.'

'Oh, Pat,' Ellie sighed, 'you're too young to fall in love. Far, far too young.' Nevertheless, she put an arm round his shoulders. 'Useless to say that when a person's in love, they're in love.'

'Yes,' Patsy agreed, 'but then love isn't something that's crossed your path yet, is it, Ellie?'

Ellie looked at her brother's reflection in the mirror behind the milk bar. She didn't really mind him getting at her about poor Mr O'Hara. That was a door that was shut for ever. There was only one way to go now, and that was ahead.

Ellie could see him far below, in the vast crowd that had come to see the liner off, waving both his hands up at her, and then taking off his hat and waving that. The sounds of the band on the quayside were momentarily completely drowned by the deep groan of the liner's giant foghorns as the tugs started to pull the ship out to sea. Everyone on the quayside waved and cheered, or waved and cried, as the foghorns again signalled the liner's departure.

The band struck up once more and the crowd started singing, as the great ship moved slowly away from them.

'*Now is the hour, when we must say goodbye!*' the voices sang across the widening gap of dark water. '*Soon

I'll be sailing, far across the sky!' Ellie could still see Patsy's hat, waving in the air as her brother tried to make his way along the packed quayside. *'When I am gone — oh please remember me!'* The hat now became stuck fast in the crowd, and a moment later Ellie had lost it, and it became just another hat in a mass of hats and handkerchieves, streamers and scarves. *'For I'll be sailing, sailing, far across the sea!'*

Everywhere lights pricked and stippled the dark swirling waters below. Behind the tugs, the sea frothed yellowy-white as the tow-boats set to in earnest to heave the massive liner from its berth and set it on its journey out into the Atlantic. The quay receded from view, slipping gradually into the darkness, and with it Boston slowly vanished, and then finally the great continent of America itself, reduced from a quite visible landmass to just a glimmering of city and harbour lights, and then finally to obliteration as the country disappeared altogether into the pitch darkness of the night.

The tugs had gone too, cast off and set back for home, their job done. The liner's foghorns honked them a melancholy last farewell, which was answered by several sharp but now distant toots from the invisible tow-boats, and then all that was left to the departing travellers was the seeming infinity of the huge dark ocean.

Ellie was one of the last to leave the promenade deck, her coat wrapped well round her to protect her from the wind coming off the now open sea. There was an elderly couple nearby, huddled together, their arms around each other, and Ellie could hear the sound of the woman weeping. The man put his arm more tightly round her shoulder, but still they stayed out on deck, apparently unable, so Ellie assumed, to accept the fact of their departure.

For herself, Ellie was cold and hungry, so she left her position on the rail and went below to find the purser's office. She had surrendered the other half of her ticket in case there might be a need for it, and the purser had gratefully accepted it, as it seemed there was a passenger anxious to change her allotted accommodation.

'The other passenger is most grateful, madam,' the purser said as he handed Ellie her promised refund. 'It seems there was some confusion over the original booking in Union Street, and contrary to her instructions the young lady had been allocated an inside berth with no porthole.'

'They say it's going to be very rough, young man,' a voice said from behind Ellie. 'Is this true?' An imperious old woman draped in furs and weighed down with jewellery pushed her way past to address the purser.

'I'm afraid the Atlantic's never exactly a millpond this time of year, madam,' the purser replied with a sympathetic smile.

'Well kindly instruct the captain to drive slowly,' the old woman commanded. 'I don't sleep as well as I used to.'

'I'll tell him to take it easy, madam,' the purser smiled. 'You can rely on it.'

Having left her coat back in her suite, Ellie decided to explore a little. The S.S. *Baltimore* had only been built the year before, and although she was just 32,000 tons, compared with the largest British ocean going liners which had over twice her displacement, she was considered to be a marvel of grace and speed, and the epitome of luxury, resembling more a Park Lane hotel than an Atlantic liner. Ellie marvelled at the fine wood panelling in the hallways and stairwells, the huge gilt mirrors, antique furniture and the deep carpeting. Except for the rolling of the ship, and the creaking of the woodwork, Ellie thought she might as well be in her late fiancé's office, so beautifully was the liner fitted out.

It was then that she saw the girl with the limp. Wandering through one of the first-class lounges, where various card schools were already in progress, Ellie had suddenly found herself in the cocktail bar. Never having been into a bar alone in her entire life, Ellie hesitated, uncertain of whether to walk on through and risk someone accosting her, or turn on her heels and get out the way she came, but thus betraying her naiveté. In the moment she paused she saw the girl, sitting up at the bar in the company of two dinner-jacketed young men. She was sipping a pale looking drink from a long stemmed glass, while seemingly ignoring the banter of her two escorts.

She didn't notice Ellie, as she was too busy staring ahead of her into the mirrors that lined the walls behind the shelves of the bar. But Ellie knew it was her, because of the stick which was hanging on the rail beside the girl, her long ebony cane with a silver fox's head for a handle. It was unmistakeable, as was the beautiful girl, who now that she was hatless Ellie saw to be a blonde, with, as she turned to look at Ellie, large bright blue eyes, the colour of cornflowers.

They stared at each other for a moment, and in that moment Ellie felt at once as if she knew this girl, as if they had always known each other. And then the girl at the bar turned away and continued to stare into the mirrors behind the shelves.

Ellie looked round, uncertain of where to go or what to do.

A steward came to her rescue. 'Excuse me, miss,' he said. 'Are you meeting someone? Or if not, would you perhaps like me to bring you a drink through to the library?' The second half of the sentence was less of a question and more of a helpful direction. Ellie thanked him, ordered an orange soda, and then allowed herself to be shown out of the bar and into the book-lined library.

As she was leaving, Artemis looked back at her as surprised to see the girl in the wedding dress as she was curious as to why she was aboard. Honeymooning, no doubt, she thought, turning her back to the bar. Honeymooning with her old husband.

'Another drink, sweetie?' the elder of her two English companions asked.

'Yes,' Artemis replied, turning back to the bar. 'I don't see why not.'

'Good show,' said the younger man. 'Then we'll all have dinner.'

'Good show,' the older one repeated. 'Yes, why not?' He looked at Artemis. 'OK?'

'Yes,' Artemis said, as her third dry martini was placed in front of her. 'Perfectly.'

Ellie was seated at a table for one at the side of the balconied dining room, but was accorded the same sort of service the guests at the Captain's table were enjoying. As she waited for her first course, she examined the details of the huge saloon, with its ornamental plaster ceiling, from where was suspended an enormous crystal chandelier, and its balustraded second floor, which overlooked the main eating area. The table cloths were of fine linen, the glass was heavy and cut, and the plates were bone china. In the corner a small string orchestra played, and were it not for the motion of the ship and the ever audible throb of its massive engines, Ellie imagined she could be in a grand hotel, or at a party in some vast private house.

The food was excellent, fresh melon, clear chicken soup, succulent sole, a tender sirloin, and a featherweight peach melba. It was quickly eaten, Ellie having no company to delay her.

Thanking her waiter for looking after her so well, Ellie rose to leave just as the girl with the limp was coming down the main staircase, in the company of the two young men with whom she had been seen in the bar. The young men were laughing and joking, while the girl with the limp, either because the ship was now rolling quite considerably or because she had drunk too many cocktails, looked deathly pale and was holding on grimly to the left handrail while swinging her bad right leg out in front of her as she made her way down the stairs. A little late in the day one of her companions suddenly remembered his manners, and offered her an arm which was at once refused.

Ellie eased herself past the threesome as it made its awkward way down, but this time the girl with the limp was too busy concentrating on her progress to notice her.

'Hard a-starboard!' one of the young men laughed, waiting for the girl to get to the foot of the stairs. 'Hard a-port!'

'Abandon ship!' called the other. 'All hands on deck!'

Before disappearing in search of her suite, Ellie gave one more look behind her as she reached the balcony and wondered why such a beautiful girl should need to keep such company.

'No.'

Ellie woke suddenly, aware of something wrong, but unsure what.

'I said no.' It was a girl's voice, from somewhere nearby. Ellie sat up and at once grabbed the rail on the wall by her bed, so violent now was the motion of the ship.

'Just one little kiss,' said a man's voice. 'Be a sport.'

'No!' The voice was now considerably raised, and contained a definite note of panic. 'Don't be such an idiot! I said no!'

By now Ellie had worked out where the voices were coming from, and was out of bed and hanging on to the knob of the intercommunicating door, the door which, had things been different, should have led Ellie through to her husband's cabin, but which now contained a girl in trouble.

'If you don't get out now,' the girl's voice continued, 'I'll ring for the steward!'

Ellie pressed her ear closer to the door in order to catch the reply, but heard nothing. So she dropped to her knee and peered through the keyhole.

She could just make out two figures on the bed, a man in evening dress, who seemed to be struggling as if in slow motion with a girl in a pale pink evening gown. The girl was being held down and was beating the man on his back with her one free hand.

Ellie knew who it was by the dress long before she saw the silver topped cane lying on the floor.

Infuriated that a man should be trying to take advantage of a girl, of whatever kind, Ellie allowed her Irish temper its full force. She shot the bolt on the door and praying that it wasn't locked the other side, turned the handle. It flew open as she fell against it, thrown off balance by the rolling of the ship, and Ellie found herself propelled headlong into the adjoining cabin.

The man didn't hear her at first, he was too busy trying to force himself on the girl lying underneath him. But the girl saw Ellie and her cornflower-blue eyes widened. They opened wider still when Ellie jumped on the man's back and with one knee in his back and both her hands sunk deep in his hair, pulled him off her. Astonished by the attack, he fell to the floor, his own balance helped neither by the amount of drink he had taken nor by the pitching of the ship.

'What on earth — ' was all he managed to utter before Ellie, hanging on to a chair which was chained to the floor, kicked him as hard as she could, and where she hoped it would do the maximum harm. The girl's assailant gasped and fell forward, clutching himself.

'Good lord,' Artemis said, sitting up and staring at Ellie. 'Where on earth did you learn to fight like that?'

'I've got four brothers. Are you OK?'

'OK,' Artemis said thoughtfully. 'Yes, I think I'm "OK", thank you.' She dwelt just overlong on the Americanism, and looked up at Ellie, staring at her with wide bright blue eyes.

Ellie half-smiled unsurely, then pointed to the man who was still lying groaning on the floor. 'Do you think we should call a steward?'

'Oh I don't think so,' Artemis sighed, leaning over

and taking a silver drink flask from a bedside drawer. 'Too many questions and answers. You know the sort of thing. A man being in one's room means one was asking for it, don't you think?' Again she fixed Ellie with her deadpan stare, before opening the top of the silver flask.

'All I know,' Ellie replied, 'is that if someone tries to take advantage of you, he should answer for it.'

'Really?' Artemis asked, pouring out two glasses of brandy. 'How quaint.' She smiled, not as Ellie might have expected, a frosty little smile, but an impish one, as if the whole incident had been a huge joke.

'Here,' she said, offering Ellie a glass.

'What about Jack the Ripper?'

'I think we can let him crawl along now, don't you?' Artemis said, picking her cane back up off the floor and prodding her assailant in the backside. 'I can't imagine he'll feel much like playing silly asses again on this voyage. Run along, Michael. Silly idiot,' she added to Ellie, 'can't take his drink.'

Still obviously in great discomfort, the man got up on his hands and knees, offering a target Artemis couldn't resist, and picking up her ebony cane, she administered a well struck blow to his posterior, which sent him scuttling from the cabin.

'There are such advantages in having a stick,' she told Ellie. 'Anyway, I'm Artemis Deverill. Who are you?'

'Eleanor Milligan, but everyone calls me Ellie.'

'From the way you fight, they should have more respect. And I should sit down if I were you. Before you fall down. It really has got quite choppy.'

Quite choppy was an understatement. The wind was howling at gale force now, and the ship was rising and falling, higher and lower into ever-roughening waters.

'Do you mind it choppy?'

'This is my first time at sea,' Ellie answered, 'so your guess is as good as mine.'

Artemis smiled and sipped her brandy. Then she pulled

thoughtfully at her pretty little chin with her thumb and index finger. 'Do you really have four brothers?'

'Yes. But only one that I like. Do you have brothers or sisters?'

'No. Did your brothers teach you how to fight?'

'One of my brothers did. My youngest brother, Patsy.'

'The one you like, obviously.'

'Obviously.'

'I have an uncle called Mary,' Artemis said, thoughtfully pulling at her chin again. 'Which I would think beats having a brother called Patsy.'

'Pasty's not a girl's name,' Ellie said defensively. 'It's a proper man's name. In Ireland anyway.'

'Well?' Artemis stared back at Ellie without blinking. 'Mary's not a proper man's name in England. Undo this, would you? I think I want to go to bed.' She turned her back to Ellie so that Ellie could unfasten her dress.

'OK,' Ellie said and unhooked the girl's dress.

'OK,' Artemis echoed and yawned, then holding on to the back of the chair, she unhitched the straps of her gown and then clung to it as it fell round her breasts. 'Thanks again, but I really must go to bed now,' she said. 'Good night.'

'Sure,' Ellie said, rising and putting her unfinished drink down on the dressing table.

'Oh you can take your drink with you, it's all right.'

'I've had enough, thanks,' Ellie replied. 'I hope you sleep well.'

'Absolutely,' Artemis agreed, still yawning gracefully.

'Come on, American,' Artemis said, shaking Ellie yet again. 'You don't sleep like a log. You sleep like an entire tree.'

Ellie stared up at the serious blue-eyed face surrounded by a mop of blonde curls which was staring back down at her.

'Are you all right?' Artemis asked. 'You haven't had the heaves, have you, Helen?'

'I was asleep,' Ellie replied. 'And my name's not Helen. It's Eleanor.'

'So come and have a walk round deck, and some breakfast,' Artemis sighed irritably. 'It's a nice morning.'

It was a perfect morning. The storm had abated sometime during the night, leaving a heavy swell but a bright blue sky. Gulls cawed overhead and hovered round the stern awaiting the next offering from the galleys, and now and then one of the last of the storm waves broke like fragments of frozen glass over the prow. The wind whipped off the sea, salting the girls' skin and taking their breath away as they turned round to face it.

'Wow!' Ellie gasped. 'I never reckoned it would be anything like this!'

'You're at sea now, you idiot!' Artemis called back over the noise of the engines and the flapping of the rigging and the crash of the ocean. 'What did you think it would be like?'

'I don't know!' Ellie laughed. 'But not like this!'

After two turns right round the promenade deck, Artemis stopped and leaned on the broad guard rail. 'Imagine falling into that,' she said, pointing at the grey-blue sea as it rushed past the hull. 'What would you do, Helen, if I fell in?'

'I wouldn't jump in after you,' Ellie replied.

'Absolutely,' Artemis agreed. 'I should think not.'

'I would if I could swim,' Ellie said.

Artemis looked at her, blue eyes widened, but without expression. 'I keep getting your name wrong, don't I?' she finally asked.

'Yes,' said Ellie.

'It isn't Helen, is it?'

'No,' said Ellie. 'It isn't.'

'And I didn't thank you properly for last night, did I?'

'No,' Ellie replied. 'You didn't.'

'I was a bit tight, you see,' Artemis said.

'That's OK,' Ellie nodded. 'I see.'

'That's "OK" then,' Artemis smiled suddenly, the first proper smile Ellie had seen her give. 'So let's go and have some breakfast.'

They turned their backs to the ever roughening wind and walked unsteadily back down the deck. As they went, Ellie held on to Artemis, and she to her.

For the next twelve hours they talked. They talked through breakfast, which soon became lunch, which then turned into tea. For ten hours they sat and talked, and walked and talked, and ate and talked, played cards and talked, and even dressed for dinner with their bedroom doors open so they need not stop talking. With the consequence that, by the time they sat in the library sipping cocktails, they felt as if they had always been friends.

'I'm exhausted.'

'Me too,' Artemis agreed, pushing an olive round the bottom of her glass. 'Let's have another drink.'

She tapped the back of a passing waiter's coat, instructing him to bring them another Martini and an orange soda, and a whole dish of olives.

'Do you always do that to waiters?' Ellie asked curiously.

'Do what?' Artemis asked, sucking the stone of her olive.

'Pull waiters' jackets like that.'

'I don't know.' Artemis tossed back her blonde hair and sighed. 'Of course you had your brother to talk to,' she said. 'Patsy.'

'And you had your nanny.'

'Yes.' Artemis shrugged. 'Though one could hardly call talking to Nanny talking. I used to talk to Rosie.'

'Who was Rosie?'

'Oh Rosie was rather fun,' Artemis replied solemnly, 'Rosie was one of the nursery maids –'

'Maids?' Ellie echoed, picking up the plural. 'How many did you have?'

'Maids or nursery maids?' Artemis asked. 'There were four nursery maids and I don't know how many maids downstairs. Why?'

'There were four maids and a nanny?' Ellie wondered. 'Just to look after you?'

'I thought you wanted to hear about Rosie?' Artemis frowned.

'Four maids *and* a nanny.' Ellie shook her head in wonder.

'Rosie,' Artemis continued after giving Ellie a small look, 'was rather big, with a sort of moon face, and always smelt of carbolic. And she had all these perfectly hideous stories about having babies. Everyone she knew was always turning black when they "birthed". And biting their fingers off. Or chewing on iron bars. And she told me if I wanted to get pregnant, all I needed was to go into the graveyard at night. That's all she heard her mother say. "Ah well", she'd say when some girl from the village got into trouble, "that's what comes of going down the graveyard".'

The waiter returned and put down a silver dish of green and black olives on the table in front of them. Artemis at once attacked them with her cocktail stick. 'I actually only drink Martinis because I like the olives. And I've just had an idea for dinner.'

'Thank you,' Ellie said to the waiter with a smile.

'Are you listening, Eleanor?' Artemis enquired tetchily. 'I said I've had an idea for dinner.'

'I'll think I'll start with the Charlotte Russe tonight,' Artemis instructed the waiter. 'Eleanor?'

'I'll think I'll start with the trifle and cream, thank you,' Ellie replied, staring fixedly at the menu.

Artemis turned to the waiter and stared up at him. 'Is there something the matter?'

'I think I must have missed part of your order, madam,' the waiter answered very gravely. 'It seems I only have down your desserts.'

'No, you haven't missed anything,' Artemis told him, having consulted his notepad. 'You have it all down quite correctly.'

'You both wish to start with a dessert?'

Artemis sighed loudly and stroked her small chin suddenly. 'No,' she said slowly, '*I* wish to start with the Charlotte Russe, and Miss *Milligan* wishes to start with the trifle and cream. I shall then have some cheese. Will you also want cheese to follow, Eleanor?'

'I think so, please,' Ellie muttered from behind the menu which was now hiding her face.

'Good,' said Artemis. 'A little ripe Camembert for us both, please. Then I shall have the *poitrine d'agneau*, slightly underdone please. Eleanor?'

'I shall have –' Eleanor began, but then lost control and had to take several deep breaths before she could start again. 'I shall have the roast duck.'

'Miss Milligan will have the duck,' Artemis repeated, in case the waiter had not heard Ellie's faint order, 'then I would like the *filet de sole* –'

'That'll do just fine for me, too.'

'Then I think the *potage à la tortue* –' Artemis ordered.

'I'll have the tomato soup, please,' Ellie whispered.

'And to finish –' Artemis paused and took a long look at the menu. 'Yes to finish I'll have some caviar. Eleanor?'

There was silence from behind Ellie's menu, broken only by the occasional faint sniff. 'I'll have –' she finally attempted. 'I'll just have the grapefruit!'

'No of course you won't,' Artemis scolded. 'That's far too dull for dessert.' She turned round to the waiter and handed him her menu. 'Miss Milligan will have the vermicelli rissoles.' Artemis took Ellie's menu from her so that she had to turn away quickly, lest the waiter see the tears of laughter which were streaming down her face.

'Would you perhaps both care for an aperitif, madam?' the waiter asked, prepared now for anything.

'Yes, please,' Artemis replied. 'We'll have some black coffee and two cognacs.'

'I think I'm going to die,' Ellie confessed after the waiter had left.

'I'll let you off that outburst,' Artemis warned her crossly, 'but if you as much as smile again, even once, before you finish the last mouthful, you lose.'

'Oh come on!' Ellie protested. 'We don't really have to eat this, do we?'

'Of course we have to eat it, you idiot,' Artemis replied. 'That's the whole point. No laughing and no leaving. Otherwise you lose.'

'OK,' Ellie sighed. 'So I lose.'

'Five pounds,' Artemis said, narrowing her bright blue eyes.

'We don't have a bet.'

'We do now,' Artemis corrected her. 'Five pounds. Which is what? About fifteen dollars.'

Afterwards, Ellie knew she would never have got through the meal had there been nothing to lose. To Ellie, every cent counted, for not knowing where her future might lie she had decided that frugality was the best and only course. She had enough cash to keep her going, until she found employment in Ireland, from the rebate on Buck's first-class ticket and from her small savings, and the collateral in the shape of the jewellery Buck had so generously bestowed on her, amounting to her engagement ring, her pearl necklace, two brooches, some earrings, and, of course, her diamond eternity ring.

But fifteen dollars was fifteen dollars cash, and Ellie could not afford to lose it. So even though each successive mouthful made her feel increasingly nauseous, she ate on. And drank on, wine on top of cognac, sherry on top of wine, and finally yet another Dry Martini on top of it all. And to make it that bit more difficult, the liner had once again run into rough waters, the sea having changed from the gentle swell it had been when they had been ordering, to what Artemis liked to call choppy by the time they were halfway through their main courses.

But Artemis seemed not in the slightest bit discomfited by the experience. In fact to Ellie she seemed to be relishing the back to front meal, conversing non-stop from the moment the waiter left the table. Having pumped Ellie all day about her life and times, it was now Artemis's turn to tell her story.

'Mother killed when I was three. Lived with Papa and stepmama in the country. In a house. And that's about it.'

'Was it a nice house?' asked Ellie as she wrestled to keep down roast duck on top of Camembert.

'Nice,' Artemis mused. 'Yes I suppose one could call it nice.'

'And yet your family sold it.'

'No. I sold it.'

Having finished every morsel of her chicken, Artemis put her knife and fork down together, and took a sip of wine, while Ellie stared at her, her duck only half finished.

'What's the duck like?' Artemis asked, leaning across and taking a bit. 'Mmmmm,' she concluded, having sampled it. 'Not bad actually.'

'Why did you sell your house?'

'I didn't want it,' Artemis replied. 'Too big.' She pointed a long finger at Ellie. 'You're going to lose.'

'So where will you live?' Ellie asked, struggling with her next forkful.

'I don't think that's a problem,' Artemis said. 'Now tell me more about Madame. Do you think she was a harlot?'

'That's a terrible thing to say!' Ellie nearly choked.

'Why?' Artemis asked, looking very puzzled. 'She was French.'

'Not all Frenchwomen are harlots!' Ellie retorted.

'Frenchwomen practically invented "it", didn't you know?' Artemis wiped up a little bit of sauce she had left on her plate with a little finger. 'She doesn't have to have been a proper harlot. You know, in a brothel. But from what you've said — anyway, there's nothing wrong.' Artemis shrugged. 'D. H. Lawrence says if a woman hasn't got a tiny streak of harlot in her, she's as dry as a stick. Have you got any harlot in you?'

'How in heck would I know?' Ellie asked, feeling her cheeks redden.

Artemis sighed, wiping her mouth carefully on her napkin. 'I'd give anything to go to a brothel,' she said wistfully. 'I mean to see what one looks like.'

Not knowing how best to deal with the way the conversation was developing, Ellie bowed her head and did her best to finish her roast duck which was now stone cold.

'Do you know anything about making love?' Artemis asked suddenly, breaking the long silence.

'No. Do you?'

'Not really. I think about it sometimes. Do you?'

'Sometimes,' Ellie confessed.

'How often?'

'I don't know.'

Artemis fell silent again, leaning back and staring up at the ceiling, while Ellie struggled on with her cold duck.

'When you do think about it,' Artemis eventually asked, 'what do you think about?'

'I guess I think about someone – I don't know –' Ellie's colour deepened. 'I guess I think about someone with their arms round me –'

'A man, I hope,' Artemis interrupted, turning her gaze on Ellie.

'Well of course!' Ellie protested and then dropped her voice as she saw someone on the next table turn to stare. 'I think about a man putting his arms around me,' she whispered, 'and we're walking along, and he's holding my hand. And he's being loving. You know. I guess I just think about someone being loving.' Ellie looked up from her food and saw that Artemis was staring at her with profound disbelief, her blue eyes opened as wide as they could go.

'Don't you kiss or anything?'

'I don't know!' said Ellie now mortified with embarrassment. 'Sure – I suppose we kiss.'

'Have you ever kissed anyone?'

'No.'

'Neither have I. No that's not true,' Artemis corrected herself. 'Someone kissed me at a party two years ago, but that didn't really count as we both had our mouths closed.'

'I don't understand.' Ellie frowned at her. 'What do you mean – that doesn't count?'

'Because we both had our mouths closed, you idiot,' Artemis repeated. 'Which doesn't count as kissing.'

'What does?'

'You must have been to the films, haven't you?'

'Sure.'

'Well.' Artemis shrugged. 'It seems they kiss differently in films. At least that's what Rosie told me. And once she made me hide with her under the back stairs so as she could spy on one of the footmen kissing the maids. But the funny thing was, it wasn't a maid we saw him kissing. It was one of the weekend guests.'

Ellie grinned. 'A woman, I hope,' she returned.

Artemis just stared deadpan at her. 'Don't you want to hear how they kissed?'

'Not particularly. I guess I'd rather wait until it happens to me.'

The waiter came, cleared away their plates, and now set the fish course in front of them. Ellie sighed and stared down at the filleted sole.

'Look,' Artemis suggested. 'Why don't you just give me your fiver now? Sorry. I mean your fifteen bucks.'

'No chance,' Ellie rejoined. 'It's getting easier by the dish.'

'Really?' Artemis smiled coolly. 'Wait till you get to the vermicelli rissoles.'

'Tomorrow,' Artemis announced, as they swayed back to their cabins, grabbing the polished handrails on either side of them to steady themselves as the liner plunged and rolled, 'tomorrow we shall be foreigners. Do you speak

French, or German, or Italian, or Spanish, or Greek, or Russian or anything?'

'Only American,' Ellie replied.

'Oh God,' Artemis sighed, as Ellie unlocked their door. 'Another whole day of pants and suspenders, knickers and purses. Oh yes! And trunks! Don't you say trunks for boots?'

'What sort of boots?' Ellie asked, as they tumbled into the suite.

'The sort of boots you call trunks,' Artemis replied.

'We don't call boots trunks,' Ellie said. 'We call boots just the same as you do. Boots. What we call trunks are the luggage compartments in motor cars.'

'That's what we call boots,' Artemis said, flopping on to the sofa. 'We call the luggage bits on motor cars boots.'

'So what do you call boots then?' Ellie enquired, sitting down beside Artemis and kicking off her shoes. 'As in what you put on your feet.'

'We call them boots,' Artemis yawned. 'What do you call them?'

'We call them boots as well,' Ellie said.

'Yes? So then what do you call trunks?'

'We've just established that,' Ellie replied. 'Boots.'

'Trunks as in bathing trunks.'

'Trunks.'

'Trunks as in luggage.'

'Trunks.'

'We have more in common than I thought. Time for bed. Tomorrow we shall pretend to be foreigners.'

Artemis started to pull herself up from the sofa, but because of the increasingly rough seas, she found it even more difficult than usual. Ellie got up and went to help her.

'No!' Artemis's eyes flashed at Ellie, as she shook off Ellie's helping hand. 'I'll tell you if I need help, thank you,' Artemis told her, still trying to struggle to her feet.

'I offered to help you,' Ellie told her, 'not because I thought you needed it, but because I wanted to, OK?'

'No it is not "OK".'

'Fine. Then that's OK with me. You just go right ahead.'

Ellie stood back and offered no further assistance as Artemis tried again to get up off the sofa and on to her feet, while the ship rose and fell in the heavy seas. Finally she conceded defeat, and she lay back with her eyes closed.

' "OK",' she said, extending a long slender arm out to Ellie.

Ellie ignored it.

'I cannot – get up, Eleanor,' Artemis said, as if to a child.

'I can see that,' Ellie said. 'And I'll help you up when you say sorry, Artemis.'

'Go to hell,' Artemis said, after a silence.

' "OK",' Ellie replied and went back into her bedroom.

Artemis stared at the now closed adjoining door and tried once more to get up. But she couldn't stand. The sofa was too deep, the sea was too rough, and she had drunk far too much. And her cane was the other side of the stateroom. And her head was beginning to swim, quite violently. So rather than slip off the sofa now Ellie had gone, and crawl her way into her own cabin, Artemis lay back and closed her eyes, hoping the feeling of increasing nausea would abate. But it didn't. It got increasingly worse. She started to go hot and then cold, and the sweat began to run off her brow, until she knew she could contain her sickness no longer.

'Eleanor!' she called, marooned on the sofa.

She moaned and groaned and swore almost inaudibly to herself, wrapping her arms round the cramps in her stomach, before using the last of her strength to call out once more.

'Eleanor quickly!'

*   *   *

The sea was calmer now and moonlight was shining on to Artemis's bed, as she lay between the cool sheets, a cold flannel on her forehead and Ellie sitting by her side.

'I don't think we'll pretend to be foreigners tomorrow,' Artemis said, staring up at the ceiling.

'Pretending to be a foreigner wouldn't make you as sick as eating a six-course dinner backwards,' Ellie argued.

'It wasn't the dinner, you idiot,' Artemis countered. 'Or the storm. It was the Martinis.'

'Sure,' said Ellie.

'Yes, sure,' Artemis echoed mockingly. 'I'll just have to switch drinks. There must be plenty of other cocktails you can have olives with.'

'You were as green as a bean when you got up from the table,' Ellie said, removing the flannel and feeling Artemis's brow.

'Rubbish. And do stop fussing.'

'You really were very sick,' Ellie said, with sudden relish.

'No I wasn't,' Artemis disagreed. 'I just was mad to have had that last dry martini on top of the soup and caviar. And it's "OK". I'm all right. You can go back to bed now.'

'Look,' Ellie sighed patiently, 'let's just get one thing straight, shall we? I'm not one of your servants you can just order around, "all right"?'

'I never said you were.'

'You don't have to say, Artemis. You just do. Now settle back, lie back and I'll wait with you till you've gone to sleep.'

'I don't need you to wait.'

'I know. I know.'

Ellie waited, despite Artemis's disapproving sighs. And in spite of her disapproval, Artemis closed her eyes and turned on her side.

After five minutes, Ellie stood up very quietly, put out the bedside light and prepared to tiptoe back to her cabin.

'When we get to Ireland, Eleanor,' a voice said from the bed behind her, 'I think I might rent a house and we can go and stay there for a while. Somewhere by a lake.'

Ellie turned back and looked down on the girl in the bed, who was still lying with her back to her.

'I thought you were asleep.'

'So did I. I am.'

'OK. So sleep.'

'*OK.*'

7

Ellie couldn't wait to get topside fast enough and ran all the way up to the bridge, so as to be in plenty of time to catch the first sight of land. At dinner the night before, the captain had invited both of the girls up to the bridge in the morning when the liner would be off the coast of Ireland. Ellie had their steward call them before first light. She herself had jumped straight out of bed, but Artemis just groaned and pulled the covers back over her when Ellie tried in vain to raise her.

So Ellie left her in bed, pulled on her clothes, and hurried up on deck.

When she reached the bridge, she found they were still well out to sea, but as the sun started to rise before her, Ellie began to make out a line of cliffs through the sea fret, and then the faint outline of the country behind it. The first mate identified the landfall for Ellie as Mizen Head, which in the early days of transatlantic sailing had, it seemed, been a graveyard for ships. But, he assured her, the S.S. *Baltimore* would keep well and safely out to sea until she had rounded Cape Clear when she would change her course and head for Cork sheltered by the coast.

There had only been a slight swell on the Atlantic for the fourth day of their journey, but now even those gently rolling waves slowly subsided as the ship entered waters as calm as a millpond. The morning sun hung in a cloudless light-blue sky, and as the liner sailed ever closer to the mainland, Ellie could understand why Ireland was called the Emerald Isle, for she had never before seen fields of such a green. Off Kinsale, where after a brief flurry of activity on the bridge, with bells telegraphing the captain's directions to the engineroom far below, the liner finally came to a stop to take on board the pilot who was to guide the ship safely into Cobh. As they waited, Ellie could see seals basking in the sunshine on the rocks, paying scant attention to the fishermen as they rowed out in longboats to haul in their lobster pots.

Finally, with the pilot aboard and giving the orders the S.S. *Baltimore* set sail again halfspeed ahead.

'Apparently we don't actually dock in the harbour itself,' Ellie explained to Artemis as she heaved her luggage through into the stateroom, which had become their joint property from that first evening. 'We're too big, so we drop anchor offshore and then those of us who are disembarking here are taken ashore by tender.'

Artemis was sitting in an armchair reading a book and drinking coffee.

'I take it you've packed?'

'Packed?' Artemis queried, without looking up from her book. 'No – why should I?'

'Because we have to go up to immigration in the lounge. We disembark in half an hour'

'In that case you'd better ring the bell,' Artemis frowned, carefully turning a page, 'and send down for someone.'

Ellie looked at her calmly reading and went to say something, but instead she went through to the bedroom with the intention of doing Artemis's packing for her. One long look and Ellie turned and went straight back into the stateroom.

'What happened in there, Artemis?' she demanded. 'They left that as neat as a pin when we got back from dinner last night.'

'Nothing happened,' Artemis replied, without looking up from her book. 'I just got undressed and went to bed. And then got up again. And I am trying to read.'

'It looks as though there's been a pitched battle in there!' Ellie complained. 'Now come on. Come and give me a hand. I can't possibly pack you up without your help.'

'What?' Artemis stared at Ellie blankly, as if she had taken total leave of her senses. 'What did you say?'

'I said come and give me a hand.'

Artemis continued to stare at Ellie for a moment, and then she got up slowly and rang for a steward, who arrived almost immediately, hardly before Artemis had time to sit back down.

'Steward,' Artemis said, picking up her book and not even looking at him. 'Would you please send someone up to do my packing? As quickly as you can.' Then she looked up at the old steward and smiled. 'Thank you,' she added.

'My pleasure, my lady,' the steward replied. 'I'll see to it at once.'

Artemis turned her smile from the steward to Ellie, before returning to her reading.

'So that's how you pack in England,' said Ellie dryly. 'I always did wonder.'

'Do you remember what I said?' Artemis suddenly asked Ellie over lunch at the hotel. 'About getting a house here, that night I was tight? It would be fun, wouldn't it?'

'It would be great,' said Ellie warmly, 'but I have to earn my living. I have to find a job.'

'Why?' Artemis asked, carefully scraping the last bit of white meat from her lobster. 'I've got some money.'

'It's a nice idea,' Ellie replied, putting down her fork. 'But let's just leave it at that, shall we?'

'It isn't an idea,' Artemis said, 'it's a fact. And you're not leaving the claw, are you?' She looked up at Ellie from under her red hat. 'You can't leave the claw.'

'Pardon me?'

'And do stop saying pardon me,' Artemis sighed, leaning over and breaking the claw of Ellie's lobster open for her. 'It's terribly common. You don't say pardon me, you say "what" in England or Ireland. That's the best part – the claw.'

They were lunching in the Metropole Hotel, with Artemis obviously determined that life was going to carry on as seamlessly as it had onboard ship, and Ellie trying to savour what she knew were the last hours before she pulled herself together and faced reality.

'I don't want the claw, thanks.'

'OK,' Artemis replied, and took it for herself.

'Isn't OK common too?' Ellie asked wryly.

'Yes,' Artemis told her, perfectly seriously. 'Frightfully. That's half the fun.'

Artemis eyed her new friend, then they both lapsed into silence for a while, as Artemis scraped and delved into the lobster claw, and Ellie gazed around her at her new surroundings. They were new, but not strange, because as soon as she had set foot in Ireland, Ellie felt as if she had been there before, not as it were in a previous life, but in this one, as if part of her had always been in this country, waiting for the other part of her to join it. And now she felt happy, inexplicably so, but utterly and completely so.

'Who is this Cousin Rose of your's anyway?' Artemis went on, after taking a sip of her wine. 'She's your mother's cousin, isn't that what you said?'

'That's right,' Ellie replied. 'But that's all I know about her. It was my brother Patsy's idea for me to write to her. And tell her – ' Ellie stopped because Artemis had once more caught a passing waiter by his coat and ordered him to bring her another half a lobster. 'You've got to stop doing that to waiters.'

'Whatever for?' asked Artemis, opening her eyes wide. 'So what are you going to do? You're not just going to turn up at this Cousin Rose's? I must say it doesn't sound the *brightest* of ideas. She could be dead.'

'Of course she isn't dead.'

'She might be if she didn't write back to you.'

'She probably didn't have the time.'

'She probably doesn't know how to write.'

'Of course she knows how to write. Of course she's not dead.'

'All of these of courses. When you haven't ever even spoken to your cousin.'

'She writes us every Christmas.'

'To us. She writes *to* us. You don't write people. You write to them.'

'And she wrote *to* us this last Christmas.'

'She could have died since then.'

'Would you like her to be dead, Artemis?'

'Why?'

'Because then I'd have to throw myself on your tender mercies.'

The waiter arrived and put Artemis's second helping of lobster in front of her. 'Grand, aren't they now, miss?' he said, flicking some breadcrumbs off the tablecloth with his napkin. 'Fresh from the sea this morning. I could ate a dozen meself. And what about you, miss?' He turned and beamed a semi-toothless smile at Ellie. 'Go on. Have another. I won't charge you for it.'

'Thank you,' Ellie smiled back at him. 'But I really have had enough.'

'May I ask where you're from, miss?' the waiter enquired, sticking his index finger in the empty wine bottle. 'From what part of Americee?'

'I'm from Boston,' Ellie told him. 'Boston Massachusetts.'

'Boston, Massachusetts,' he repeated, with a nod of his head. 'Now there's a thing. Sure and don't I have a brother in Detroit?' He wandered off with another big smile, swinging the wine bottle from the end of his finger.

Artemis watched him go. Then she turned back to stare at Ellie. 'Is that what your father is like?' she asked.

'No-o,' said Ellie thoughtfully. 'My father has more teeth. To bite you with.'

' "OK",' Artemis began again, scooping out the meat from her second lobster. 'What I thought was we could stay here, in the hotel – '

'You just don't *listen*, do you?'

'Eleanor,' Artemis continued, ignoring Ellie's protest, 'it need only be for the summer. Then after the summer's over you can go to your stupid cousin's then. And start scrubbing floors, and washing dishes, doing the laundry, or whatever it is you intend to do for the rest of your so-called life.'

'Excuse me,' Ellie said, rising from the table after a moment's silence. 'I have to put in a telephone call to my poor dead cousin.'

It took a good while for the various local telephone exchanges to make the connection between the Metropole Hotel, Cork and Strand House, Ballinacree, not it appeared due to any technical difficulties, but because each of the operators down the line wished to pass on the latest news and exchange the most recent gossip. After a good ten minutes delay, Cork was finally joined to the exchange at Ballinacree, and the operator asked to be connected to Ballinacree, two, five.

'That's Miss Lannigan's number,' the distant voice said. 'Who's that that'll be wanting her?'

' 'Tis a young American girl,' Cork replied. 'Just off the liner today.'

'Ah sure, that'll be Miss Lannigan's second cousin Miss Milligan,' Ballinacree said, and then in a raised voice for Ellie's benefit, 'is that right now? Is that you, Miss Milligan?'

'That's right,' Ellie answered with some astonishment. 'Yes, this is Eleanor Milligan.'

'Ah God love you,' the voice from Ballinacree sighed. 'Didn't I know your mother as a child, and wasn't she beautiful, God rest her soul. And are you as beautiful as she, Miss Milligan? No – no ye've no need to say a thing, Miss Milligan, for sure won't we be able to see for ourselves when you come on your visit? There now, that's your cousin's telephone ringing now.'

'Your cousin's telephone is ringing now, Miss Milligan,' the Cork operator confirmed. 'She shouldn't be too long in answering now, provided, God willing, she's at home.'

'She's never out on a Windsday,' Ballinacree chipped in. 'And anyway, hasn't she just had a call from the doctor? Here she is now.'

'Hulloooo?' said another voice, faintly and rather formally. 'This is Ballinacree twenty-five. Who is this now?'

'Hullo?' said Ellie.

'Hullo, Miss Lannigan,' said the Ballinacree operator. 'I has your second cousin Miss Milligan on the phone from Cork.'

'Have ye indeed?' Ellie's second cousin asked, 'and is she there now?'

'Whisht now and we'll see, Miss Lannigan,' Ballinacree replied. 'Hello, Cork? Jeannie – do you still have Miss Milligan there? Or have you her lost?'

'I have her still here, Marie, God love you,' Cork confirmed, 'and I'm putting her through now. Go ahead now, Miss Milligan. Go ahead if you will, we have Miss Lannigan waiting.'

'Hullo?' Ellie raised her voice, uncertain of the distance it had to travel. 'Cousin Rose?'

'Ah – Ellie darling,' the voice in her ear sounded as if it were on the edge of tears. 'Eleanor sweet is that really ye?'

'It's really me, Cousin Rose,' Ellie replied. 'I'm in Cork.'

'Isn't that wonderful?' Cousin Rose sighed. 'In Cork! Who would ever have believed it?'

'Did you get my letter?' Ellie asked.

'I did,' her cousin confirmed. 'Yes indeed I did. I got your letter, yes indeed I did.'

Ellie waited before continuing, expecting to hear the reason why her cousin hadn't replied. None was forthcoming. 'I wondered whether I could come and see you?' Ellie ventured.

'Did ye ever hear the like?' her cousin demanded to know.

'I did not, Miss Lannigan,' the Ballinacree operator replied.

'Wonder indeed,' Cousin Rose laughed. 'Hasn't yer bed been made up this last calendar week? You're to come out at once. This minute.'

'How do I find you, Cousin Rose?' Ellie asked.

'There's a train to Bantry at half past three,' Cork volunteered. 'But she'd need to hurry.'

'Didn't she say she was in the Metropole?' Ballinacree said. 'Sure that's no distance to the station.'

'Oh, I'd say she's time enough to make that easily,' her cousin agreed, apparently forgetting Ellie was still on the line.

'We'll have Jeannie ask her,' Ballinacree suggested.

'Are you still there, Miss Milligan?' Cork enquired. ' 'Cos if you are, they need to know if yous is able to catch the three-thirty train to Bantry.'

'I should imagine so,' Ellie said, grinning to herself and looking at her wristwatch. 'It's now only two-fifteen.'

'Grand,' she heard her cousin say when the message was relayed to her. 'Tell her I'll send the trap to the station. Goodbye.'

'Goodbye now, Miss Lannigan,' Ballinacree said. 'And goodbye to you, Jeannie, and may the Lord bless you.'

'God love you, Marie,' Cork replied, 'and God bless you too.'

'Goodbye,' Ellie said, but exactly to whom she wasn't quite sure, for it seemed they'd all gone off the line.

When she returned to the dining room, Artemis was gone, too. Assuming this was because she'd been away too long, and discovering from the waiter that she'd paid the bill, Ellie went in search of her friend, expecting to find her in the lounge or the lobby, sitting in an armchair, absorbed as always by some book or other. But there was no sign of her anywhere.

'Now this would be the young lady from England,' the desk clerk recalled, 'in the maroon suit and walking stick.'

'Yes,' said Ellie, wondering why she had begun to panic, because she had already learned in their brief association how totally unpredictable Artemis could be. 'Did she book a room here?' she asked.

'No, miss,' the clerk said, having consulted his ledger. 'No, no, no. No there's not a single booking anywhere. Devil the one. Just the two single ladies from Tralee.'

Ellie checked with the porter to see if Artemis's luggage had gone, but her four cases were still there with Ellie's two, lined up in a row in a room off the foyer. Having discovered she would be well advised to leave at least half an hour to get from the hotel to the station and on to the train, Ellie sat down in the lobby to wait.

Artemis didn't come back. At five to three Ellie wrote a note leaving her cousin's telephone number and explaining where she was going, and then, having waited until the clock in the lobby had finally marked the hour, climbed into the waiting cab, and left to catch her train. As the cab drove through the streets of the city, Ellie sat on the edge of her seat staring out of the window in the vague hope of catching sight of Artemis, but there was no sign of her anywhere. Several times she thought she should get the driver to return her to the hotel, so that she could ring and postpone her visit to Ballinacree. But in a way, she decided, that would be giving in. Artemis had wilfully abandoned her without leaving any indication as to her whereabouts. Whereas Ellie had left her a note explaining in full where she herself was to be. If Artemis was bothered, she'd call Ellie at her cousin's, and come and visit. And if she didn't bother to do just that, then she wasn't really worth bothering about.

As it happened, the moment Ellie relaxed and sat back in her cab, she passed right by Artemis. But she would not have seen her, for Artemis was sitting one floor up in offices belonging to Neill and O'Dwyer, a firm of lawyers who specialized in the letting of properties. As Ellie's cab passed below the office windows, Mr O'Dwyer was just putting on the desk in front of Lady Artemis Deverill details of a most charming small house which was for rent on the shores of Lough Caragh.

The place where Cousin Rose lived was nothing like Ellie had imagined it. In her mind's eye she had visualized a small whitewashed cottage, set among the rocks and bog, with the smoke curling up to the sky, like the pictures of Ireland she had seen in books. For her second cousin on her mother's side must surely be poor, Ellie imagined, as were most people living in the Irish countryside.

Cousin Rose's annual Christmas letter never gave her or Patsy any hint of her standing in the community. They were random, full of snippets of family gossip, or news of Milligan relatives. Her father never said anything indicative about his dead wife's cousin, except 'Poor old Cousin Rose.' So Ellie had imagined exactly that. A poor woman, and an old one, which left her totally unprepared for the sight she saw ahead of her now as the pony and trap swung off the country road and up a long potholed drive. For there at the top was a beautiful old grey stone house. There were steps leading up to the front door, either side of which were stone pillars, half sunk in the stonework. Above the door was a glass fanlight, and the windows of the house itself were long and delicately latticed, the sills of the ones on the ground floor hidden behind an uncontrolled tumble of bright spring flowers. Lawns ran up to the house from where the drive turned its last corner, the last part of the grass rising steeply as a bank, up to a terrace where a woman sat under the shade of a huge umbrella, although by now it was early evening and the sun was beginning to set.

Standing slightly behind the woman, whose age Ellie was as yet unable to determine, was a man of immense height in what looked like an old fashioned frock-coat, pin-striped pants, and a bowler hat. As the driver pulled the trap into the carriage sweep, and drew up in front of the house, Ellie could see that the man was also wearing an old pair of rubber gardening boots, which seemed to have had their top halves hacked off with a knife or a pair of scissors, or at least so Ellie surmised from their ragged edges.

Neither the woman nor the man moved as the trap drew to a halt. Then the woman put one lace-mittened hand up to shade her eyes against the sun which was setting in the sky behind the trap, and peered out from under her hand at Ellie.

'Hulloooo?' she called in enquiry. 'Is that ye, Eleanor?'

'Cousin Rose?' Ellie called back, as the driver helped her down the steps of the trap.

'It is, Tutti, it is!' the woman said, turning to the man behind her. 'Will ye just look at her!' She rose and brushing down her skirts, stood for a moment with one hand to her cheek, before walking to meet Ellie with open arms.

'I'd never have thought it,' she said, having embraced Ellie and now holding her away from her to take a good look. 'Ye even have yer mother's eyes. Will ye look at this now, Tutti?' She turned back to the man who was still standing by the abandoned chair. 'Come over here, man, and see for yerself.'

'I will not,' said the man from where he stood. 'I'll do no such thing.'

'I have eyes like you, Cousin Rose,' Ellie said, looking at her relative, a fine, handsome woman in only her middle-age, nowhere near as ancient as Ellie had imagined her to be. 'They're just the same colour. Grey, with brown flecks. Patsy has them, too.'

'Trouts' eyes,' her cousin told her, squeezing Ellie by the shoulders. 'Lannigan eyes. Dear heavens, but you're yer mother's likeness. When I saw the trap drawin' up, I thought ye were a spook. I did. Didn't I, Tutti? Didn't I say to you my God! 'Tis this ghost of my cousin!'

'You did not,' said the man, still unmoving, 'you said no such thing.'

'Pay no attention to Tutti,' Cousin Rose advised Ellie, as she took her arm and led her up to the house. 'He's in a fret because I took tea outside.'

'I am not,' said the man from behind them. 'I'm in no such thing.'

'You should have been a parrot, Tutti!' Cousin Rose called back over her shoulder. 'Not a butler!' She drew Ellie closer to her and smiled in confidence. 'Ye'll not mind him now. He's a heart of gold, he has, but he has a piece of steel in his head. From the war.'

They were up the steps now and Cousin Rose swung open the front door.

'This place is just beautiful,' Ellie said, turning back to have another look out across the lawns and grounds which ran practically into the sea itself. 'It is. This really is heaven.'

'Ah. Well. Ye've come at a good time,' her cousin said. 'For the garden's in a grand old mood.'

They stood in silence for a moment, looking at the lush vegetation, the purple and green hills beyond, and the last sparkle of the day dancing on the waves of the distant sea.

'Now,' said Cousin Rose, breaking the spell, 'ye'll be in need of a wash and brush up, and then we'll have a drink or two, and we'll hear how everything's been since the very beginning. And what sort of business it is that has brought ye here.'

She kissed Ellie suddenly and fondly, and Ellie felt suffused with a feeling she had never known.

'There,' her cousin said. 'Tutti'll show you to your room and bring up yer things.'

'I will not,' the butler said, arriving at the door and heading for the stairs armed with Ellie's two cases. 'I'll do no such thing.'

'He went right through the war, ye know,' Cousin Rose confided to Ellie as her butler passed them by. 'With devil the scratch. Only God help him to be shot in the head in the second battle of the Marne. Sure that's no sort of luck. No sort of luck at all.'

Ellie paused at the foot of the stairs, before turning back to her cousin. 'I'm so glad to be here, at last,' she said softly, 'Cousin Rose'.

'Will ye not call me cousin now?' her relative demanded. 'It's Rose or it's nothing.'

'OK, Rose,' Ellie smiled. 'But I'm still real glad to be here.'

Rose watched her young relation go up the stairs, and then called after her. 'When yer mother was a girl, Eleanor!' she said. 'Did you know? Did your father not tell ye – people used to stand on stone walls to see her pass by!'

As Ellie and her second cousin Rose were sitting in the drawing room having their second glass of sherry, the butler came in, dressed as he was before, except for his rubber gardening boots which he had exchanged for a pair of old felt bedroom slippers, and rang a small brass gong which he held aloft in one hand. He struck it forcibly but without success. No sound came.

'Dinner,' he announced adding as an apparent afterthought, 'madams.'

'Don't pay the slightest attention to that,' Cousin Rose warned Ellie as she saw Ellie trying to hurry through her drink. 'We've a good half-hour yet.'

There were no lights on in the room, although the sun was all but finally set. Ellie could barely make out her surroundings, and yet she felt comfortable and at ease. The chair she sat in was upholstered in velvet, and the round table by her side was also draped in the heavy material, topped off by a fine lace cloth. On it were various framed photographs, of whom or what Ellie had no idea since it was too dark to see, and a big vase simply spilling over with late spring flowers. The french windows at the west end of the room were still open, and a cool breeze blew in off the sea, bringing with it the heady evening scent of columbine, mixed with the tang of the brine.

So far the talk had been general, Ellie telling her cousin how all her brothers were doing, paying particular attention to Patsy, since he was Cousin Rose's godchild. She told how it had always been a struggle for her father to raise the five of them until the boys were old enough to work, and how it had been just as well she'd been a girl and able to help him. Cousin Rose listened in silence. In the half darkness it was impossible for Ellie to make out what her relation was thinking, because she couldn't see the expression on her face. Perhaps because of this she finally stopped.

'Yes, go on, go on,' urged Rose.

'That's all there is, nothing more. Not really.'

'Interesting,' her cousin nodded. 'And what I've always thought. When people tell ye their histories, there's no need for romances.'

The butler returned to try and sound his small hand-held gong for the second time. 'Will yous both come and eat?' the butler demanded. 'Before Aggie packs her bags for good?'

There were no lights on anywhere, so Ellie followed her cousin, who from habit obviously knew her way in the dark.

'Keep to the right along here!' Cousin Rose called ahead of Ellie down the corridor. 'For there's precious few floorboards to your left!'

Ellie did as she was told, running her right hand along the wall to guide her. And then at last there was a flicker of light, as the butler threw open the door of the dining room.

Cousin Rose waited for Ellie at the threshold, and took her arm before Ellie could enter. 'Ye'll need to go steady here too, Eleanor,' she announced. 'Go round this side here. For the floor's gone by the fire, too.'

As she made for her place, Ellie could see what Cousin Rose meant. On the far side of the room there were no floorboards at all. The candlelight flickered and danced over an empty dark space where once had been laid a polished wooden floor.

'It was a damp old winter,' Cousin Rose informed her. 'So we had to burn more of the floor than usual, but we'll soon have it all to rights.'

'We will not,' the butler replied, pulling out Ellie's chair for her. 'We never do.'

The table was quite beautifully laid, with Irish linen, Waterford glass and heavy silverware. And from what Ellie could see of the room, that too was beautiful, with its fine mahogany furniture, and the paintings on every wall. Every wall that was except one which was totally bare except for a large crack which zig-zagged down it. There was also a pile of rubble in the corner by the bare wall, which seemed to be old plaster which must have come from the ceiling, for there was a gaping hole above, just to the right of the long sideboard. And there was trouble with the fireplace too, since as her eyes became accustomed to the candlelight Ellie could see it was being kept standing thanks only to a couple of sturdy timber supports.

'We won't have the electricity,' Cousin Rose said as she sat down. 'Will we, Tutti?'

'You won't, madam,' the butler replied, flapping at something unseen on the sideboard with a napkin. 'I could do with some, personally.'

'I won't have the electricity,' Cousin Rose continued, 'because it wouldn't do for the house. Besides, I've heard it gives ye headaches.'

The butler sighed and left the room, while Cousin Rose threw open her stiff linen napkin which she then laid over her bosom, high up near her chin, like a child.

' 'Tis the mice, Eleanor,' she said. 'They have us annoyed.'

Whatever the disrepair of the room the food was delicious and Ellie, who by now was starving, tucked in to the fresh brown trout which was served with just one fluffy cream coloured potato, the roast lamb served with more potatoes, fresh spinach and baby carrots, a mouthwatering savoury called Devils on Horseback, and a pudding made from whipped honey and cream, served with little sweet biscuits which Cousin Rose called 'ratafias'.

'Aggie's a grand cook,' was Cousin Rose's only comment on the meal, 'when she's half sober.'

To Ellie it was a dream, a fairy-tale spun round both the place and the people. For all this could surely not be connected to her dead mother's past? Ellie had always understood that her mother's family were poor. That they were of peasant stock, who had worked land belonging to others, and who had lived in rented shacks like the poor who lived and worked further down the line outside Boston, the poor whom Ellie had once seen and never forgotten when she had journeyed by train to visit a relative in Chicopee. And yet here she was, sitting in a grand house, albeit one which needed some repair, furnished with antiques and silver, fine paintings and glass and owned by a wonderful and striking woman who was her dead mother's first cousin.

'You enjoyed that,' Cousin Rose said, as the butler brought in a tray of coffee and chocolates. 'I can see from yer face.'

'I'm enjoying everything,' Ellie replied, 'most of all just being here.'

'I'll bet ye,' Cousin Rose said, squeezing a chocolate carefully between a thumb and a finger to ascertain its complexion, 'that yer wonderin' why yer mother ever left this place.'

'I was wondering about a lot of things, as a matter of fact,' Ellie answered. 'This isn't at all what I expected.'

'What ever is?' Cousin Rose sighed, rejecting one chocolate for another. 'What ever is? Thank God.'

'Am I really like my mother?'

'Child — yer the spit of her. The spit. Only taller.'

'My father –' Ellie lapsed into silence.

'If anything,' Cousin Rose removed her linen napkin from her bosom and stared at Ellie. 'If anything yer actually even better looking than she.'

'But my mother was *really* beautiful. My father keeps saying how beautiful she was.'

'Don't you ever look in the mirror, child?' her cousin asked her, 'or have you always been too busy down on your hands and knees?'

Ellie stared.

'You can tell the truth and not a word of a lie, and you still won't have told the truth,' said Cousin Rose, nodding at yet another chocolate. 'And isn't that the truth?'

The two of them sat on as the fire sunk into a grey dawn of its own making.

'Yer mother would never have left these shores, Eleanor,' Cousin Rose finally told her as somewhere in the dark of the room the grandfather clock chimed two, 'she'd never have gone at all, if it hadn't been for the tragedy.'

'What tragedy might that be, Rose?' Ellie asked.

'Your mother was engaged to be married, d'ye see?' said Cousin Rose impatiently.

'Yes. To my father.'

'Ah, before that, child,' Cousin Rose corrected her, with growing irritation. 'Yer mother was engaged first to be married to a local boy. Thomas Hackett. The rector's son. He was as handsome as could be, and yer mother and he they made a grand couple. And then he was drowned, early one spring morning. Out by himself, he was, with the mayfly just hatched, hardly a mile up river from here, tickling trout. And didn't he fall into the pool, dash his head on a rock, and wasn't he killed. We thought that wouldn't be the only death. We all of us thought yer mother would also die, from her grief.'

'How old was she?' Ellie asked quietly, and shivered in the growing chill of the room. 'How long was it before she met my father?'

'It was the year before. She was seventeen. And the year after, midsummer, yer father arrived from America, to see his own father, who was in Cork General, dying of nephritis. Ye know the rest. Yer mother was looking after yer grandfather, ye'll remember. I'd paid for her to take up nursing after Thomas was drowned, do you see? And when her grandfather died, yer father proposed marriage just a week later. And yer mother agreed, and no wonder. For by jingo — but yer father was a sight! He was a fine-looking man. Strong boned and upright, and with the charm of the devil. Ye'd have to say he quite swept yer mother clean off her two feet.'

'And then she followed him to America?'

'She went and was married to him six months later, wed to a man she'd barely known three weeks. Still, she had to go. Better that than staying here.'

'But you said she loved it here.'

'She'd not have married here, Eleanor,' Cousin Rose replied. 'All she'd have done was mourn. And been a spinster like meself.'

'Why?' Ellie asked her. 'Are there not enough young men?'

'There are not,' Cousin Rose replied. 'But that's not the reason why I never married.'

'May I ask?' Ellie said after a moment, 'what was your reason?'

'Of course you may, child,' her cousin replied, with a laugh. 'I'd no mind to have a man bossing me around and isn't that a caution? For look at me now?'

Tutti appeared in the door of the old room, his shadow elongated by the flickering light of the lamps. 'Come on now, have you no mind of the hour?'

Ellie looked across at Cousin Rose. 'I see what you mean.'

8

'Hullo,' said a voice after nearly six weeks.

'Artemis?' said Ellie, trying not to sound surprised.

'Where exactly are you?' Artemis enquired. 'I thought I'd drive over and see you.'

Ellie paused to take stock of things before replying. Since she had left the note with her address and telephone number for Artemis at the desk of the Metropole, she had heard nothing from her, not a word.

'Eleanor?' she heard Artemis ask. 'Are you there?'

'Listen,' Ellie said, trying her best to sound as matter-of-fact as Artemis was sounding, 'where are you?'

'On the edge of a lake,' Artemis replied. 'In Kerry. I've tried to find Ballinacree on the map but I can't. Someone said it was on Bantry Bay.'

Ellie confirmed that it was then explained the route she should take down from Kerry, to Kenmare, on to Glengariff and then west along the coast road until she reached Adrigole Harbour. 'Then before you come to Derreeny,' Ellie finished explaining, 'there's a little road marked private. You go down that, and we're at the bottom. Opposite Loughure Island.'

There was another silence.

'I've got the map here,' Artemis said eventually, 'and I'm just measuring it with my fingers. It's just over twenty miles as the crow flies. Except I'd better stick to the road, the one here.' There was another silence. 'Look,' she concluded. 'It can't be more than forty or fifty miles at the most. So I'll see you for lunch.'

And then the telephone went dead.

Artemis finally arrived mid-afternoon. Ellie had intended to take the trap into Bantry to collect some more floorboards, but had cancelled the trip after Artemis had called and instead persuaded Aggie to change her day off until the morrow so that she could cook lunch for her and her guest, since Cousin Rose was away visiting in Ballydonegan. Aggie, who was three parts drunk by mid-morning, nonetheless managed to assemble a delicious looking confection of fresh prawn salad and salmon poached in white wine and cream, which sat on the dining room sideboard under glass covers until lunchtime came and went. Rather than concede defeat, Ellie ate a piece of freshly made soda bread with some cheese, and then went back to her work relaying the floorboards.

Since Cousin Rose had quite strenuously opposed the notion of Ellie leaving her house in order to start earning her living, Ellie had agreed to stay on only if she could work for her keep. She was as determined to work as her relative was to have her stay, so finally Cousin Rose agreed that in return for her board and lodging, Ellie could do odd jobs around the place. The sort of jobs Cousin Rose had in mind were helping Aggie occasionally in the kitchen, and driving with Tutti and herself into town when there was any special shopping to do. By odd jobs she did not mean the complete renovation of Strand House, which is what Ellie had in mind.

For in the five weeks since Ellie had started 'odd-jobbing', with the help of the garden boy, the hall had been reboarded and painted, as had the dining room. The holes in all the downstairs ceilings had been repaired and the dining room fireplace had been reseated. The only floors that were still awaiting new boards were on the landings and corridors of the uppermost floors, which must have been a source of plundered firewood for years, since all that remained anywhere was just a single one plank gangway.

In fact Ellie was just on her way up to join the boy on the third floor to take up one or two boards which were rotting and dangerous, when she heard the high whine of a motor car engine coming up the drive. Forgetting that she had left him hammer in hand, Ellie rushed outside, just in time to see a little dark blue ragtop juddering to a halt in the carriage sweep, with Artemis at the wheel. Behind her sat a tall thin dog with a serious and lofty expression, and a coat of long wiry brown hair. It yawned as the car came to a halt, stood up and stretched, and then leapt effortlessly and gracefully out to go and inspect the adjacent undergrowth. Artemis, meanwhile, turned the ignition off while the gearbox was still engaged, so that the little car gave one last final leap and heave before lapsing into silence.

'Blast,' Artemis announced. 'That's the bit I always forget.' Too late she disengaged the gear lever, before turning round to smile at Ellie. 'Hullo,' she said.

'Hi,' Ellie replied, opening the car door for her guest. 'I take it not only did you not take the crow's route, I imagine you didn't even bother with the roads.'

'Irish signposts are very deceptive,' Artemis said, reaching for her stick and pulling herself up out of the car. 'They say one thing, but mean quite another. What a good spot.' Artemis stood and looked for a moment out into the bay, the breeze ruffling her soft blonde hair.

'What's your "spot" like?' Ellie asked.

'I prefer the sea to lakes,' Artemis replied. 'Lakes can sometimes get awfully doomy. Brutus?' She called to her dog who was happily rolling in something private. 'Brutus, stop that and come here.'

The big dog got up, shook his slim body, and wandered over to sit by his mistress, who laid a hand on his fine head. He looked up at Artemis and then at Ellie, as if to seek an introduction. He had very pale and slightly squinty eyes, set quite close together, which gave him a distinctly comical air. He held a large paw up and dandled it at Ellie, waiting for it to be taken. Ellie, unable to resist the look in his eyes, took the paw and solemnly shook it.

'Don't you think he's fun?' Artemis asked, turning to look at the house. 'He wandered up to the house one day and adopted me. Haven't a clue where he came from, although at least six people have tried to take money off me for him. He didn't belong to any of them, because he barked at them all. I had to leave my two terriers in England, so I'm rather glad really. I do like this house. It's about 1780 isn't it? My favourite.' Artemis began to wander across to the house, and as soon as she moved the dog was at her heels following.

'Artemis – ' Ellie started, preparing now to demand an explanation for her friend's behaviour.

'I suppose I've missed lunch.'

'It's practically teatime, actually.'

'I'm starved,' Artemis said, turning round to Ellie and wide-eyeing her. 'I could eat lunch and tea.'

Which she did. They both did, after Ellie had fetched Aggie's cold collation out to the terrace where they sat in the warm afternoon sunshine, and devoured the lot, followed, after a decent interval of an hour or so, by tea and scones.

'Aren't there any staff?' Artemis enquired, as Ellie returned with the strawberry jam for the scones.

'It's cook's day off,' Ellie explained, 'or rather it was until you phoned and said you were coming for lunch.'

'Sit,' Artemis instructed her dog before feeding it a scone, and ignoring Ellie's comment. 'And don't snatch.'

'And there's a butler called Tutti,' Ellie finished, 'who's driven Cousin Rose over to Ballydonegan.'

'Is he Italian?' Artemis enquired. 'The butler?'

'No,' Ellie replied. 'Cousin Rose called him "Tutti" because when he first arrived, years ago, all he would say was "tut, tut, Miss Rose". As a matter of fact, he still does on occasion. Whenever Cousin Rose asks for another sherry, or a second helping or something. It's so funny to hear him. I didn't know where to put myself for the first few days.'

'What's Cousin Rose like?' Artemis asked, buttering and strawberry jamming yet another scone.

'I guess she has to be just about the nicest person I've ever met,' Ellie replied with a smile.

Those were the first direct questions Artemis had asked since they sat down to eat. Although Ellie had tried to elicit information from Artemis as she ate her way through the cold salmon and salad, Artemis either totally ignored Ellie's questions, or answered them with a series of typical Artemis non-sequiturs, so that by the time they were drinking tea and eating home-made scones, Ellie was really none the wiser as to what exactly had happened since she had left the table in the hotel that day and gone to ring Cousin Rose.

'Artemis,' Ellie started again, determined to sort matters out. 'You really still haven't told me exactly why you vanished that day in Cork.'

'I wouldn't be here if I'd vanished,' Artemis replied. 'Don't be an idiot.'

'I see,' Ellie nodded. 'It's just quite normal, is it? I mean it's normal behaviour not to leave word as to where you've gone? And why?'

'What was the point? You weren't interested in my proposition.' Artemis shrugged and bent down to scratch her dog's chest.

'That doesn't explain why you just got up and went,' Ellie retorted. 'If I hadn't left *you* a note – '

'If you hadn't left me a note,' Artemis said, suddenly looking up at her, 'I wouldn't be sitting here now. Can you drive?'

'No I can't,' Ellie said. 'And I don't see what that's got to do with what we're talking about now.'

'Come on,' Artemis rose, and her dog rose with her. 'I'll teach you. It's terrific fun.'

Ellie sighed and got up to follow.

' "OK",' Artemis said slowly, staring at the dashboard. 'First you turn this key, then you press this button.' Artemis followed her own instructions and the car jerked suddenly forwards, catching Brutus off balance on the back seat so that he fell in a heap between the two girls.

'That must be wrong,' Artemis said with a frown. 'Of course. First you have to pull this stick back here, so that it waggles.' She demonstrated what she meant, disengaging the gear stick and setting it in neutral. '*Then* you press this button,' she continued, pressing the starter, 'and the engine should start.'

It didn't. No matter how often Artemis pressed the button. Ellie frowned and tried to help fathom it out.

'Perhaps you shouldn't have turned this key back off,' she said, pointing to the ignition key.

'Of course I shouldn't,' Artemis said, turning it back on. 'Quite right.'

This time the engine fired first time, bursting into life and then ticking over in the manner of a large sewing machine.

'OK,' Artemis continued slowly, pulling suddenly at her small chin and as she tried to recall what she should do next. 'Yes! *Then* you push this stick here!' Artemis had hold of the gear stick which she was trying to ram up into first gear, but without depressing the clutch:

'That can't be right!' Ellie yelled over the quite fearful grating noise.

'No!' Artemis agreed, looking down and frowning. 'It can't be, can it? No – of course. I forgot. You have to press a pedal. This one. That's right. The one on the left.' This time she managed to engage first gear almost noiselessly, with just a single clunk, while still frowning deeply and staring at the car floor. 'And then – ' she said, doing her best to remember. 'I know. Then you let the pedal go – sort of slowly.'

It was all done with deep concentration. Ellie too was staring down at what Artemis's feet were doing, quite fascinated, and quite unprepared for the subsequent stall the engine abruptly suffered as Artemis removed her foot from the clutch without opening the throttle, which this time threw them both backwards, but the dog again forwards, so that he became quite firmly wedged between the two front seats. Artemis tried to push him off with her left elbow.

'Do sit down, Brutus,' she ordered. 'You're really not helping. Let's start again. Key on, press the button. Shove down the pedal, push up the stick. So what did I do wrong here?' There was a short silence while Artemis racked her brain for the answer. Then she suddenly banged her hands on the steering wheel. 'Of course,' she said. 'Press the other pedal. The one that makes the stupid thing go.'

Because of her bad right leg, Artemis's seat was pushed as far forward as it would go, practically jamming Artemis against the steering wheel, so that she had to steer with both elbows stuck out at right angles. Now she rammed her right foot down on to the accelerator, until the engine practically reached the limits of its revolutions.

'And then!' she yelled, turning to Ellie, 'then you let go of the left pedal – like this!'

She disengaged the clutch and the car shot suddenly forward again, but this time, thanks to the engagement of full throttle, in a series of much more violent bounds, forcing Ellie to cling to the top of her door, and the dog to abandon ship altogether over the side. Finally the engine stalled, nearly shooting Ellie out of the open top and wedging Artemis even more firmly against her steering wheel.

'I must still be doing something wrong,' Artemis said, totally bewildered.

'You don't say,' Ellie retorted, rubbing her bruised knees.

'The handbrake, idiot,' Artemis suddenly said to herself. 'You forgot the stupid handbrake. Key. Button. Left pedal. Stick thing. Right pedal. Honestly – it's like falling off a log once you remember what to do. Other pedal – left pedal that is – and handbrake. And that's it.'

Free at last, the little blue car shot off at speed round the carriage sweep with Brutus chasing it, barking joyously all the while.

'We'll just go round the sweep a couple more times!' Artemis called. 'Until I'm absolutely used to it again! And then we'll go off to the beach!'

They seemed to Ellie to be going very fast, but this was an illusion caused by the car being driven flat out with the engine still engaged in only first gear. Which is the gear in which it stayed as without warning Artemis suddenly swung out of the carriage sweep and started to head down the drive, hurtling through every single pothole so that Ellie had to keep hold of the sides of her seat lest she be bumped out of the car altogether. Artemis bounced up and down beside Ellie in perfect synchronization as the car rose and fell and rose and fell through all the potholes, Artemis's elbows sticking out at right angles while she clung on for her own dear life to the very proximate steering wheel.

And then as the car rounded the last bend in the drive, it met Cousin Rose and Tutti coming in through the gateway in the pony and trap.

'You'll have to wave them out of the way!' Artemis yelled. 'I don't think I can stop now!'

Ellie found herself on her feet, grabbing hold of the top of the windshield with one hand, and waving violently with her other and shouting for Tutti to pull the trap over. He did so, just in time as the little car screamed past, and as Ellie sat back down in relief, she looked over her shoulder only to see the pony and trap disappearing into the laurel bushes.

'Do you want me to go back?' Artemis yelled as Ellie told her. 'Because I can't!'

'It's all right!' Ellie yelled back, taking another look. 'They're out of the bushes! And they're back on the drive!'

'I would have thought your cousin would have had a car!' Artemis said above the protests of the straining engine, as if that would have altered history. 'Now which way do we go for the beach?'

All the way to the beach, which fortunately wasn't very far, Artemis drove in first gear. Ellie, who knew no better, just thought that the car was very noisy.

'I agree,' Artemis shouted back. 'That's the only thing I don't like about it! In fact I was thinking of trying to buy a quieter one!'

'Don't you have to have a licence to drive?' Ellie asked, as they turned off for the beach, straight in front of another trap whose driver tumbled slowly from his seat into the ditch as his pony shied away from the little blue car.

'A licence?' Artemis pondered. 'Oh I shouldn't think so. Not unless you're carrying passengers, probably.'

'So who taught you?'

'No-one really,' Artemis replied, stopping the car on the edge of the beach by applying the handbrake and then turning the ignition off while the car was still in gear, occasioning yet another series of precipitous jolts. 'I picked it up sitting on one of the grooms' knees when I was small, and he was driving the tractor. There's not very much to it, you know. I mean it's not like riding a horse, for instance. You just have to do things in a certain order.'

The beach, a long pale yellow curl of sand running round a sparkling cove, was totally deserted, which was just as well since initially Ellie was an even worse pupil than Artemis was a teacher. It took Ellie a full quarter of an hour to get the car to go further than three feet without stalling it. By this time, Ellie was quite helpless with laughter, her sides aching with the pain of it, and the tears coursing down her face. Artemis did not find Ellie's amusement at all funny, which only made Ellie laugh all the more.

And then quite suddenly Ellie got the knack of the clutch and they were off, careering down the strand in first gear at nearly ten miles an hour, with the dog lolloping alongside them, happily splashing through the tiny waves and barking with joy.

'This is easy!' Ellie yelled. 'Once you have the knack, it's just easy! And fun, too! Oh boy!'

Ellie started weaving back down the strand in a series of zig-zags, swinging the steering wheel from side to side, up to the water's edge on one lock, and then to the top of the beach where the sand was still firm on the other. Finally she drove round and round in circles, big sweeping ones at first, and then down to the smallest she could make the car, until Artemis caught Ellie's infection and began to laugh quite helplessly as well.

'I've forgotten how you said you stop the darned thing!' Ellie yelled.

'Turn the key off!' Artemis yelled back. 'And pull on the handbrake!'

Ellie did as she was told and the car stalled abruptly to a stop. 'Now that was fun!' Ellie exclaimed. 'I mean it! But this has to be a very basic car, you know, Artemis. Because compared with what I've been driven in back home, it's kind of rough. I should reckon this is a beginner's model.'

'Do you think so?' Artemis frowned. 'Yes. I suppose it is quite titchy.'

'Titchy?'

'Small. And I did ask for one one could manage. And the man in the village yes — he did say one couldn't get much simpler than this. It used to belong to a very old lady.'

'Sure,' Ellie agreed. 'And she wouldn't want anything too fancy. Or too fast. Still, if it only does ten miles an hour, you could almost do that on a bicycle.'

'Do you think I should get something faster then?' Artemis enquired.

'Maybe,' Ellie answered cautiously, the memory of the drive to the beach still all too fresh in her mind. 'When you've had a bit more experience.'

'I wouldn't mind something a bit faster,' Artemis mused, watching her dog playing at the water's edge. 'It did take an age coming over today.'

They fell silent, Ellie unwilling to encourage Artemis any further, and Artemis slipping into one of her brown studies.

'Come on,' she suddenly said, opening her car door. 'I'm going for a swim.'

'Yes?' said Ellie. 'Have you brought your costume?'

'You don't need a costume,' Artemis replied. 'Who's going to see?'

Ellie looked around. There was no-one in sight anywhere. 'There could be someone in the grass or something,' she argued.

'So what?' Artemis replied, kicking off her shoes and then sitting down on the running board to roll down her stockings.

'You're not going to strip right off, surely?'

'No,' Artemis said. 'I'm going to keep my camiknickers on. Sorry. I mean I'm going to swim in my "pantees".'

Artemis looked at Ellie and grinned impishly, before unbuttoning her skirt and blouse, and peeling them both off. Then she turned round to face Ellie with her arms folded demurely across her chest, but with a frown on her face. 'You can't swim, can you?' she said. 'Of course.'

'Don't let it stop you,' Ellie replied. 'I'll have a paddle.'

Artemis gave Ellie one of her long blank looks and then shrugged. ' "OK",' she said, and started to walk towards the water.

Ellie followed on cautiously, as if it was she who had no clothes on. 'Are you sure you shouldn't have a robe on?' she asked. 'They'll throw you in gaol, I bet. If anyone sees you. There was a party of nuns here yesterday.'

'Nonsense,' Artemis retorted. 'I swim like this the whole time in Kerry. Come on, Brutus!' She called to her dog who was now chasing seagulls, and the dog, with one last despairing leap at an escaping bird, turned and cantered back to his mistress.

Artemis needed her stick to get her to the sea, but tossed it away behind her as she reached the water's edge. Ellie, pausing to roll her skirt up and tuck it into her underwear, realized what this meant to Artemis. For in her state of undress, Artemis's deformity was all too visible, and it was impossible to dismiss it any longer as just a bit of a limp, particularly when seen in relation to the rest of her really quite perfect body. Her right leg was not only considerably shorter, but it was twisted below the knee almost at right angles, and the muscles and ligaments both above and below the knee, although not wasted, were considerably tighter and smaller than those on her good leg. To judge from the shape in which they now were, her right hip and the right side of her pelvis had also been badly damaged in the fall, for instead of roundness and symmetry there was a flatness and inequality, and both at the top of her right thigh and running even as high as her waistline, there were large areas of scar tissue. It was a body which had suffered what must have been a devastating accident.

Ellie hurried to catch her friend up, who was already testing the water with one foot, the foot of her bad right leg. Ellie arrived beside her, and ran straight into the water and then straight out again.

'Gee!' she cried. 'That is cold!'

'Don't be such a baby,' Artemis said. 'Of course it's not cold.' And started to walk without flinching until the water was up to her waist.

Ellie didn't mind what Artemis thought, but to her the sea was cold. It was cold but wonderfully clear, clearer than any water Ellie had ever seen. Through its small shimmering waves she could see the sand and the pebbles crystal clear below her, as she stood waiting to wade in further. Artemis by now had plunged herself under, and was already swimming, with an intensity and vigour which quite astonished Ellie. She watched Artemis swim way out to sea, with long, quick and strong strokes. From the way she was swimming, it would have been quite impossible to tell she had an infirmity.

A good way out from the shore now, Artemis paused, trod water and looked back to Ellie whom she saw still standing in the shallows, a Venus returning to the sea. She waved at her and Ellie waved back, before hoisting her skirts even higher and beginning to paddle. Artemis watched her, and then swam lazily back to within hailing distance.

'This is another reason I prefer the sea,' Artemis called to Ellie, as she turned to float on her back. 'It's far easier to swim than to walk.'

'From what I've just seen,' Ellie called back, 'you could swim in custard.'

'I love water,' Artemis replied. 'There have been times when I could have swum out to sea, and – just disappeared.' And then, she was gone, turning back on to her front and jack-knifing herself neatly into the gentle blue sea, to surface again what seemed an age later, gasping for air, laughing and shaking the water from her ears and eyes.

'It's so clear!' she called. 'I've never swum in a sea so clear!'

Ellie watched with growing envy as Artemis disappeared below the waves again, to reappear twenty yards or so further along. She then swam a good hundred or so yards out to sea once more without stopping, before turning and swimming all the way back to the shallows, where she lay letting the water break over and around her.

'Marvellous,' she said. 'Simply wonderful.'

'I don't suppose you could teach me to swim,' Ellie asked, paddling out of the clear sea.

Artemis eyed her. 'I don't see why not,' she said. ' "OK".'

There was no-one around on the beach when they got back to the car, and no sign in the sand that anyone had been anywhere near. Just the marks of their own shoes and feet, and the paw marks of the dog. They looked very closely to make sure, and with good reason, because after they'd dried themselves off on Artemis's car rug, and Artemis had got fully dressed again, they found their shoes were missing.

'That's the little people,' Cousin Rose told them over sherry. 'They're forever taking people's shoes. Isn't that right, Tutti?'

'It is not,' the butler replied. 'It's got nothing to do with it.'

'But there were no footprints round the motor car, Tutti!' Ellie explained. 'Only our own!'

'My very point, miss,' the butler nodded, 'which I was just about to make, had I been allowed. For if it had been the little people, there'd have been some little footmarks.'

There then followed a long and earnest argument between Cousin Rose and her butler as to who then the culprit could be, Cousin Rose sticking staunchly to the leprechaun theory, despite the lack of physical evidence, while her manservant elaborated on the possibility that a seabird might well have made off with the shoes in order to make itself a nest.

'Did ye ever hear the like?' Cousin Rose snorted. 'And what size of seabird would it have to be, man? It could hardly be a gull, because it wouldn't be strong enough. So at the very least it would have to be a Gannet or even a Shag, would it not? And then it would be too something big to sit and nest on a girl's little shoe! I mean did ye ever hear the like?'

'There were no other footprints, madam,' said the butler, 'so that is conclusive.'

'Aha!' Cousin Rose cried, halfway through the soup. 'I have it! It could have been one of the little people! On the *back* of a Shag!'

After dinner, Artemis having been invited to stay the night, she and Ellie walked in the gardens and watched the moon rising above Bantry Bay.

'Everything grows like mad here apparently,' Ellie explained, as they walked past the lush vegetation and under the shadows of the palm trees, 'because we're on the end of the Gulf Stream.'

'It sounds as if you've found a home then,' Artemis said.

'Why do you say that?' Ellie asked.

'You didn't say "they're on the end of the Gulf Stream", Eleanor. You said "we",' Artemis replied. 'And why not? If I were you, I wouldn't budge from here.'

'OK,' said Ellie. 'So don't.'

' "OK",' said Artemis. 'I won't.'

Cousin Rose was only too happy to have Artemis to stay, and for as long as she liked. On the morning of the second day, Artemis announced she was going to drive back to Lough Caragh in order to fetch what she needed, but Cousin Rose at once scotched such a notion, saying it was too far for a young woman to be driving alone and that Tutti would drive her. Ellie and Brutus squeezed in the back of the little blue motor and the party set off on a fine sunny midday with the bowler-hatted butler at the wheel.

'Wait,' Artemis ordered him as they were no more than halfway down the drive, 'what did you do then? With that thing?' Artemis pointed to the gear stick. 'You moved it,' she said, accusingly.

'Of course I did, miss,' Tutti replied. 'Otherwise I could not have changed gear.'

Artemis stared in unconcealed amazement as the butler proceeded to take the car up through the gears, until they were driving down the road at a steady and relatively quiet forty miles an hour, with only the wind noise now to pitch their voices against.

'It goes backwards as well, miss,' the butler told Artemis, after she had admitted her ignorance.

'It doesn't?' wondered Artemis. 'What – without pushing?'

After they had arrived at Artemis's hired house, which nestled in the woods on the shore of the beautiful lake, Artemis indicated all the things she wanted to take back to Strand House, and left Ellie and her hostess' butler to do the packing, while she took herself off to practice changing gear up and down her drive. She returned after nearly three quarters of an hour, flushed with triumph and carrying her shoes.

'I've got it,' she announced. 'Not only that, I even managed to get the wretched thing to go backwards.'

'Great,' Ellie said as they stood by the front door with all Artemis's luggage. 'But where's the car now? I don't see it.'

'No, well you wouldn't,' Artemis replied. 'It's in the edge of the lake.'

Soon it was high summer. The garden at Strand House resembled nothing less than something out of the tropics, full of lush vegetation and the fattest bumblebees Artemis had ever seen. The weather was particularly fine, with long hot days, and short warm nights, so that the chill went from the sea, and Artemis and Ellie took to bathing every day long before breakfast. Ellie might have been slow to master the knack of driving, but she soon learned to swim under Artemis's excellent if somewhat impatient tutoring. She had to, otherwise she most probably would have drowned. For having spent the first few days of her coaching teaching Ellie the rudiments, with Ellie buoyed up on an inflated inner car tyre, one afternoon when the sea was as calm as a millpond, Artemis lured the unsuspecting Ellie well out of her depth, and then with the aid of a pin she had concealed, punctured her tyre. Ellie screamed for help and thrashed around as the air gurgled out from the rubber tube, but all Artemis did was swim away and yell at Ellie to follow her.

Which Ellie did, having first swallowed what seemed like half of Bantry Bay. She found herself swimming, at first far too fast, as she thrashed through the water in her panic, and then, once she realized she was alive and afloat, slowly and with complete amazement.

'Hey look at me!' she yelled at Artemis, who was swimming ahead of her. 'Look, Artemis! I'm swimming!'

'Of course you are, you idiot!' Artemis called back. 'If you weren't, you'd be drowning!'

After that, the days took on an easy shape, with Ellie, after their morning swim, working on the house until midday, while Artemis lay reading in the garden, or helping Cousin Rose garden, followed by a long slow lunch outside, a doze and then either a trip in the car to fish somewhere, or to explore the coastline as far as Crow Head and sometimes even round into Ballydonegan Bay and beyond to the mouth of the great Kenmare river. Before dinner there would be a few games of croquet, Cousin Rose and Ellie against Artemis and Tutti, the latter being such a formidable combination, Ellie and her second cousin were rarely in serious contention. Then there would be dinner, which was invariably taken late, since the croquet matches were sometimes still being played as dusk was falling, particularly once they had changed the sides, and Artemis was saddled with playing with her hostess. For Cousin Rose had a style of croquet all her own, swinging the mallet not through her legs but round from the side, in a wildly disorganized arc. She also had a habit of hitting the wrong ball, since she was colour blind, and going the wrong way round the lawn, since she also seemed to be, as her butler described 'directionally agnostic'.

On occasion, when they finally sat down to yet another of Aggie's delicious dinners, cooked, as Cousin Rose always said, at the grumble, Ellie wondered how she wasn't dead from laughing, particularly since Artemis apparently took it all so seriously, trying to correct and control her partner's lunatic swing and detailing complex tactical plans which Cousin Rose hadn't the faintest chance of executing. They were never any of them in bed until well past one o'clock, but the two girls were always up with the dawn.

One boiling hot morning, when Ellie had driven off with Tutti in the pony and trap to fetch some more bags of plaster, Artemis drove her little car down to the beach to take an extra dip. As always there was no-one about on what Ellie and she had now come to regard as their private strand, so, finding that she had left her bathing things back at the house, Artemis didn't think twice about stripping down to her usual minimum and making straight for the sea.

He must have arrived as she was swimming away from the shore, Artemis thought, as she stood treading water and wondering how she was to get to the safety of her car unnoticed, because she was quite certain there had been absolutely no-one about earlier. Yet there most certainly was someone there now, a man seated at an artist's easel, halfway along the golden strand.

It wasn't so much the thought of the odd sight she would make in her soaking underthings that made Artemis swim as far out as she dared before turning to swim parallel to the shore but away from the stranger, but rather her natural reluctance to expose her infirmity to a total stranger. It had taken all her gum, as her godmother would have put it, to take that first dip that day with Ellie, so she was certainly more than a little unwilling to be seen stripped by a stranger.

Not that it mattered to her personally, Artemis kept telling herself, as she swam steadily away from him, but it might give him a bit of a start.

It was a long hike back to the car from where she finally came ashore, but it was worth it because she seemed quite safely out of vision, the artist appearing to be sitting with his back to her. She had left her cane where she had first got in the water, so her progress back towards the car was a little slower and more painful than usual.

And then, alerted by Brutus's delighted barking as he rejoined his mistress, he turned round. Artemis froze, her arms crossed protectively across her. She saw the sun glint on what she thought must be the man's spectacles. He seemed to be staring directly at her, so she dropped to her knees, hoping the car would shield her from his sight as Brutus reached her and started smothering her with kisses. After a seemingly endless moment she looked up, and found that the man had turned away again, and was once more busy with his work, so busy that Artemis made the safety of the car unseen, where she then collapsed on to the nearside running board to catch her breath, while Brutus ran round in circles, barking with delight.

It was so hot she had no need to dry herself. She just slipped straight into her clothes which she smuggled from the car, and was back in her Tyrolean blouse and long embroidered cotton skirt in no time. Now all she needed was her stick.

'Fetch,' she ordered Brutus, looking round the car and pointing to where it lay by the water's edge. 'Fetch it, you idiot.' The dog ran off, wagging his tail and barking, and brought Artemis back a piece of seaweed. 'No, you stupid hairy chump,' Artemis scolded. 'My stick. Look! Fetch!'

This time Brutus retrieved a small piece of driftwood, which he dropped on Artemis's left foot, and then wagged his tail in anticipation of his next exciting task.

Artemis sat back against the car and sighed. Since the tide was nearly out when she had gone to swim, her stick was a good hundred yards from the car and thus directly in view of the painter. She knew she could make it, if she took it steadily, but she also knew that she would be seen, and if she was seen, the man might feel the need to get up and help her, and for some unknown reason that was the very last thing she felt she wanted.

So she decided to remain where she was, until such a time that the man either went home, or Brutus got it into his thick skull to retrieve it.

'Is this yours?'

Artemis looked up and saw a man in a straw hat with his back to the sun. He was holding up her stick.

'Yes it is.'

'I thought it might be,' the man said, dropping it on the back seat. 'Cheerio.' He doffed his hat and went off in the direction from which he had come.

Artemis had no idea of what he looked like, or of what age he might be, because his face had been in deep shadow with the sun right behind him. She pulled herself up, holding on to the side of the car, and looked after the retreating figure, who was ambling up towards the dunes, his easel under one arm, and his box of paints under the other, a tall untidy figure, in a fading canvas suit and bare feet, the song he was whistling fading away with him as his figure became just a shimmer in the haze of heat which hung over the dunes.

'That's very like John Piper,' Artemis observed.

The man in the straw hat turned round, surprised. Artemis saw she had been right and that he did wear glasses, very round and with brass frames. And that he was also young, serious and tall and good-looking, with long fair hair, grey-green eyes, and a deep sun tan.

The artist dipped his brush in the mixture of oil and spirit and stared at his work. 'Don't you know that's the rudest thing you can say to a painter?' he asked amiably. 'That something's very like somebody else's work?'

'I like John Piper,' Artemis replied. 'I'd take that as a compliment.'

'I like John Piper too,' he agreed. 'But I still don't take that as a compliment.'

He began to paint again and Artemis watched in silence.

'I've been here for ages,' Artemis suddenly announced.

'Yes I know,' the painter replied, disappointing Artemis who imagined she had surprised him, so quietly had she approached his easel. 'Where's the dog?' he enquired, without looking round.

'Why?'

'I just wondered. He looks rather a nice sort of chap.'

'He's totally brainless and extremely vain,' Artemis informed him. 'And I left him behind because he drank seawater yesterday and did what he shouldn't all over the person I'm staying with's bathmat.'

There followed another long silence, broken only by a sigh from Artemis, which made the artist momentarily stop painting. He looked round at her, to find she was still staring at his work.

'Something the matter?' he asked.

Artemis shook her head without looking at him. 'You must have been here ages,' she said. 'Judging from your suntan.'

'I've only been here a couple of days,' the painter replied. 'I got the tan in Egypt.'

'Are you an archeologist?'

'Not really. My father is. In an amateur way. He spends quite a lot of time in the Middle East.'

Artemis took off her large floppy sun hat and ruffled out her short blonde hair, staring out to sea. 'I'm Artemis Deverill, by the way,' she said. 'Who are you?'

'Hugo Tanner,' he replied, and then resumed painting.

'Is that what you were?' Artemis asked. 'Tanners?'

Hugo Tanner looked out at the view he was painting, and then started to mix a colour on his palette. 'No,' he replied. 'My father was a brewer before he retired. And my grandfather was. And my great-grandfather.'

'So really you should be called Brewer.'

'Probably.'

Artemis put her hat back on and leaned on her stick. 'Do you like Stanley Spencer?' she asked.

'I've only seen the stuff at the Tate,' Hugo replied. 'And the War Museum. I'm not sure I care for it.'

'He had a state of sureness, you know. Unlike most painters. That's why he could see Cookham, where he lived, as Heaven. And Jesus living there. Because of it. It must be rather nice. Having a state of sureness.'

'Really?' Hugo mixed some more paint.

'I think so.' Artemis leaned forward to stare more closely at the painting. 'You've been influenced by the post-Impressionists.'

Hugo stopped painting and looked round at the young woman behind him. Once again, she paid no attention whatsoever, but merely continued to study his work, allowing him time to take her in. She was very pretty, standing there with her floppy brimmed straw hat back on her head, hands sunk deep in the pockets of her long white cotton skirt, slender and tanned, and with a pair of the brightest blue eyes he had ever seen. But there was something sad about her, too, which seemed to have nothing to do with her infirmity, but concerned something unseen, something metaphysical.

'The island isn't right,' she ventured out of the silence.

'It's only a sketch,' Hugo replied. 'I've hardly begun the island.'

'You've made it look like a whale,' Artemis continued.

'It won't do when I've finished,' Hugo assured her, somewhat tetchily.

Artemis turned and looked at him, blankly, as if she didn't believe a word of it. 'I'm going now,' she announced. 'Goodbye.'

The next morning the car was there before Hugo was, but as he set up his easel, he could see no sign of the girl. He looked out into the bay in case she was swimming, but could see no-one, so he continued with his preparations, opening his canvas stool, mixing the linseed and turpentine, squeezing out the worms of colour on to his palette, and selecting his brushes. By the time he had been painting for an hour, and there was still no sign of her, Hugo suddenly stopped as the thought hit him. He stood up, scanning the calm sea, and then putting down his palette, his brushes and his paint rag, he ran at speed to the water's edge, for some reason expecting at any moment to catch sight in the water of a dead and floating body.

What he found instead was a set of human footprints headed west where the tide had receded, two bare feet and the imprint of a walking stick. By the human foot-marks were the spores of a madly circling dog, who had obviously been running round and round its owner and in and out of the water. Shielding his eyes against the glare, Hugo looked to where the beach curled to an end, before disappearing round the headland, and sure enough, just coming back into sight out of the shimmering haze were the figures of a young woman and her dog.

Hugo was back and hard at work by the time Artemis walked by.

'Hello!' she called, but more *en passant* than in greeting.

'Good morning!' Hugo called back, doffing his old straw hat. 'Beautiful again, isn't it?'

'What is?' Artemis stopped and peered at Hugo from under one hand held to the brim of her own hat.

'The weather!' Hugo called back, feeling rather fatuous.

'Oh!' Artemis dropped the hand from her hat and waved with it, once. 'I'm going to be late for lunch!'

'If you wait I'll walk back with you!' Hugo shouted, beginning hastily to pack up.

She didn't wait, but Hugo still caught up with her easily, because her car was parked down the far end of the strand.

'You don't work for very long,' she said.

'It's quite long enough in this heat,' Hugo replied. 'And anyway, I do some more when I get home. After I've eaten.'

'You don't work from photographs?' Artemis turned to him and stared, almost accusingly.

'Why?' Hugo asked. 'I have done, yes. But no – not on this sort of painting. No.'

Artemis walked on, replying nothing.

'Where have you been?' Hugo asked.

'For a walk.'

'I know that. I saw you coming round the point.'

'Yes?' Artemis stared out to sea.

'I haven't been round the point,' Hugo said. 'What's it like?'

Artemis shrugged. 'Go and see,' she told him.

'Is it worth it?'

'I wouldn't tell you to go and see if it wasn't.'

'What's round there?'

'More sea,' Artemis said. 'And more sand.' And then she smiled at him, the first smile she'd smiled at him, more from the eyes than the mouth, the sun coming out from behind a cloud. 'And there are seals,' she said. 'Masses of seals. Would you like a lift?'

She drove him back up from the beach, along the dusty sandy track and up to the road.

'Which way now?'

'This is fine,' Hugo told her. 'I can walk from here. You're going to be late.'

'No I'm not,' Artemis replied, engaging first gear. 'If you can walk it, it can't be that far.' She turned and looked at him questioningly, as she continued to drive down the middle of the road.

'Turn left. And I'm just down the bottom there.'

'Yes, there's a whole colony of seals round the point,' Artemis told him, as they drove along, hatless, with the wind ruffling their hair. 'I've made friends with one.'

'Not with the dog in tow, surely?'

Artemis suddenly laughed, once, and then stared at Hugo as if he were mad. 'The dog?' she said, looking in the mirror at the happy panting sight behind her. 'That silly idiot went and hid.'

The road was a cul-de-sac, ending in a sand dune. To one side, on a hard standing by a rough field, was a gypsy caravan, painted red with yellow scrolls and curliques.

'Tinker, tailor,' Artemis said, staring at it, 'brewer, tanner? Painter?'

'I'm on holiday,' Hugo smiled. 'It's not my profession.'

'What fun,' Artemis said. 'Goodbye.'

And drove off.

'There are tinkers below, madam,' Tutti told Cousin Rose at lunch. 'Below in the field.'

'Do we need anything fixing, man?' Cousin Rose asked.

'That's not my affair, madam,' the butler replied. 'That's for Aggie to say.'

'Then ax her so,' his employer instructed. 'Ax her if she's any pots or pans.'

'Are you sure they're tinkers?' Artemis enquired, filleting her fresh mackerel.

'There's a caravan, Miss,' Tutti replied. 'And where there's a caravan, there's tinkers.'

'It could be someone on holiday,' Artemis said vaguely.

'On holiday?' Cousin Rose asked with a laugh. 'Did ye ever hear such a thing? Did ye ever? In a tinker's caravan? I never heard such a thing!'

'It belongs to a friend of mine,' Hugo explained to Artemis the next morning, 'who has a house down here. One of the MacGillycuddies. He bought it off a tinker and had it in his drawing room as a conversation piece.'

'I don't see why not,' Artemis replied. 'Much better than the weather.'

'There's little wrong with this weather,' Hugo mused, continuing to paint. 'I was told to expect nothing but rain.'

'Absolutely,' said Artemis. 'Would you sell that painting?'

'I thought you didn't like it.'

'That's not what I said,' returned Artemis. 'I asked if you would sell it.'

'Yes,' Hugo agreed. 'Why? Do you want to buy it?'

'No,' Artemis said. 'Because if you're willing to sell it, it can't be any good.'

'Why not?'

'Oh – because you're an amateur painter. And amateurs never sell the paintings they like. They sell only paintings they don't think much of.'

Artemis stared at him, and then picked his sketch book up from the top of his paint box, only for Hugo to take it back from her at once. 'I only wanted to look,' she complained.

'And I don't want you to look,' he stated.

The next time he stopped painting to turn and talk to her, she was gone. Hugo looked down the beach and saw her getting back into her car. He stood up to wave and call, and then thought better of it and sat slowly back down.

Artemis did not go back to the beach the next day, nor indeed for several days. The following morning she persuaded Ellie to put down her paintbrush and go fishing instead on Glenbeg Lake, where they caught several good trout. They then drove round Ballycrovane Harbour and up to Kilcatherine Point where opposite Inishfarnard, under a clear blue sky, they ate the picnic lunch Aggie had prepared them.

'Cousin Rose says they haven't had a summer like this since before the war,' Ellie said, shading her eyes against the sun.

'You do know there's going to be another war, don't you?' Artemis announced, beginning to peel a hard-boiled egg piece by careful piece.

'Not today, Artemis,' Ellie sighed. 'We've had this over dinner all week.'

Artemis threw a crust of bread to a circling gull, who swooped and plucked it out of the air. 'I suppose Hitler's just playing games,' she said after a silence. 'Having all those people assassinated so he could become chancellor.'

'It's a beautiful day, Artemis,' Ellie groaned. 'Can't we just leave politics alone for once?'

'It's probably a beautiful day in Germany, too,' Artemis replied, pulling herself up on her stick. 'The same sun's probably shining on all those young men who are being forcibly conscripted. And all the Jews they've passed laws against. I suppose they're all thinking what a beautiful day, I'll bet.'

Ellie watched Artemis walk off with her big brown and white coated dog loping behind her, but knew better than to get up and follow. Instead, she packed the picnic up, put it back in the car, and then wandered down to the tiny beach below, where she lay down in the sun to doze.

The next day Ellie was persuaded to go for another expedition, but that too fizzled out in what Ellie considered pointless argument, this time concerning America's apparent indifference over Mussolini's invasion of Abyssinia. The third day they drove down the finger of land the south side of Bantry Bay to Sheep's Head, round the north side of Dunmanus Bay and down to Mizen Head, a trip specially requested by Ellie as she wanted to stand on the very bit of Ireland she had first glimpsed from the S.S. *Baltimore*. It was yet another fine, clear summer day, and Ellie did her very best to relish all the wonderful country and coastline they drove through and along, but she found her enjoyment confounded by the increasing darkness of Artemis's mood.

'I don't know what's going on,' Ellie said as they neared Mizen Head. 'But I just don't seem to be able to say a thing right.'

'That's right,' Artemis agreed. 'You don't.'

'What the hell's got into you anyway?' Ellie rounded on Artemis. 'It's as if these past few days you've taken me out on these trips just to take it out on me!'

Artemis said nothing. She just stared round briefly at Ellie and then drove on.

'Aren't you going to get out?' Ellie asked when they'd arrived at the top of the great cliffs which form the Mizen headland. 'Don't you want to see the view?'

'I can see from here,' Artemis said, settling herself below the level of the windscreen.

'It's hardly the same experience,' Ellie protested.

'You Americans and experience,' Artemis sighed. 'You'd honestly think you invented it.'

Ellie stood on the edge of the cliffs, with the Atlantic

far below her, and for the first time since she'd arrived in Ireland, as she looked back across the great ocean, she realized with some surprise she felt homesick. At this moment she would have given anything to be home, seeing Patsy coming home with something for her, a bunch of violets, a second-hand book, a new magazine, to tell her a joke he'd heard at the office or a story he'd overheard down at the drugstore. Whenever the others were out, she and Patsy would sit in the kitchen and talk for hours, about what they were going to do, and the people they both hoped they one day might meet.

Ellie looked into the wind that was blowing off the Atlantic and thought how wrong she had been to leave America. She should have stayed home and seen it out. No-one could run away from their future. The future was already a part of you, she remembered her father saying, and you can't run away from your future.

Ireland was lovely, but Ireland was just a party, a diversion, a ceilidh as the natives called it, a lark and a caper before facing the serious business of life which had now to be faced, because it seemed the party was soon to be over, certainly in Europe, and according to Artemis the balloons were all just about to burst. When it got dark they'd probably find that these forces of evil had managed to take even the moon away.

Then Artemis suddenly appeared at her side, startling her. 'You know,' she said, slipping her arm through Ellie's. 'I really don't know what I'd have done. If you hadn't been on that stupid boat.'

They talked for the rest of the day, mostly about the past, as if Ellie's unspoken thoughts had prompted Artemis into unaccustomed frankness, first as they lazed on Barleycove sands and then on the long slow journey home, during which they took it in turns to drive.

'What about the house? Was there really no way you could prevent it being sold?'

'Short of murdering my stepmother, no.'

'What about your father?'

'My father's favourite play is *Macbeth*,' Artemis replied enigmatically. 'Come on, it's your turn.'

Artemis braked suddenly, but Ellie was rarely caught unawares now, since when Artemis drove Ellie spent the whole time with her arms braced against the dashboard.

'Your turn to drive,' Artemis announced. 'Except do try and drive a bit faster this time.'

They changed places and Ellie took the wheel, proceeding to drive at the sensible speed at which she always drove, and which occasioned a series of deep groans from Artemis.

'God,' she said, 'you certainly haven't got much of what my godmother would call dash.'

Ellie smiled, ignoring the jibe. She preferred to suffer Artemis's good-natured insults rather than her recent long dark silences, for she had realized early on the jibes were not meant to wound. On the contrary, they were Artemis's way of expressing affection. And besides, it was the most perfect of early evenings, with the waning sun making glinty stars dance on the waters of Bantry Bay as they passed through Glengariff and headed for home.

'I'm reading this book *Wine From These Grapes* at the moment,' Artemis said after a long and peaceful silence. She was lying back in her seat, staring up at the skies overhead, and trailing her left arm over the side of her door. 'It's by Edna St Vincent Millay. And she says, "childhood is a kingdom where nobody dies." '

'I think that's how I thought, when I was very small.'

'I think I probably did as well,' Artemis agreed. 'But it didn't last very long.'

She continued to stare above her, at the skies and the edges of trees that passed through her vision, and fell silent again. Ellie started to sing in a light and charming voice snatches of a song Artemis couldn't identify, while Artemis settled lower into her seat and wondered why she hadn't told Ellie about Hugo Tanner.

And then she wondered why she was wondering, because she knew perfectly well what the reason was.

She had wanted to keep him as her private friend, in that kingdom where nobody dies, which was absurd and selfish of her. As from tomorrow Hugo Tanner would no longer be her secret. She would bring him up to meet and be met by everyone at Strand House.

'What was that you were singing?' Artemis asked, still staring at the evening sky.

' "Smoke Gets In Your Eyes",' Ellie said, changing down a gear and turning into the drive. 'The new Jerome Kern.'

Artemis was sitting on the terrace reading when Hugo arrived. He was wearing his crumpled canvas suit and battered straw, with a clean white tennis shirt, a red bow tie spotted white, and not so white tennis shoes worn without socks. When he took his hat off to say good evening, his thick fair hair was still matted with sea-salt and sand, which in addition to his deep tan made him look as though he had stepped straight out of a coracle.

'Did you know the Irish monks sailed the Atlantic in those extraordinary boats?' Artemis asked as they sat waiting for the others, drinking home-made lemonade. 'They got as far as Iceland, apparently. In something like 6 BC.'

'Greenland, actually,' Hugo corrected her. 'In 4 BC.'

'They're only wickerwork and canvas, you know,' Artemis continued blithely, as if he hadn't spoken. 'It's unimaginable.'

'Religion is a powerful force,' Hugo replied. 'People will do anything for their religion.'

'Except live for it,' Artemis said. 'Here are the others.'

Hugo rose as two women came out of the house, followed by an oddly attired butler who was carrying sherry and glasses on a silver tray. The older woman, introduced to him as Miss Lannigan, was defiantly handsome, with a magnificent leonine head on a strong and well boned body, dressed in a black gown embroidered in gold thread at both the neck and half-sleeves, which by its length and shape identified it as belonging to the very early Twenties rather than the now mid-Thirties. She had piled her mass of still dark brown hair up on top of her head and wound it convulsively into what looked for all the world like two bunches of large and hairy grapes, divided in turn by a large fresh red rose cut straight from the garden. Hugo knew that to be the case, for he could see the greenfly in it, still alive and at work. But somehow, such was Cousin Rose's character and presence, the end result which should by rights have been risible was nothing of the sort. It was eccentric perhaps, and idiosyncratic certainly, but it was also utterly entrancing and oddly glamorous.

There was nothing oddly glamorous about the young woman, however, who was standing by her side, and was introduced to Hugo as Miss Ellie Milligan, Miss Lannigan's second cousin from across the water. As far as Hugo Tanner was concerned, Miss Ellie Milligan had stepped right out of a dream. He tried to remember if he had ever seen such original beauty as flesh and blood, and standing before him shaking his hand, rather than as a lifeless photograph in some fashionable magazine, or as a flickering image up on a silver screen. By the time he had finished gazing into those strange grey-green eyes with flecks of brown, set in the most open and expressive face he had ever seen, Hugo decided that the nearest he had come to being in the presence of such natural divinity, if indeed there was such a thing, was when he had stood entranced and staring up at the girl in the centre of Millais' painting of *Autumn Leaves*.

The girl in the painting had long brown hair, whereas this girl's hair was considerably shorter, but the expressions were the same, open and accessible, but also sad and private. He remembered how he had stood before that painting for what seemed like hours, oblivious to everything but the face of that wonderful girl, lit by the warmth of the bonfire of leaves, and how he had found himself falling in love. And now it seemed he was standing in front of that mythic creature's double, a brown-haired girl with deep soulful eyes, lit by the glow of the late summer sun.

'I must paint you,' he said to her, much earlier than he had intended. They had drunk some sherry, played an eccentric game of croquet, and now, at Cousin Rose's insistence, he was enjoying a refreshing gin and tonic, as she sipped lemonade.

'Mr Tanner's a Sunday painter,' Artemis explained, eating a slice of lemon.

'I do wish ye wouldn't do that, darling,' Cousin Rose admonished her with a sigh. 'For heavens it dries up all one's gastric juices.'

'It's terribly good for the skin,' Artemis replied.

'Could you perhaps call me Hugo?' their guest implored. 'The "Mr" sounds so formal.'

'I agree,' Cousin Rose said. 'It's a bit like being in stuffy old England. You must call me Rose.'

'And me Ellie,' Eleanor agreed.

Artemis said nothing. She just reached for another slice of lemon.

'And you?' Hugo finally asked her.

'What's in a name?' Artemis replied. 'Why not call me Tom?'

'If that's what you'd prefer,' Hugo said.

'Maybe I'd prefer Maud,' Artemis countered. 'It's up to you.'

'Much more suitable,' Cousin Rose replied, finishing her gin. ' "Maud with her exquisite face, and wild voice pealing up to the sunny sky, and feet like sunny gems on an English green". Much more the thing. Shall we go in now everyone?'

' "Birds in the high Hall-garden," ' Hugo said as they rose. ' "When twilight was falling, Maud, Maud, Maud, Maud, they were crying and calling." '

'Actually, come to think of it, I actually prefer Tom,' Artemis said, walking in ahead of him, her stick searching on the wooden floor for the sounder of the boards.

Dinner initially was a disaster. For once Aggie failed them, which Cousin Rose suspected might be the case when what was intended to be iced cucumber soup came out of the tureen at near boiling point, and which Cousin Rose decided definitely to be the case when the pheasant casserole was set before them minus the necessary pheasants.

' 'Tis the company, isn't that the case, Tutti?' Cousin Rose enquired of her butler.

'It is not,' the butler replied. 'That has nothing to do with it.'

'She's always the same when we've company,' Cousin Rose continued. 'We had the suffragan bishop here last Christmas, and she shrank the turkey to the size of a walnut.'

'Because she was blind dead drunk, that's the reason,' the butler said. 'And that's how you'll find her now.'

'Well you sure can't eat this,' Ellie said, getting up, 'what's left of it. It's nothing but onions and a few carrots. I'll go and see if I can fix something.'

'Don't you love Americans?' Artemis asked. 'They fix food, they don't cook it.'

'I don't suppose you'd like to help?' Ellie asked Artemis.

'Not really,' Artemis replied. 'Someone's got to organize a diversion.'

Ellie went off to the kitchen, with Tutti bringing up the rear, carrying the inedibles.

'Cook was insensible at teatime, Miss,' the butler's booming voice echoed down the corridors. 'I'd to hold her up under the arms while she made the soup.'

The kitchen was a fearful sight, as if a war had been raging there, with one of its combatants apparently lying dead in a chair in the corner. A closer inspection by both Ellie and the butler revealed Aggie still to be alive, but fast out.

'There's not a whit between her and a scag,' Tutti said, nudging the prone form with a booted foot. 'For all the use she is, she might as well be an old cigar butt.'

Luckily there was plenty of cold food in the larder, chicken and ham, salmon and trout. There were plenty of cooked potatoes too, as always, since as Ellie had discovered, the Irish would rather have the roof off their house than to be found without a potato cooked anywhere. She made a perfect mayonnaise, a French dressing for the salads she had prepared, and sliced the potatoes up with butter and fresh parsley.

'With cheese to follow,' Ellie said, 'and then plenty of raspberries and cream, I don't think anyone will go hungry.'

Aggie groaned as the butler held the door open for Ellie. ' 'Tis a wonder she didn't stew the raspberries,' the butler sighed, looking round at the cook, 'the state she was in.'

Hugo and Cousin Rose were all but hysterical with laughter when Ellie brought in the food.

'It's absolutely hopeless,' a stone-faced Artemis announced. 'We've been trying to play word association, but we can't get anything past Rose.'

Hugo wiped a tear from his eye, and still laughing helplessly, apologized to no-one in particular.

'I don't see what's so funny!' Cousin Rose cried, weeping into her napkin. ' 'Tis the daftest thing I've ever heard!'

'Just listen,' Artemis nodded to Ellie, as she and Tutti started to lay out the picnic. 'Fair,' she said.

'Foul,' Hugo said.

'Egg,' said Cousin Rose, to the detriment of Hugo who all but disappeared under the table.

'Why egg?' Artemis asked as patiently as she could.

'Sure why not?' Cousin Rose asked her back. 'Sure what else do fowls do but lay eggs?'

At this, Hugo fell off his chair and disappeared under the table completely.

'See?' Artemis challenged Ellie, as if it was all her doing.

'Egg!' said a voice from under the table, accompanied by the hammering of fists on the floor. 'Egg!'

Hugo's hysteria only made Cousin Rose cry with laughter all the more, and she now grabbed the edge of the tablecloth to dry her eyes. 'Ah the man's mad!' she howled. 'Ye've brought a loon to the house!'

After dinner, Cousin Rose persuaded Ellie to play the piano, while Hugo and Artemis played Racing Demon. Tutti brought in a tray of fresh coffee, and at his employer's behest, poured the company all a glass of malt.

'Have one yerself, man,' Cousin Rose instructed, 'for we've a party going, and then give us a song.'

The butler poured himself a glass of the whisky, and then loosened his collar and tie.

'One voice only!' Cousin Rose instructed. 'One voice only, now!'

The butler found the sheet of music for which he was searching, and handed it to Ellie. And then he sang.

He sang in Gaelic, and the song he sang was 'Danny Boy'. But such was the meaning in his voice, that all understood his lament, and tears were openly shed for the poet's plight.

Later, Artemis sat on the end of Ellie's bed, leaning against the wall, her knees pulled up under her chin.

'A kingdom where no-one ever dies,' she said. 'Our life now could be like that.'

9

Hugo became a regular visitor at Strand House, as the summer began to slip imperceptibly into autumn.

'How long exactly is your holiday?' Artemis asked him one day, as she beat him once again at cards.

'As long as I choose to make it, Tom,' Hugo replied, using the name that had stuck since the night of the dinner.

'Don't you have to go and make beer or whatever it is you do?' Artemis enquired, dealing out the next hand.

'No,' Hugo said. 'I have things to do, but making beer isn't one of them.'

'I hate beer,' Artemis said. 'I think it smells like sick.'

Ellie came in with a tray of tea and scones, which she set down on the table at a window overlooking the bay. It was raining, a fine spray which drifted off the sea and across the beds of slowly fading flowers to run silently down the glass.

'Everything's so soft,' Ellie said as they all three sat buttering their scones at the table. 'I love this kind of day.'

Hugo took a bite out of his still warm scone, and then got up to fetch his sketchbook. As he sat down again, Artemis asked when he was going to start actually painting. Hugo told her that he had already done so, much to the surprise of both the young women.

'But I haven't sat for you yet,' Ellie said.

'You won't have to,' Hugo said, looking at her and then sketching. 'I've nearly finished you.'

'These are the paintings you do with a camera, I suppose,' Artemis said, glancing at Ellie.

'Then you suppose wrong, Tom,' Hugo said. 'You suppose wrong.'

Artemis stared at him for a moment, then quite abruptly pulled herself up from her chair.

'You are painting Artemis as well,' Ellie began, but too late, as Artemis was already by the door.

'Come on, Brutus,' Artemis called to her dog. 'Walks.'

Ellie watched her go, miserably.

'What did you say about painting Artemis?' Hugo asked, distracted by his sketching.

'I said you are going to paint her as well.' Ellie replied.

'Of course. I've sketched her already. Several times. I just haven't started the actual painting yet.'

Hugo looked up at Ellie to study her further, then continued with his drawing. Ellie watched Artemis crossing the lawn and clicked her tongue. 'She hasn't put a coat on,' she sighed, and then looked at Hugo, who had his head down, sketching. 'Hugo?' she asked. 'Hugo – don't you think you should take Artemis her coat?'

'She's all right,' Hugo muttered, 'it's only a light drizzle.'

'She needs a coat, Hugo.'

Hugo was too busy drawing. 'You take it then,' he said.

'No,' said Ellie, 'I have things to do. I have to cook for tonight, because Aggie's off. And I haven't even cleared away lunch. Go on. Go and catch Artemis up. She won't have got very far.'

'She doesn't want me, Ellie,' Hugo said, in quite a different tone. He put down his notebook, and stared out of the window after the disappearing figure of Artemis. 'She keeps making that perfectly clear.'

'She doesn't want people feeling sorry for her,' Ellie corrected him. 'That's all. I know. She's like that with me. Or rather she was. It's easy to mistake how Artemis is, and half the time what she says – '

'If I go after her,' Hugo interrupted her, 'it'll only be to give her her coat.'

Ellie frowned at Hugo, then turned away. 'I'd better go and clear the table,' she said, and hurried out.

Artemis heard the footfalls behind her, but much as she wanted to, resisted turning round to see who it was. She just walked on, throwing Brutus the large stick he kept fetching back to her.

Hugo caught her up as she was crossing the road to the beach. 'Here,' he said. He was carrying Artemis's raincoat, which he held out to her. 'Ellie said I should bring you this.'

'Really? I don't see why.'

Brutus dropped the stick once more at her feet, Artemis picked it up and threw it for him, and then continued walking towards the sea.

Hugo hesitated, then caught her up. 'Would you like to see the painting?' he asked. 'I'd like to hear what you think.'

'No you wouldn't,' Artemis replied, walking on.

'OK!' Hugo called after her. 'I've a better idea! Why don't you go and have a look for yourself?'

Ellie was in the kitchen washing up when Hugo returned. He sat down at the table, putting his sketchbook in front of him.

'You weren't gone long,' she said in surprise.

'She doesn't want me with her,' Hugo said, brushing the rain from his hair. 'She doesn't want anyone.'

'So where's she gone?'

'I don't know. I told her to go and look at the painting.' Hugo shrugged as he picked up the carving knife to sharpen his pencils.

The canvas was at the front of a stack of paintings, some of which were finished, some only half realized, all carefully stacked against one wall of the caravan. Artemis picked it up and put it upright on the bed, so that she could see it better in the light from one of the half-curtained windows. It looked almost finished and was so perfect it seemed as though it had been painted at

228

one stroke, in one sitting, in one moment of inspiration. There were no other portraits among the other canvases, just one of Ellie.

The technique was impressive, and in this instance seemed to show the influence of John Singer Sargent, elegant, fluid, assured. The portrait was alive and glowed with Ellie's life force, her oddly contained vibrancy. The warmth of Ellie's nature, and the softness that shaped both her body and her loving personality had all been captured.

Artemis stood back from the canvas and stared at it, for a moment unable to understand how the artist had been able to paint such a true likeness without his subject there, just from his sketches. And then it came to her, when she remembered how artists did their best work. Artists did their best work when they were inspired. She picked the canvas up and replaced it against the wall, without giving it another glance.

Outside the caravan she crossed the road to the beach where she walked by the thundering waves of the incoming tide with her face turned into the wind. Hugo could paint Ellie with his eyes shut. She walked on, into the rain and the sharp tangy seaspray. He knew her face and her essence so well he could probably paint Ellie in his sleep. She walked on and on until the damp of the rain forced her to turn back.

On returning to his caravan, Hugo half-hoped Artemis might still be there, sitting in the rug-covered chair, perhaps ready for argument. Even though he teased her about the peremptory judgements she passed on his work, he valued her criticism because he'd sensed early on that her asperity was a valued part of her defences. But when he opened the half doors of the gypsy caravan, he found it empty. In fact, had it not been for a few tell-tale long wiry brown hairs from the ever faithful Brutus which had strayed on to the wool rug on his bed, he wouldn't have known he'd had a visitor.

He poured himself a drink and sat down on the caravan steps, looking over to the beach, hoping to catch sight of a young woman and a dog returning from a walk, but the tide was too high for walking now, and the road back to Strand House was deserted. Reaching behind him, Hugo pulled his sketchbooks out from under the bed. He selected one in particular and then started to leaf through it. It was full of nothing but sketches of Artemis, a set of drawings he had begun the first day he'd seen her, not the day Artemis had taken her swim, but the day before, when she'd no idea he even existed.

He'd been strolling through the dunes following a bright blue butterfly, and had all but stumbled upon her as she lay sleeping in the sands. She hadn't awoken, she hadn't even stirred, and he was so taken with the sweetness of her face, and the slenderness of her young body as she lay at ease in her slumber, that he'd sat hidden in the grass of the dune opposite her and drawn her where she lay, one arm up and resting on her straw hat which tilted over her forehead, the other stretched out by her side, her long white skirt falling over her half tucked up legs, and the neck of her pink blouse undone just enough to let the hot sunshine warm the white of her lovely breasts.

Hugo stared at the drawing for a long time, and then turned to the next page and the next. Some of the drawings were done from memory, some done quickly and swiftly when his subject wasn't looking, profiles drawn with one continuous pencil line. Or head and shoulders, again in one line, jotted down in a trice, or less, images stolen, charcoal memories pegged to a page of cartridge paper.

He looked at them all, right through the book, from the first page to the last, before closing the book and fetching the portrait of Ellie from the pile of canvases. He propped that up against the wall of the caravan, on the bed, just as Artemis had done, standing back to study it. And then after some time he put it back with the rest of his work, and pulling on his coat, went out to walk among the sand dunes.

'Have you anything to ride?' Artemis asked Cousin Rose the next day.

'No,' Cousin Rose replied. 'We've nothing that's up. I don't bring the hunters in for another two weeks yet, and why I do I wouldn't know.'

Ellie was upstairs helping to make the beds, but the windows were open and the voices drifted up from below. Deeply puzzled by Artemis's out-of-the-blue request, Ellie stopped shaking out the eiderdown, and moved out of sight to the side of one window the better to hear.

'Dan Sleator has a few hirelings,' Cousin Rose was continuing. 'You could try him.'

'Has he anything with a bit of dash?' Artemis asked from the bench, where she sat briskly brushing Brutus who stood by with a martyred air. 'I don't want some tired old cob.'

'Why don't you drive over and see?' Cousin Rose suggested, giving her the directions.

Ellie caught Artemis when she came up to her room. 'Are you crazy?' she demanded. 'You haven't been on a horse since your accident!'

'You shouldn't eavesdrop,' Artemis replied, pulling on an old crew-necked sweater. 'You only ever hear things you shouldn't.'

'You don't even have any riding clothes!' Ellie continued.

Artemis sat on the edge of her bed and started unbuttoning her skirt. 'That would make a difference, would it?' she asked.

'I don't see why all of a sudden you want to go riding,' Ellie replied, digging in her toes.

'You don't have to,' Artemis retorted. 'And your cousin has lent me some old jods.' She pulled off her skirt and started to struggle into the borrowed riding trousers which had been lying beside her. Artemis sighed and pointed to a pair of old brown jodphur boots on the floor. 'Pass me those up, would you?'

Ellie did so, and then watched in silence as Artemis, whistling tunelessly to herself, pulled on the leather jodphur boots and then stood up to fetch her well-worn check tweed jacket off the back of a chair. Hooking a finger through the loop inside the back collar, she threw it over one shoulder, and walked towards the door.

'Have I done something, Artemis?' Ellie asked. 'Something to annoy you?'

'Why do you think you're meant to have done something, Eleanor?' Artemis asked. 'Don't be an idiot.'

Ellie ran after Artemis down the stairs. 'Then why are you behaving this way? If I haven't done anything?'

'Behaving in what way?'

'Can't we talk?'

'What about?'

'I don't know! Look,' she said as Artemis reached the front door. 'If you wait, I'll come with you.'

'You can't ride,' Artemis said. 'So there's no point.'

Dan Sleator's farm took some finding more because of, rather than in spite of, Cousin Rose's directions. When Artemis finally reached it, up a long pot-holed path, Dan Sleator was leaning on the gate, smoking an old clay pipe. He showed Artemis the horses which were standing loose in his barn, and discussed their various merits and demerits. Never once did he refer to or even glance at Artemis's stick, nor ask her even whether she was up to his animals.

'The bay with the star,' Artemis pointed at a tall dark horse which was busy trying to eat the mane of his neighbour. 'What did you say his name was?'

'Knocklomena,' Sleator answered, without removing the pipe from his mouth. 'But sure everyone calls him Boot.'

'Saddle him up, please,' Artemis said. 'I'll ride him.'

While Dan Sleator went about slowly getting the horse ready with the help of a gangly lad who appeared from the whitewashed cottage, Artemis leaned with her back on the gate and began to whistle tunelessly.

'Here you are, ma'am,' Sleator announced once the horse was saddled. 'If ye'll just remember now, this horse is a racer.'

'Is a racer?' Artemis enquired, as Sleator cupped his hands together to leg her up. 'You mean he still races?'

'On the sands, ma'am,' Sleator replied. 'Just on the sands.'

And then in answer to Artemis's request as to where she should ride, Dan Sleator spelled out the best ride, before opening the gate and flapping the horse on its quarters with his folded cap.

Five minutes later the telephone rang in Strand House.

'Hulloooo!' Cousin Rose called into the mouthpiece. 'Ballinacree twenty five!'

'I steered her into old Knocklomena, Miss Lannigan,' Dan Sleator told her down the line. 'The one they all calls Boot. So may that be an end to your worries. He's that sort of horse you could put an unborn baby on.'

Ellie brought in a tray of coffee and biscuits, and set them down by the fire. As they sat and took their mid-morning refreshment, Cousin Rose told her that Artemis was quite safely horsed.

'I still don't understand why she suddenly got it into her head to go and do such a crazy thing,' Ellie said. 'On the journey over she more or less admitted she was too frightened ever to ride again.'

'So perhaps that's why she did it,' Cousin Rose replied. 'She might kill herself.'

'Mightn't we all?' Cousin Rose sighed. 'Isn't life without the courage for death like a gin and tonic without the gin?'

'I think there's more to it than that.' This time it was Ellie who sighed.

'Hmmm,' said Cousin Rose. ' 'Tis one of life's pickles, I've always said. Whatever the space, there's never room for the three.'

They had reached the top of the track, where there was an open gate and then nothing but a long gentle roll of green to the top of the hill. For the first mile, they had not broken out of a walk, the big horse happy just to stride out and warm himself through in the autumn sun. Artemis had found at once, both to her surprise and relief, that the animal was properly schooled, and she was quite able to ride him through her hands and her seat.

But now she was faced with the test, in the shape of the long open space which stretched out in front of her from the open gateway, and leading to Artemis knew not where. If she had been riding side-saddle, she knew the difficulty would have been greatly lessened, since her damaged right leg would have been out of the way, held in place by the upper pommel of the saddle, and her good strong leg would have been the only one stirruped. Astride, without the help of any devices, and with her right leg in a stirrup hitched three holes shorter than the left one, it would be all too easy to unbalance the horse if she dared canter him, or even, more importantly, she could well become unbalanced herself.

There was no need for her to canter. The horse, although fidgeting slightly under her with excitement at the thought of stretching out, was such a good natured and tractable sort that Artemis knew she could either easily turn him away from the tempting stretch of grass-land and just hack on up the hill at a walk, or face him away altogether and walk back home. After all, had she not proved enough for one day? Hadn't she actually bitten the bullet and climbed up on to the back of a horse, something she had thought would never again be even the remotest possibility?

And yet the gallop beckoned. It beckoned because Artemis not only wished to recover her nerve, she also wanted her pride back. She wanted to be able to respect herself again.

So she shortened her reins, sat down into the horse and squeezed him to go on. She sat his trot and squeezed again, urging him on straight into a canter. The horse responded easily and smoothly, changing his pace from the trot to a perfectly collected canter. Artemis sat down and through the stride and softened her rein once she knew the horse had accepted the bit. A feeling of intense exultancy ran threw her, as she and the horse became as one, two creatures in absolute harmony, enjoying total trust. The breeze ran unseen fingers through her hair and called her name, as together she and the big bay horse bounded across the springy turf, he with his proud head held into his chest and his great neck half-arched, and she with confidence restored, holding the reins in just her right hand, her left one resting on her thigh.

In a dip, Artemis sat and reined back, and the horse came down through his paces to a perfect halt. They stood together in silence for a moment, a quiet broken only by the faint sigh of the breeze in the grasses. Being alone, Artemis laughed aloud with the joy of the moment, and leaned forward to wrap both arms around the neck of the horse, who, in his turn snorted and stamped at the ground with one hoof, proclaiming his own love of life.

'Come on!' Artemis called to him, as she collected up her reins. 'Let's see exactly what sort of racer you are.'

She turned the horse once, as if to gather the courage for them both, before setting him off up the gentle slope at a canter which in six strides she had got him to switch to a gallop. This was a very different game they were playing now, this was no dressage canter, no polite park pace, no handy dawdle. This was Epsom, this was Aintree, this was the hill at Cheltenham. This was three-quarters of a ton of horse travelling nearly as fast as her little blue car, only with no brakes to stop him, just a one-and-a-half-legged, seven and a bit stones girl to pull him up. There was no thrill like it, and Artemis knew it, as the gentle breeze which had turned into a wind whipped through her hair and smarted her eyes. Longer and longer strode the horse as faster and faster his rider urged him, until finally the hill started to run out in front of them and turn to just sky.

As soon as she asked him, the horse began to pull up, happily and easily. In a moment they were down to a trot and then a walk, ambling along the ridge while they both caught their breath. Then they stopped, and looked down at the green country below them.

'I love you, horse,' Artemis said, pulling his ears and stroking his neck. 'I love you as I love nothing else.'

They were all to go to the party. Artemis insisted. Cousin Rose protested she was far too old for it, but Artemis was at her most resolute.

'Dear – it's fancy dress, darling!' Cousin Rose complained.

'When isn't it?' Artemis replied, with unconcealed contempt. 'It seems no-one can ever give a party without making everyone dress up.'

'But God love us, what shall I *go* as?' Cousin Rose enquired. 'I've been to so many of the confounded things, I've been as everything!'

'Go as Tutti,' Artemis suggested. 'I'll bet you've never been as your man.'

Cousin Rose was greatly taken with that notion, and at once forgot all her objections, as she hurried off to find her butler to break the news and receive instruction as to how best to dress herself.

'What about me?' Ellie asked.

'You,' Artemis replied, 'can go and invite Hugo.'

'Why me?' Ellie objected. 'Why not both of us?'

'Don't be an idiot, Eleanor. It doesn't need two people to deliver an invitation. And while you do, I'm going up to the attic to look for things.'

Ellie took the car and drove down to Hugo's caravan, a part of her hoping he was out so that she could just leave the written invite, and a part of her hoping that he was in, so that she could see him.

He was there, sitting on the step of the caravan, drawing yet another view. He saw Ellie long before she saw him, because she was concentrating on her driving, and he was only pretending to draw, because once he had seen her, all else went from his mind. She was so beautiful she rendered him not only speechless on occasions but often thoughtless as well. And so he pretended to draw, while he waited and longed for her finally to arrive.

All the time, as he was painting her portrait, Hugo had wondered how best to describe the irradiance of her beauty, but had as yet not found the perfect adjective. She wasn't gorgeous. Gorgeous girls were redheads, sexy, opulent. Nor was she ravishing. Ravishing girls wore a lot of makeup, and were fast. He had toyed with devastating, but the remaining image was always one of destruction, of a chaos created by a sultry blonde. Exquisite was too fragile, and heavenly too effete. Dazzling was sheer Hollywood, sublime suggested an experience rather than a person, faultless was feeble, superb was too sporting, and wonderful belonged to the make-believe world of advertising. She was all of these words, certainly, every one of them, but she was not any one of them in particular.

'You shouldn't frown like that,' she said, as she pulled the car up in front of him. 'You'll get tramlines.'

'I've been trying to find a word to describe you,' Hugo replied, getting up to go and open her car door. 'And at last I think I've found it. You're beautiful.'

'I don't think so,' said Ellie.

Which were the last words Ellie spoke for what seemed like an eternity, because seconds later Hugo kissed her.

Afterwards Ellie tried to recollect the sensation, of spinning, of a dark crimson delight, darkness, and the thrill of it all. But just as Hugo had failed in his search for the word which would perfectly describe Ellie, Ellie found nothing else in her head to say about her trip to the stars except that she had been kissed.

'You shouldn't have done that,' was all she eventually found to say, as she stood looking up at the person who'd made her feel this way.

'I agree,' Hugo said. 'That was probably the worst thing I ever did in my whole life.'

Ellie sat down suddenly on the wooden steps of the caravan and rubbed her puzzled forehead with one hand. 'You really shouldn't have. I mean it.'

Hugo sat down beside her. 'I had to,' he told her.

'Why?'

'Because I wanted to.'

'But you shouldn't have.' Ellie felt ridiculous, inexplicably sad, when in reality she should have been dancing. 'I've never been kissed by anyone before,' she said.

'I have,' Hugo replied. 'Plenty of people. And I'll tell you something. About all those kisses. I've forgotten them all.'

'Perhaps it's just being kissed,' Ellie added hopelessly. 'Perhaps first kisses do this to people.'

'Do what?'

Ellie paused, and then held out one of her hands. It was shaking visibly.

'Me, too,' Hugo held out his own.

'Anyway,' Ellie said, doing her best to recover her senses, 'this isn't why I'm here. I came down here to ask you to a party.' She turned back to the car and produced the invitation, which Hugo took and stared at without seeing the words. 'Well?' Ellie asked him. 'Will you come?'

'Yes,' Hugo agreed. 'But only if you'll marry me.'

Ellie's eyes widened as far as they would go. 'That's not funny,' she said.

'It wasn't intended to be.'

Ellie stared at him in silence.

'So that's OK, is it?' she asked. 'You'll come to the party?'

'Yes,' Hugo replied. 'I will, if you'll marry me.'

A moment later and she was gone, into the car, having finally driven off after a desperate and frantic attempt to do everything at once, slam the door, start it and engage gear, all at the same time.

Hugo watched her go and then sat down and sighed. 'It's the only solution,' he said to the donkey in the field.

Ellie danced with everyone except Hugo. She hadn't spoken to him since her visit to his caravan, and she didn't address one word to him all the way to Sneem, a journey undertaken in Cousin Rose's motor car, the big black Humber which lay under its cover for most of the year in the garage, generally only to be brought out for what Cousin Rose described as 'comings and goings'.

Tutti was at the wheel, in his old regimental uniform, his butler's livery having been purloined by his employer, who was now dressed as him. Artemis had got herself up as a more than passable Charlie Chaplin, a costume which cleverly allowed her full use of her stick. Hugo, with considerable help from Artemis, was dressed as a lookalike Douglas Fairbanks pirate, and Ellie, again thanks to Artemis's skills, looked quite and utterly bewitching as Coppelia, with chalk white face, rouged cheeks, and carefully painted on eyelashes.

There was a sense of high excitement on the journey across, with Cousin Rose at her most garrulous, and Artemis at her most provocative. Everything Hugo said she disputed or challenged, and for the most while the two of them were locked in controversy, a state which, to judge from Hugo's hoots of laughter and Artemis's persistence, both of them enjoyed enormously.

For her part, Ellie sat quietly in the corner of the back seat, watching Ireland darkening in the September sunset, trying to sort herself out. She was still undecided as to whether or not Hugo's proposal had been real or mock, a conclusion she found all the more difficult to reach since in the land in which she was now living everything that happened seemed to be all part of a tease. 'Ah sure 't'was only a tease,' her cousin was forever saying long after having led Ellie up yet another garden path. 'You didn't think I was serious?' And although Hugo wasn't Irish, even so it seemed to Ellie he too had become touched with the feyness that was so universal it surely had to be in the very air they were all breathing. She looked at him now, from the corner of her eye, as he sat laughing and making merry with Cousin Rose and Artemis. He didn't look in the least like a man with serious intentions. A man with matrimony really on his mind would hardly be sitting in the back of a car doubled-up with laughter as his hostess failed yet again to cope with one of his terrible tongue twisters.

The party, held in a ramshackle castle on the edge of a large dark lake, was astonishing, and, unsurprisingly, quite unlike anything Ellie had ever attended before. It was hosted by an extraordinarily beautiful and very eccentric White Russian princess, who was called by everyone, and quite inexplicably, Babs. She was over six feet tall, smoked cigars, and was dressed so they learned as Shirley Temple had been in *Glad Rags to Riches*, in a huge peek-a-boo bonnet, baby socks and shoes, a white scooped-neck top decorated with leaves, and a pair of sequinned diapers, held together at the front with an enormous gilded safety pin. She appeared never to speak to anyone, but glided constantly through her assembled guests, suddenly choosing someone of either sex to seize by the shoulders and kiss passionately on the mouth. In her drawing room was an enormous church organ, which she played occasionally throughout the evening, and whenever she did so, a succession of outraged cats appeared howling and hissing from the mass of iron piping.

In the great hall a game of cricket was in progress, with a full complement of players, and an attentive and appreciative crowd of deck-chaired spectators.

'What fun,' Artemis remarked as they arrived and Hugo fielded a well struck cover drive. 'I wish we'd had some of these sort of things at home.'

'Was your house as big as this?' Ellie wondered as they explored all the rooms.

'Yes,' Artemis replied. 'Bigger really. And it was always full of people. But nothing ever really went on, nothing fun.'

There was music, too, besides Babs's sombre organ recitals, to which none of the guests paid the slightest attention. There was a danceband in the dining hall, and a trio of violin, accordion and flute in the kitchen, playing Gaelic music to which an enormous red-bearded man would sing at irregular intervals, lifting one foot to knee height in order to stamp in time on the floor.

Ellie found the whole atmosphere completely intoxicating, and even Artemis's mask of indifference soon slipped.

But it was Hugo dancing with Artemis that Ellie would remember always. She and Artemis had been watching the cricket match in the hall, where a tall and elegant elderly gentleman dressed as a rabbit had just scored a text book half century. Artemis was explaining the niceties of the game to Ellie when Hugo had reappeared by their sides.

'I think I like this one,' Artemis said, listening as the band struck up 'Body and Soul'.

'So come and dance to it then,' Hugo asked her.

For a moment Ellie thought Artemis was going to hit Hugo, as her blue eyes darkened and Ellie saw her make little fists of her hands.

'No thank you,' she said finally instead, and picked up where she had left off explaining cricket to Ellie.

'Please,' said Hugo. 'Please, Tom.'

'Go and ask someone else,' Artemis replied. 'Ask Ellie.'

'I don't want to ask anyone else, Tom,' Hugo said. 'I want this dance with you. Besides, Ellie keeps refusing.'

There was complete silence between the three of them, Artemis for once stuck for a reply. 'Actually,' she said at last, 'the point is I don't dance.'

'Fine,' Hugo said. 'Then I'll teach you. It's very simple.'

'I didn't say I can't,' Artemis corrected him. 'I said I don't.'

'It's one and the same thing to me,' said Hugo.

Artemis had no further time to protest before Hugo lifted her off the oak table on which she and Ellie were temporarily perched, and holding her a couple of inches off the ground with his right arm round her waist, started to dance for the both of them. After a moment, Artemis's stiff body visibly relaxed and she looked up at Hugo, almost curiously, without smiling.

'See?' Hugo stopped dancing for a moment, but kept Artemis still held up, the toe of her good left foot just reaching the floor. 'I told you there was nothing to it.' And with that he started dancing again, and slowly disappeared with Artemis into the throng in the dining hall.

They reappeared later, when the elderly rabbit had scored what Ellie reckoned to be another thirty-four runs. Hugo had his left arm round Artemis's waist, thus acting as her right leg. He lifted her back on to the oak table and as he did so Artemis placed a hand on either shoulder.

'Thank you,' she said to him.

'That was fun,' Hugo said.

'Yes,' Artemis replied. 'It's a really good band.'

Hugo now turned to Ellie. 'Well?' he said.

Ellie could have married him then, just for the look on Artemis's face. It wasn't a smile, it wasn't gratitude, it was quite simply happiness.

'Well?' Hugo repeated, standing in front of her once again.

'Yes,' Ellie said. 'I will.'

'Sorry,' Hugo said. 'You will what?'

'Come and dance,' Ellie smiled.

She lost count of how many dances they had. All Ellie knew when it was time to go home was that when

Hugo held her in his arms all the dreams she'd never had came true.

Later Ellie found it impossible to sleep. There was too much in her head. Several times she sat bolt upright and stared into the pitch darkness, as she thought about the real consequences of marriage to Hugo. She knew now that she loved him, but if he loved her and she loved him, there would be no-one for Artemis.

'Are you asleep?' she whispered, pushing open Artemis's bedroom door. There was no answer. 'Are you asleep?' she asked again.

'No,' came the gruff reply. 'Or if I was, I'm not now.'

Artemis was just a shape in the bed, turned with its face to the wall. Unable to see where she was going, Ellie collided with a chair, and Artemis's stick clattered to the floor.

'Can I come in?' she whispered, halfway across the room.

'I'd love to know what else you think you're doing,' Artemis replied, laughing suddenly but still not turning round.

Ellie came to the edge of her bed. 'I couldn't sleep, I'm sorry.'

'Yes,' said Artemis, pulling the covers up almost over her head. 'I'm sorry too.'

It had started to rain heavily, down from the dark clouds which had been gathering round the moon as they drove home. There was not a bite of wind, so the water fell straight from the sky, thundering into the ground below, drumming on the grass, pounding the earth, drilling holes in the sands and soaking the turves. It fell remorselessly, leaping off the slates and missing the gutters, knocking leaves off the trees and heads from the dying flowers. As she turned to stand and watch it at the window, Ellie could imagine all nature out there running for cover, down holes and burrows, under bushes and hedgerows, as the dark landscape flooded with a river of rain.

'I'm trying to get to sleep,' Artemis complained, as Ellie just stood in silence.

'I know,' Ellie replied. 'I was as well. I just couldn't.'

There came a deep sigh from the bed, and then silence. Finally Artemis shifted her position and turned round to lie on her back. 'Any particular reason?' she asked. 'Why you couldn't sleep?'

The rain started to fall even harder, cascading off the roof.

'I don't know how to tell you this.'

'What?'

'Hugo wants to marry me.'

'Yes?' Artemis replied after a moment. 'So why's that so difficult to tell?'

'I don't know what to do, Artemis,' Ellie said, turning from the window. 'I really don't. I just don't know what to do.'

'Of course you do, don't be an idiot,' Artemis told her, sitting up to plump her pillow. 'You know perfectly well what to do.' She lay down and settled back on her side with her face to the wall. 'Marry him,' she said. 'That's what to do. And be happy. Why not? He's the nicest man anyone could meet.'

Ellie waited for a few moments longer, watching the rain bouncing off the terrace. Then she went and kissed Artemis goodnight on the top of her now submerged blonde head and tiptoed back to her bed where, within five minutes of climbing into it, she was fast asleep.

Artemis, on the other hand, didn't finally close her eyes again until the dawn had begun to light up the sky.

10

The weather had broken. The soft sunny days of September had given away to early October rain, or mornings of heavy autumnal mist which shrouded the landscape. Even so, they all still went out walking whenever possible, in heavily oiled waterproofs bought from the village store, the girls in Aran berets and gloves, and Hugo in a fisherman's sou'wester which looked a little out of keeping with his donnish brass-rimmed spectacles. And everywhere they went they went as a threesome, as if by tacit agreement there was still a *status quo*, for no direct inference had been made to the future or the likelihood of change.

Everything to do with Hugo and Ellie was left deliberately vague, in keeping with the spirit of the country they were in. The date was to be sometime in spring. They were most probably going to get married in England, but they still might in Ireland if it could be organized. It was likely that they would live mostly in England, but since they had both fallen in love with Ireland, they were determined to buy somewhere in Cork, or south Kerry, so that they could spend an equal amount of time out west as well.

'Listen to ye,' Cousin Rose said. 'I never heard people so full of possibilities. If all your ifs and ans *were* new pots and pans, there'd certainly be no call at all for poor old tinkers.'

Cousin Rose, however, had been delighted at the news of her young relative's engagement, and declared the whole thing to be great sport. Using the change in the weather as a good reason, Hugo was invited to return his borrowed caravan, and come up and stay at Strand

House until he had to go back to England, whenever that might be.

'It could be this year, Rose,' he warned her, 'or it could be next year. Or it might be some time, or even never.'

'While there's whisky in the jar, young man,' Cousin Rose replied, 'and yeast for the dough, there'll be linen on the bed.'

As a result of the arrangement, there was nothing regular whatsoever about Hugo and Ellie's courtship. They spent very little time alone together, not because they were shy of each other's company, in fact the opposite was true, but because of the natural gregariousness of the company. At first Artemis made to hold back, but neither Ellie nor Hugo would hear of excluding her.

'We'll have all the time in the world when we're married,' Ellie explained to her, a remark which precipitated one of Artemis's unexplained and abrupt disappearances. But Ellie had long since learned that whenever this happened it was best to leave well alone. And sure enough the next morning when Ellie suggested all three of them should drive into Bantry to shop for the weekend, Artemis, who was sitting by the fire reading, agreed quite readily.

From then on things had been plain sailing. For the next two weeks they all three went everywhere together, whether it was fishing for mackerel from a rowing boat in the bay, sitting in *Twomey's Snug* in Castletown sipping porter and John Jameson in a fog of Sweet Afton cigarette smoke, driving into Cork one wet Saturday to see Leslie Howard and Norma Shearer in *Smilin' Through*, or just wandering along the headlands, watching the winter seas build up.

In the shortening evenings they played endless games of cards, not adult games like bridge or poker, but raucous and childish games of snap, beggar your neighbour, oh well, and pip-pip, until it was time for Artemis and Cousin Rose tactfully to take themselves off to bed.

Hugo and Ellie knew so little about each other. They used this time to find out more of those things which other couples might have learned of on first meeting.

And so Ellie spoke to him tactfully and honestly about her background, while on his own behalf Hugo was more reticent.

The middle one of three children, the other two both being girls, it seemed his mother had died from pernicious anaemia when he was fifteen, and his father, whom he loved but rarely saw as a boy, was a strong if absent influence. They had a house in London and one in Hampshire, the latter of which his father wanted to sell since his children were all now grown up, in order that he could buy what he called a 'challenge', a property which he could restore to its former glory.

'He's always been very keen on the fine arts and architecture,' Hugo explained. 'And archeology. And now that he's retired, he's determined to pursue to the full interests he's previously only had time to treat as hobbies.'

For themselves, it was decided that they should live in a flat at the top of the family's London house initially, while they looked around at their leisure for somewhere to live. Hugo assured Ellie the house was sufficiently large for them to lead a private existence and that in any case his father was so rarely in London, since he spent most of his time driving round the country looking at old houses, that privacy would never really be a problem.

'Do you work for your father?' Ellie asked.

'Yes,' Hugo answered. 'Yes and no.'

'And what's that supposed to mean? I mean surely either you do, or you don't.'

'Yes I do work for him,' was all Hugo would tell her, 'and no I don't. And in England we say eye-ther, Ellie. Not ee-ther.'

'I know, Hugo,' Ellie returned. 'And in America we say ee-ther, not eye-ther.'

'Meaning?'

'Meaning,' Ellie replied, 'ee-ther you work for your father or you don't.'

Hugo, who at that moment had one arm round Ellie's waist as they sat on the floor in front of the fire, feigned sudden seriousness, before squeezing Ellie's waist, an underhand move which instantly reduced Ellie, for whom even the thought that someone might tickle her was enough, to a gasping heap of helpless laughter. A minute later he gathered her in his arms and kissed her passionately.

'I can't wait to be married,' he told her.

But wait they must, despite the increasing fervour of their passion. Now, whenever they were in company, Ellie would hardly dare even look at Hugo, because just the meeting of their eyes was quite enough to make her forget mid-sentence what she was saying. And if Hugo ever twined one of his feet around one of Ellie's under the table at dinner, Ellie would drop her fork with a clatter on the plate, or spill her wine, or just simply start to go crimson slowly and very visibly from her neck up.

'Do you know what happens?' Artemis asked her, when Ellie was doing Artemis's hair one evening.

'If you mean what's going to happen on our wedding night,' Ellie replied, 'I guess I don't, you know I don't.'

'I remember asking Rosie once, on one of our walks,' Artemis said. 'I suppose I was about twelve. I remember asking Rosie because she was talking about babies as usual – '

'You mean *you* were, I'll bet,' Ellie interrupted.

'Probably. Anyway I asked her how, no I didn't – I asked her where they came from,' Artemis continued.

'Once someone had been to the graveyard and mysteriously gotten pregnant,' Ellie grinned.

'Yes. And Rosie said it was just the same as animals. I remember laughing so much I thought I'd be sick. Have you ever seen horses doing "it"?'

'No,' Ellie said with a sinking heart. 'Is it awful?'

'Let's just hope,' Artemis sighed, 'that there's a little bit more to "it" than that.'

As Ellie and Hugo were getting to know each other even better, Artemis and Knocklomena were doing the same. Artemis rode him daily, generally before breakfast as it was now both too cold and too late in the year for any more early morning swims. They formed an attachment as passionate in its own, but very different, way as that of Hugo and Ellie. Artemis lived to ride the big bay horse, who in turn appeared to have formed a particular affection for his disabled rider.

'Before ye took to him,' Dan Sleator told her, 'I'd any amount of trouble gettin' him in off the field. Now he stands there waiting for ye.'

One day Artemis arrived with a side-saddle she'd persuaded Cousin Rose to borrow from one of her hunting cronies. 'I want to jump Boot today,' Artemis told Dan Sleator as she helped him saddle the horse up. 'And I think this is more practical.'

'Do ye want me to send the boy out with ye?' Sleator asked, as Artemis climbed the mounting block.

'No,' said Artemis. 'But if I don't come back, you can send him out after me.'

She and Boot tackled a three-foot hedge first, which the big horse flew with ease, standing well off and not needing to be asked. Artemis sensed at once he was a horse who liked to jump and who would jump as he liked, so she simply read the stride with him and gave him his head. In return, he jumped straight and true and sensibly, rounding his back and getting his forelegs well under him and out of the way. Finally Artemis put the horse at a line of stone walls at more than a good hunting clip, and he jumped them superbly. But more importantly, which was what Artemis most needed to know, he got away from the obstacles quickly, and in no time at all was back at the gallop.

'Good,' Artemis said, as she handed the horse back to Dan Sleator. 'How much do you want for him?'

They were just all getting over the excitement of Artemis's purchase, and finalizing the arrangements with Cousin Rose to have the horse stabled at Strand House with Cousin Rose's hunters, when a telegram arrived.

At first Hugo didn't realize it was for him, he was so busy arguing with Ellie and Artemis about her plans to ride Boot in point-to-points that he didn't hear Cousin Rose calling for his attention.

'I don't understand what these "point-to-points" are,' Ellie protested. 'So I don't know why you're getting so heated.'

'Point-to-pointing,' Hugo sighed, 'and particularly in Ireland, is the nearest thing you'll find to organized suicide. It's the sport of amateur steeple-chasing. They used to ride from point A to far point B over natural fences trying their utmost to kill each other or themselves for a purse or a wager. Now the difference is they do it in a circle in full view of everyone and call it a sport.'

'Hugo?' Cousin Rose tried again, flapping the small brown envelope at him.

'You're mad even to think of it, Tom,' Hugo declared, rounding on Artemis. 'Totally and utterly mad!'

'Cousin Rose wants you,' Artemis replied, pouring herself another sherry.

'You need that pretty little head of yours dismantled,' Hugo said, 'to see if there's any sign of a brain in it at all.'

'Hugo,' Cousin Rose repeated, having finally got his attention, 'there is a telegram for ye, I keep saying a telegram.'

Hugo opened it, and then after a moment looked up with a frown on his face, his eyes suddenly searching for Ellie's. She took the piece of paper from him as he hurried from the room.

Ellie frowned at the words. 'Hugo's father has died,' she told Artemis and Cousin Rose.

Cousin Rose sighed. 'Don't I hate those things, they're worse than magpies,' she said to no-one in particular, then she too left the room.

Hugo decided to return to England himself, since it didn't seem to be the best time to introduce Ellie to his family. He promised to be back well before Christmas.

He failed to return, or communicate in any way. Finally, Ellie, unable to bear or understand the silence, gave in and telephoned him herself.

It seemed that he had also been ill and he didn't wish to be a burden to anyone. Ellie tried to plead with him to let her come over and look after him, but Hugo refused.

'As a matter of fact, I'm going to Florence. On my own. To get things in perspective,' he told her.

'Would "things" include me?' asked Ellie.

'Of course. But I have to try and make sense of everything. I know I met you long before my father died, but when we marry, I must be myself.'

'I don't understand, Hugo. I don't understand one thing you're saying. We loved each other long before this happened. Your father's death can't change how we feel, surely? I mean why should it?'

There was a silence on the other end of the line, broken finally by the sound of Hugo clearing his throat. 'You're right, Ellie,' he said eventually. 'Of course you are. I know you're right. It's just that I'm a bit confused. It was all so completely unexpected. What I'm trying to say is although I never saw much of my father when I was very small, as I grew we became very close. I went everywhere with him: on his explorations, on his digs, to Africa, the Middle East. We became more like brothers. We'd sometimes know in advance of seeing each other, we'd know things about each other. What had happened since our last meeting. Things like that. Even once, once he knew what I'd be wearing when I came through the door. And I knew when he'd fallen in love again, long after my mother had died. I even knew the colour of the woman's hair.'

There was another silence.

'What are you trying to tell me, Hugo?' Ellie asked. 'Are you trying to say part of you *knew* your father was going to die suddenly? And that because part of you knew it – this is why you fell in love?'

'I don't know, Ellie,' Hugo replied after a long pause. 'Perhaps, yes. But I really don't know. I'll be myself, Ellie, I know I will,' he finally continued. 'When I've had a time to think, to sort everything out. It's just so difficult, with all the family here.' There was another deep and heartfelt sigh. 'Particularly now I'm the head of it,' he said.

'Why don't you at least try coming over here?' Ellie pleaded with him. 'Here where you've been so happy. We'd look after you. All of us. We'd look after you so well.'

'I know you would,' Hugo replied. 'That's one of the things of which I'm most afraid.'

To Artemis he didn't speak, he wrote to her instead. Up as always before the rest of the household, and just back from a ride on Boot, that morning Artemis got to the post first. She took the letter straight upstairs and read it sitting on her bed, still in her riding coat and bowler hat. And then once she had read it and re-read it, she made her way as quietly as she could back downstairs and rang Hugo in London.

Ellie found it when she was tidying the bedrooms. It was the day for fresh linen and when she was making the bed she found the letter tucked under the pillow. She recognized the handwriting instantly, and felt quite giddy and faint. It wasn't the fact that Hugo had written to Artemis, that wouldn't have bothered her one bit. It was the fact the letter had been hidden.

It lay staring up at her, torn open jaggedly at the top, as if the recipient had been anxious to get at the contents. The actual letter protruded from the envelope, stuffed back apparently as hastily as it had been extracted. Ellie could read the greeting. 'Dearest Artemis', it said. Dearest Artemis.

After what seemed like an age, Ellie put the letter on Artemis's bedside table, made the bed up with fresh linen, and then tucked the letter back under the pillow.

Artemis said nothing to her before lunch, nor during it. Cousin Rose was on terrific form but even so the meal seemed to drag. Afterwards, when she had taken herself off for a rest, Artemis sank down in a big deep armchair by the fire.

'Well?' she said eventually.

'Well what?' Ellie enquired.

'I suppose you read it,' Artemis said, without looking round.

'You suppose wrong,' Ellie said.

'You must have seen it, Eleanor,' Artemis said, in the clipped tone she used when she was put out. 'You couldn't have made the bed up without seeing it.'

'If you mean Hugo's letter.'

Artemis bent round the side of the chair and stared at Ellie with her eyes deliberately over-widened. Then she sat back and started throwing balls of rolled up newspaper into the wood fire.

'I didn't read it, Artemis,' Ellie said, pouring herself another coffee. 'Of course I saw it. But I didn't read it.'

'Because?'

'Because.'

'Because I thought you'd get the wrong impression, you idiot,' said Artemis factually.

'For God's sake will you stop calling me an idiot and will you stop treating me like one all the goddam time!' Ellie suddenly banged her fist on the table to the side of her.

'There's no need to shout, Eleanor,' Artemis said. 'And bang the table.'

'Do you know how infuriating you can be.'

Artemis nodded sagely in agreement, which proved even more infuriating, somehow. 'Don't you want to know what the letter said?'

'I get the feeling you're going to tell me anyway.'

'When I was nineteen,' Artemis began again, sitting back in her armchair, 'I had to see a doctor. Except he wasn't a doctor really. He was a psychologist. My stepmother had made me come out. You know, do The Season.'

'No, I don't know.'

'You know what a debutante is, don't you?'

'I reckon so.'

'So I was a debutante,' Artemis continued, lighting a match and watching it burn. 'Not for very long, but I was. I can't say I enjoyed it. For a start, I couldn't dance.'

'It must have been tough.'

Artemis stared at Ellie's reflection in the mirror above the fireplace, and then threw the twisted dead match into the fire. 'Yes it was "tough" actually,' she agreed. 'Anyway, what with one thing and another, it all got a bit too much, hours spent sitting it out on gilt chairs, etcetera. And Diana Lanchester, my godmother, she knew this chap. This doctor. This psychologist. And sent me to see him.'

'And did he help?'

'I'm still here, aren't I?' Artemis replied. 'Yes, actually he was rather good. Hugo wrote to me to find out his name.' Artemis's face suddenly appeared round the side of her chair to stare at Ellie. 'Hugo's in trouble, you know. Quite a lot of trouble.'

'Yes,' Ellie finally agreed after a long silence. 'I know.'

'He's not going to Florence,' Artemis continued. 'That was just so as you wouldn't worry. He's hoping this man will take him into his clinic for a couple of weeks. Do you see?' Artemis looked at Ellie, giving her one of her sudden attentive stares, and stroking her small chin at the same time.

'No, Artemis,' Ellie said after a while. 'I guess I don't see. Why should he tell me one thing, and you something else?'

'He doesn't want you to worry, or for you to think he's going cuckoo.'

'Is he?' Ellie enquired. 'I mean what exactly *is* wrong with him?'

'This chap will do the trick,' Artemis assured her, sitting back again in her chair. 'He's not going dotty. He's just at a loss. People sometimes are.'

There was another long silence as they both stared at the fire, while it crackled and hissed.

'This wood's too green,' Artemis announced.

'Yes,' Ellie said thoughtfully, 'but I guess it's not the only thing round here that colour.'

Artemis smiled, then picked up the bellows to fan the weakening flames.

Nothing further was heard from Hugo by the time Artemis was set to ride her first point-to-point in March. She had not only hunted and qualified Boot with the West Carbery, but she had also travelled twice a week to Tipperary to receive coaching from Ireland's finest woman race-rider, Mrs Dunne, the Master of the Tipperary, and a relation of Cousin Rose's. There were no restrictions in Ireland as there were in England about women racing against men, so with more races to choose from, it was a little easier for Artemis and her helpers, Mrs Dunne, Dan Sleator and Cousin Rose, to select one of the less competitive races in the calendar for Artemis's debut.

Boot ran a blinder, jumping fast but accurately. He pulled his way to the lead after the fourth fence, and Artemis, riding side-saddle, found they were still there with only two to jump. But then he began to tire, as did his pilot, and from being two lengths up in the lead going to the second last, he faded to finish fourth, ten lengths down on the winning horse, in a field of thirteen other maidens.

Dan Sleator and Cousin Rose were beside themselves when Artemis rode Boot in to the unsaddling enclosure. After patting Boot's rump, and hugging him round the neck, Dan Sleator lifted Artemis from her horse, set her gently on the ground, and handed over her walking stick.

'You're the stuff of good stories sure ye are, ma'am,' he said, as Artemis, tucking the stick under one arm, bent to ungirth her horse. 'We'll have ye winning be May.'

'I wasn't anywhere near fit enough, Dan,' Artemis replied, pulling the saddle down off her horse. 'You should never have let me ride.' With that Artemis disappeared to weigh in and change.

'You mustn't mind her,' Ellie began. 'She says these things, but –'

'Now beggin' your pardon, ma'am, but ye've no need,' Dan Sleator nodded. 'Sure don't I know the difference between her ladyship's complaints and her compliments?'

'But she never complains. Not really.'

'And don't I know that equally well?' Dan Sleator replied, before leading the horse off to be washed down.

When the party finally returned to Strand House, there was a fresh telegram awaiting. This time it was addressed to Ellie, and it simply read:

'Will you marry me in Leckford Parish Church. Saturday, 23 May? Hugo.'

11

'Artemis can't make it,' Ellie announced, telegram in hand. 'She's had a fall, and the doctor says she has to lie flat for a week.'

Hugo took the wire from her and stared at the message. 'Typical Artemis,' he said. 'Four days off the wedding, and she doesn't even say she's sorry.'

'Artemis only ever apologizes for things she considers her fault,' Ellie said, determined not to show her disappointment. 'And obviously the fall wasn't her fault.'

Hugo took off his spectacles to rub them clean on the end of his tie. 'Don't you sometimes wonder, if anything ever is Artemis's fault?'

'No I don't.'

'Well I'm afraid I do. Although, perhaps she has to be excused this one. Even so, I warned her. I said she'd kill herself if she raced.'

'She hasn't killed herself.'

'From the look on your face, I should have said that's just what she has done.'

'That's because I did so want her to be there. She's my only family, as it were.'

'And Cousin Rose definitely can't come either?'

'You know poor Aggie was taken to hospital?' said Ellie absently.

Hugo put his arms round her and kissed her, but Ellie just sighed. It wouldn't be the same without Artemis, they knew that, although Hugo kept shrugging off his disappointment as if he hadn't expected anything different. Fortunately, his sister Jane agreed to take Artemis's place as Maid of Honour. But even as the dress was being altered for Jane, Ellie kept hoping for an eleventh-hour miracle.

'But she's not here, Ellie darling!' Cousin Rose boomed back across the Irish Sea, when Ellie telephoned her. 'Did you not know? Did she not tell you that? She had the fall racing up in Limerick, and she's back at her own place, at Caragh Lodge!'

'Is she really too bad to travel?'

'Darling girl!' Cousin Rose replied. 'The horse right behind her kicked her in the back! Would the child be missing yer wedding otherwise?'

'And you're sure you can't be there either?'

'I'm doing all I can, darling. But sure poor Aggie's 'flu has gone to her chest.'

Ellie then called Artemis direct at Caragh Lodge, but all she could get was the engaged tone. Finally a distant voice somewhere along the line in Kerry informed Ellie that there had to be something wrong with the line, because everyone kept complaining of the very same thing.

She hardly slept the night before her wedding. She had gone to bed early and lain awake in the dark, thinking of what might be and of what might have been. Ellie had heard nothing from her family since she had written to tell them the news, nothing from her father to wish her well, and nothing from her three elder brothers, not a word even of simulated affection. Eventually Patsy had written, delighted for her and thrilled, but unable to come over despite Hugo's offer to pay his fare. He was off to Los Angeles the very day he was writing his reply, off to Hollywood where a pal with whom he used to spar down at the gymnasium was working as a stunt man and had promised to get him a job. So much as he would love to get over for his sister's wedding, the chance he was being offered in Hollywood was, it seemed, the chance of a lifetime. He was sure Ellie would understand. Of course she understood, but it didn't stop her feeling, lying there in the dark, her dress all laid out, as if she was quite alone. Not even Madame Gautier had written.

As she lay in her darkened bedroom, Ellie found she was once again looking out into the unknown. Her life was about to change once more, and in a way she couldn't even begin to imagine. Because of this, a panic began to overcome her, causing her to shiver, and pull the bedclothes more tightly around her. She loved Hugo. But she had never really been alone with him, not for any length of time, not as she was about to be, for the rest of her life, and the prospect daunted her.

There had always been the three of them, Artemis, Hugo and Ellie. Even when Ellie and Hugo had been left alone together, Artemis had always been there with them, in their talk, and in their thoughts, a sort of perfect trinity.

Ellie's own thoughts drifted into half-thoughts and soon she had fallen asleep, dreaming of a ship, a vast and silent liner on which she was sailing with Hugo, on a flat, black sea. Behind them was a tiny fragile boat, a rowing boat, fixed to the ship's stern by a long ribbon. Then the ribbon broke, and Hugo and she watched with growing helplessness as the little boat drifted and slowly spun away from them, on this strangely calm but lustreless ocean, until it was no more. And as it disappeared Hugo took hold of Ellie and said something to her, repeatedly, gripping her hard by her shoulders, his face getting closer and closer to her's, saying words which Ellie could not hear.

She awoke, panic-stricken, and sat up to turn on her light. She was soaked in perspiration, just as she had been when she was a child and fell asleep after one of her father's thrashings.

That same night Artemis awoke from a dream. She'd been riding on a horse that wasn't Boot, over fields that weren't Irish fields, but the fields were known to her. And then she remembered the fields and where they were. They were the fields of Brougham.

Brutus, who slept quite illegally but unpunished on Artemis's bed, stirred in his own sleep, stretched, yawned, and then resettled. Artemis reached out for the jug beside her bed and poured herself a glass of water, sitting further up in bed and pulling the blankets up around her. Afraid to sleep again, in dread of dreaming again of those beloved acres, she decided instead to sit and watch the dawn break over the lake below her window, and listen to the song of the early birds greeting the light.

She must eventually have dozed, because the next thing she knew the sun was up and trying to pierce the mists that hung over the Caragh waters. Brutus growled good naturedly as Artemis shifted to look at her little gold clock, and saw it was half past six.

Later, at about the same time as Ellie was getting dressed in a gown of antique French silk, Artemis was restrapping a heavy bandage round her ribs and the small of her back. She winced at the pain as she twisted and turned in order to fasten the support, and then sat slowly down on the bed to pull on a pair of wool socks. Ellie stood to check her silk stockings, running her hands up each leg in turn and adjusting her garters, before slipping her feet into a pair of white shoes. Artemis pulled on a dark blue polo-neck sweater and her breeches, gritting her teeth as she tugged on her half-boots with great difficulty. Ellie had help in Hugo's sister Jane, who adjusted the floor length fall of Bruges lace which made up Ellie's headdress, and straightened the fabulous gown out at the waist. But Artemis had no-one as she struggled with her right boot, leaning against the bedroom wall to catch her breath before once more tucking her bad leg up behind her in order to try again.

A Rolls-Royce took Ellie to the church, accompanied by one of Hugo's uncles, since there was no-one from her family to give her away. Artemis left in her small blue Austin, with Brutus in the passenger seat, and with her side-saddle, habit and bowler slung unceremoniously in the back. Both of them reached their destinations in good time and as Ellie walked slowly up the aisle on the arm of Hugo's uncle, Artemis walked into the paddock at Kinsale on the arm of Dan Sleator, the better to disguise her limp. Five minutes later, as Ellie stood before the altar beside Hugo, handsome, tall and fair, but slightly tousled as always, as if he had dashed straight off the tennis court, or got up from his easel, with barely enough time to scramble into his morning dress and hurry on to the church, Artemis cantered Boot down to the start where she answered the roll call in the company of eight other lady riders just as Ellie and Hugo were plighting their troth.

And then, as Ellie came down the aisle of the beautiful parish church of All Saints in Leckford, on the arm of her smiling husband and under the appreciative stare of the mass of fashionable guests, Artemis, roared on by the crowd, was half a length down going into the last fence and a length up coming away from it.

So that as the happy couple left the church and walked out as man and wife into the dazzle of the bright May sunshine, Artemis urged her brave horse on and up the hill to win her first race by two and a half lengths.

They stopped for dinner at an inn near Malmesbury, where they drank champagne and dined on dressed crab and tournedos cooked in madeira. They lingered over their dinner, staring at each other, touching fingers, and talking almost in whispers. They forgot all about time, with the consequence that they did not reach their destination until after midnight.

They had driven there through the warm May evening and now the night in Hugo's Alvis, to a destination about which Hugo refused to say anything except that it was beautiful.

It was a perfect night and neither was in the mood for sleep. For the last few miles, Ellie had rested her head on Hugo's shoulder and entwined both her arms through his left one, as they left the main roads and made their way slowly along lanes and finally along and down what seemed just like a track which fell away into dark woods.

'Where *are* we going, Hugo?' Ellie asked, as the car started bumping over deep potholes, and the woodland turned to forest.

'Wait and see,' Hugo said. 'Just wait and see.'

At first sight all Ellie could see as the car finally stopped was the silhouette of what looked like a cottage in the woods. But then as her eyes got used to the dark, she saw it was not a cottage at all, but something which more resembled a thatched chapel.

'What is it, Hugo?' she asked, holding tight to his arm. 'I mean, are we here?'

'Yes, my darling,' Hugo replied, 'we are here.'

He picked her up off her feet in both his arms and kissed her. 'Welcome, Mrs Tanner,' he smiled at her. 'Welcome to your new home. Welcome to the Convent.'

'You're putting me in a convent *already*?' Ellie teased, peering at the strange building and trying to make out more detail.

'I'm locking you away in the woods,' Hugo said, lifting her up in his strong arms. 'I'm putting you where no-one else can ever find you.'

Kissing her again, Hugo carried her up to the doorway and over the threshold. It was pitch dark inside, and Hugo was suddenly gone from Ellie's side.

'Hugo?' she called, half-alarmed. 'Hugo?'

He returned, lit by the soft glow of the candle he was carrying. 'Come on,' he urged, 'come through.'

Their shadows danced on whitewashed stone walls as they walked down the short corridor and then into the main room, where Hugo lit more candles, on the table, on the sideboards, and finally on the walls. As he did so, the exquisite little place came alive, in the gleamy dancing quiver of a dozen flames.

It was quite unlike any house Ellie had ever seen, with tall gothic windows, finely traced, and vaulted ceilings arching up into the flickering shadows, thick oak doors, and worn flagstone floors. Hugo was now lighting a fire someone had left laid in the hearth, and within moments because the wood was so dry, he had it aflame, adding warmth and colour to the enchanted room.

'Where are we?' Ellie whispered. 'It's like something out of a fairy-tale.'

'It is now that you're here, Ellie,' Hugo replied. 'This is the Convent, really it is. But don't worry. I mean knowing your antipathy to churches, I shan't force you to pray.'

'I got married in a church, didn't I?'

'Yes,' Hugo agreed. 'But not your church.'

'I don't have "a" church,' Ellie said quickly. 'You know that.'

'I know,' Hugo said. 'I know, don't worry. Just as long as you believe in the vows we took.'

'You know I do. Now, tell me about this wonderful place.'

As he led Ellie from room to room Hugo explained that the little house had never been a convent but had been built as a folly in the previous century, by someone very rich, for his mistress to use as a place where she could go to read and write letters, although Hugo doubted if that was all it was used for. Eventually the place had fallen into disrepair during and after the First World War and Hugo's father had found it when staying nearby and bought it, thinking that Hugo might like it as a little country retreat.

'It's not so little,' Ellie said, climbing the staircase. 'How many bedrooms are there up here? Three?'

'Only two,' said Hugo. 'The middle room is a bathroom.'

Hugo opened a door and went in ahead of Ellie, putting down one of the two candles he was holding on a chest of drawers and holding the other one so that Ellie could see the room. It was small, but perfect, rush matting on the floor, with oak furniture and the prettiest four poster bed imaginable. The ceiling sloped down to two small gothic windows, which looked out on a view of dark trees and hills.

'This is heaven, Hugo. Really. It is. It's just – heaven.'

'Would you like something to drink?' Hugo asked her after a moment. 'I've some champagne downstairs.'

'No thank you,' Ellie whispered. 'Do you want some?'

'No,' said Hugo. 'No.' He took Ellie's hat from her head, and brushed a hand through her soft brown hair. 'No, Ellie,' he said. 'No that's not what I want at all.'

Ellie smiled.

'What are you smiling at like that?' Hugo peered at Ellie studiously, over his brass-rimmed glasses. Then caught by the infection of her smile, he smiled too. 'Come on,' he said.

'I'm just smiling,' Ellie replied, 'because I'm so happy.'

They were having breakfast outside, a tray of toast and coffee at their feet on the grass, while they sat side by side on an old wood bench.

'You know something?' Hugo whispered in her ear, after kissing her cheek, 'I think you've been married before.'

'You know I haven't been married before,' Ellie retorted. 'You're the one with the experience.'

'The "experience"?' Hugo grinned.

'Oh Hugo,' Ellie sighed, as she felt herself blushing.

Hugo buttered a fresh slice of toast. 'Ellie,' he said eventually, leaving his toast uneaten. 'You and I. Heavens, I'm not very good at this, you know.' He turned and took one of her hands in both of his. 'What happened between us last night.'

'Yes,' asked Ellie. 'What did happen?'

'Well, yes,' Hugo stumbled unsurely over what he was saying and lowered his voice, although there was no-one around for at least ten square miles. 'That's exactly what I mean, Ellie. What happened between us – well. It doesn't often happen. Apparently.' It was Hugo's turn to redden. Ellie put the back of her other hand to his face, as if to cool his cheek. 'It doesn't, Ellie,' Hugo continued. 'It was extraordinary.'

'I know.'

'I don't think that sort of thing happens to well – to many people,' Hugo whispered. 'If at all.'

'I don't think it can ever have happened before,' Ellie said quietly.

'Not that I'd know,' Hugo said. 'I wasn't exactly Casanova before I met you. But I did know this woman, she was much older than me. Well – by much, I mean five, six years older.'

'That's old enough.'

'It certainly seemed so at the time,' Hugo said, shifting and putting his arm around Ellie's waist. 'Anyway, as the old saying has it –'

'She taught you everything you know?'

'You're – what do you call it in America?' Hugo asked.

'Fresh,' said Ellie.

'That's right!' Hugo exclaimed. 'That's just what you are. *Fresh*.' He made the word sound like a new word, a word invented to describe someone who was just like spring, someone with skin so soft, and hair so silken, and a look so pure that he now only had to think of her for his heart to miss.

'I want to hear what this old woman told you,' Ellie whispered, when Hugo had stopped kissing her.

'It doesn't matter,' Hugo said. 'All you need to know is that I never knew, I never thought for one moment – never. That making love could be like that.'

'I did,' said Ellie.

'How?' Hugo asked in astonishment. 'You couldn't possibly!'

'But I did, Hugo,' Ellie replied. 'I knew it the moment I saw you.'

It was late morning, and the sun above them filtered through the trees as they walked in the forest. There were still bluebells out, great drenches of sudden blue in the glades among the greening beeches, filling the air with the scent of late May.

'You know I love you, don't you, Ellie.' Hugo stated rather than asked.

'Yes, Hugo,' Ellie replied. 'As you know that I love you.'

They walked on hand in hand, along paths of hard red earth, past banks of wild indigo rhododendrons, until they came to a track where the trees met overhead, to form a long tunnel of dark green, a shade only occasionally relieved by the flicker of sunlight.

'Where are we going now?' Ellie asked, holding his hand a little tighter as though this part of the woods might be dangerous.

'You'll see,' Hugo replied. 'We're nearly there.'

Ahead of them a deer suddenly crashed out of the woods, scattering birds and rabbits in its bolt. When it saw Ellie and Hugo, it became momentarily transfixed, staring at them with black-brown eyes. Then it leaped into the other side of the woods, and Ellie watched enthralled as it made its escape, jumping up the slope in a series of extraordinary bouncing bounds.

'I always imagined deer just ran. I never knew they bounced.'

'They're like humans,' Hugo told her solemnly. 'They only bounce when they're in love.'

By now they had reached the end of the tunnel of trees, and Hugo led Ellie into a sun-filled clearing, along the edge of which Ellie could see the tops of some trees.

'We must be very high up here,' she said, not venturing any further.

'You're perfectly safe,' Hugo told her, keeping firm hold of her hand. 'And yes, we are high up. And you'll be amazed. This is one of the most wonderful views in England.'

Hugo led her on, up a little path and round a corner, till they both stood on a plateau. Ellie caught her breath when she saw what lay below her, and as she did so, Hugo turned and just smiled.

It was a vision from a dream, a picture from an age long gone, an image of perfection. Far below them was an ornamental lake, bordered along one side by specimen trees, and surrounded by azaleas in flower, whose vivid colours were mirrored in the calm waters they adorned. A stone bridge spanned the lake, leading from a carriage drive which long before it reached the gates disappeared out of sight behind a line of tall trees. On the other side of the bridge the drive ran up to a pair of enormous iron gates hung on decorated iron pillars, before ending in a carriage sweep in front of the most beautiful house Ellie had ever seen.

Built of a stone which glowed warmly in the sunshine and lying in the folds of the rolling park as if resting in the palm of some vast green hand, the house was fronted by a magnificent double exterior staircase, either side of which ran two gently curving colonnades which connected the main house with its two wings.

It seemed that it even had its own church, for Ellie could see, half hidden behind the left wing and seemingly part of the house, a spire rising above the roof.

'What a wonderful place,' Ellie said, after staring at it in amazement. 'What's it called?'

'Brougham,' Hugo told her. 'Pronounced Broom.'

'Yes?' said Ellie. 'And who lives here?'

'We do,' Hugo replied.

On 4 June, Artemis received a letter at Caragh Lodge from her godmother. It read:

Darling Artemis,

Have you heard? I'm sure you must by now but anyway, in case you ain't, the old family home was sold again. Did you know? Some chap called Tanner bought it, he of the big brewing family. But then he fell off the perch rather suddenly and his son's living there now with his new American bride. Odd to think, don't you find?

The only juicy bit is the bit about the chap who bought it off you. Wilfred Brooke he was called, and word has it that there was some kind of dirty dealing going on, because Brooke apparently was one of those beastly estate agents who does all his business with – guess who? The famous old family firm of Grafton, Grafton and Grafton. It doesn't take a lot of reading between the lines to see how you could have been 'talked out of the place', for it to be bought cheap and then sold on well. Anyway, that's what everyone's saying at dinner-time. I can't honestly believe those lawyers of your father's were acting in what's known as 'your best interests'. But then which lawyers ever do!

And when are you coming back to civilization? Not turning feral are you, taking to the bogs for good? That would be simply too much!

And besides, I miss my goddaughter.
Love
Diana.

Artemis sat in her drawing room overlooking Lough Caragh, and read and re-read the letter. Then she called Brutus, and piling him into the back of her little car, drove off up the mountains, not returning until nearly midnight. At a few minutes after twelve she sat down and replied to her godmother's letter. On the back of a postcard she finally wrote:

Thanks for yours, and please excuse postcard, but have only just returned from abroad. Yes I'd heard about Brougham. Guess what? I know the new owners! Ah well. It's only a house.
Love Artemis.

In the morning, as Artemis slept on, the housekeeper began to tidy the downstairs drawing room. She found endless piles of screwed up writing paper scattered on the floor around Artemis's desk. Naturally she unhesitatingly flattened most of them, and then stood with interest trying to decipher the writing on them. Some began 'Darling Diana', others 'Dear Hugo', and yet others were addressed to someone by the name of Eleanor. There was little of interest written after that. Only each bore a date, and some got as far as 'How are you?'. Or 'Guess what?' Or again 'I thought I must – '

And that was all. Nothing of interest, nothing scandalous or even vaguely passionate. The old woman gave a small sigh of disappointment, and then carefully laid the pieces of writing paper under the logs in the kitchen stove, before setting a match to them.

12

The invitation came as a complete surprise. Through her success at racing Artemis had quite naturally made many new acquaintances, but she'd also made quite sure that was how they stayed, as casual relationships rather than possible friendships, preferring instead to return home to Caragh Lodge alone, where her housekeeper, Mary, arrived every day from out of the hills behind in a donkey cart driven by Tim, her only unmarried son, who would then tend to Artemis's garden, or row her out on the lake for a morning's fishing.

Artemis never entertained, nor was she ever entertained. At first everyone tried to get her to their tables, or failing that at least into their drawing rooms for drinks. Artemis politely but firmly refused all such solicitations, and gradually, when it became obvious that no-one could tempt her out, everyone stopped asking her. Thus she was able to confine all socializing to the outdoors, which worked most satisfactorily, since it seemed that everyone in the south-west of Ireland either owned horses, rode horses, trained horses, sold horses, or bred horses, or if they did none of these things, then either they were just about to or had just done so. In this way Artemis's was the name on everyone's lips, but an absentee at all their parties, an arrangement which happily appeared to suit everyone.

Except the sender of the newly arrived invitation. He was not a man to be bested, as Artemis was about to discover. He was not a man who took no for an answer. And he had a determination equalling that of his quarry's.

It was a printed invitation to dinner, with Artemis's

name handwritten in copperplate in one corner, delivered in a sealed envelope which bore no postage stamp.

'Did you see who brought this?'

'No, ma'am, I did not,' Mary replied, bent over her pastry making. 'The dog barked, but when I opened the door, they was gone.'

Artemis looked at the invitation again, pondering on its formality. Most people who had tried coaxing her out had done so by telephone, or by direct contact. The only printed invitations she had ever received in Ireland were for dances and hunt balls.

'Do you know anyone called Masters?' she asked her housekeeper. 'The Honourable Mr Sheridan Masters?'

For a moment Mary stopped rolling out her pastry, leaning her hands on both ends of the pin. 'That I do, ma'am,' she said.

'Who is he?' Artemis enquired.

'Mr Masters is yer landlord, ma'am.'

Artemis had never given any thought to who might actually own Caragh Lodge. Having signed an agreement with the lawyers in Cork, she had simply paid her rent each month and considered the house as her's. Nothing in life had ever prepared her to think of herself as a tenant, so it came as a shock to realize that someone out there, some total stranger, had rights over her. She threw the invitation on the fire, without even bothering to answer it.

A week later, he called. Brutus heard him first, cocking his boss-eyed head and curling up one corner of his brown lipped mouth in a low growl. It was late, past nine o'clock at night, and no-one ever called at that hour.

Artemis put down her book and listened. Brutus was still only growling, so she thought perhaps it was only an animal the dog had heard moving about outside, because if it had been a human he would have thrown back his big shaggy brown head and started to bark it off. But he hadn't. He was just sitting there, with Artemis's hand on his neck, where she could feel the risen hackles.

Even when the sudden knock came on the door, which made Artemis stiffen, Brutus still didn't bark. The dog just backed off from the drawing room door and hid under the table, where he lay still growling.

Artemis lifted an oil lamp, grabbed her stick and went to the front door. 'Who is it?' she called.

'Hullo!' came the reply. 'It's your landlord!'

The voice sounded cheery enough, so Artemis turned the big key in the lock and opened the door, holding the lamp up in front of her. A very tall man stood on the threshold, staring at her with piercing light-blue eyes, while the wind which had got up that night ruffled a head of blonde hair. He was wearing a full length dark-green cloak, with a high collar, fastened at the neck with a gold chain, and if he had not been smiling such an engaging smile, Artemis knew she would have been frightened.

'I do have a telephone.'

'I know you do,' her landlord replied. 'But old Maggie Tomelty's husband is fighting drunk again, so she's had to abandon the switchboard and go fetch him on home.' He lifted the phone off the wall by the door and handed Artemis the earpiece. 'You can try for yourself if you don't believe me.'

Artemis replaced the receiver without bothering to double check. There was something so good humoured in her visitor's manner that it would have been impossible not to believe him.

'I'd never have called without telephoning,' he smiled, 'but I was driving this way and I was curious to know whether or not you received my invitation.'

'Yes, thank you,' Artemis replied. 'I did.'

'You haven't replied.'

'No I haven't.'

'Why not?'

'I don't really know as a matter of fact.'

'Perhaps you forgot.'

'Yes. Perhaps that's it.'

Not once had his eyes left her face as they exchanged words. A silence fell.

'My name is Sheridan Masters,' he said eventually to break it. 'May I come in?'

Artemis didn't want to let him in. She didn't know why, but everything in her wished to forbid it. She seemed to sense in some strange way that once he was over her threshold she would never be rid of him. Nevertheless she found herself standing aside and admitting him, and following on without a word as he led the way into the drawing room.

'How charming,' he said, swinging off his cloak to reveal a perfectly cut velvet smoking jacket. 'You've made this old place so – snug.' He turned and looked at her and Artemis was fascinated to find she was quite taken with his looks. He was strong, very much the Viking, with a cleft in his chin, and blonde hair swept back from a fine high forehead. But still she said nothing, just watching him, leaning on her stick.

Brutus spoke for her, suddenly erupting under the table into another rumble of growls.

'Ah,' Masters said, 'the dog that barked.'

'He's not barking now.'

'No,' Masters smiled at her. 'He's not, is he?'

'He barks at everyone else.'

Her visitor nodded, but said nothing in reply. Instead, he looked round the room, appraising the way Artemis had furnished it.

'This was a terrible damp old place.'

'Yes it was.'

'You've done great things. Great things. Who did this painting?'

'A friend of mine,' Artemis replied, wishing for some unknown reason that it wasn't one of Hugo's delicate watercolours which had taken his attention.

'What's his name?'

'Why?'

'He's very good. I might like to buy one.'

'He doesn't sell,' Artemis informed him. 'He only gives.'

Masters nodded without looking round at Artemis and examined the rest of the paintings and drawings Artemis had collected since she'd been in Ireland.

'So, you'll come to dinner then?' he asked eventually, after he had made his way slowly round the room. 'It's Saturday. This Saturday.' He put his hand out towards the dog to pat him.

'I shouldn't.'

'You shouldn't what? Come to dinner?' Masters smiled at her.

'No. I shouldn't touch the dog,' Artemis replied carefully.

Masters just smiled, no longer looking at the dog, but watching Artemis. After a moment, Brutus crawled out on his stomach from under the table and licked the stranger's hand. Masters ruffled the top of the dog's head, and Brutus rolled over on his back, offering him his throat.

Artemis pushed at Brutus in an effort to make him get up. 'I'm going to the races on Saturday.' She ran a nervous hand through her now longer hair.

'That's all right, we won't be eating until late,' Masters replied. 'I'll send a car.'

'I haven't said yes,' Artemis reminded him.

'And you haven't said no,' Masters smiled. 'So unless you do, I'll send a car at eight.'

The headlights of the car and the glow of the dusk revealed Shanangarry House to be a long low dwelling, built on two floors, and painted a dead red. The drive ran up straight in front of it, past lawns either side on which peacocks roamed, to end in a rectangle where a number of cars were already parked. Artemis, sitting as far back as she could in her seat as if afraid to be seen, now regretted her acceptance of the invitation even more. She had a sudden urge to tell the driver to turn and take her back home, but it was too late. A servant was already on his way out to escort her in from the car.

There were lights in all the windows Artemis noticed as she walked to the front door, and the noise of laughter and chat. A maid took her coat, and a butler, who must have stood nearly seven feet, led her into the party.

'Lady Artemis Deverill!' he announced, in a very high voice, to which no-one paid the slightest heed, except a small and pretty middle-aged woman dressed in bright red velvet, and wearing a magnificent set of Edwardian garnets, who at once flew over to Artemis's side.

'I'm delighted,' she said. 'Absolutely delighted. And you're every bit as pretty as they said you were. I'm Sheridan's mama, and please call me Leila. Everyone else does. So you will as well, won't you? I know you will.'

Artemis liked her hostess at once. She was a woman in her fifties, with silver hair, small delicately chiselled features, and pale slender hands which she kept anxiously putting up to her face without, so it appeared to Artemis, any due reason.

'Now then?' Leila Masters wondered aloud, taking Artemis's arm and leading her across to a group by the fire, 'I wonder who you'd like to meet? It won't really make much difference,' she laughed. 'They're all talking horse.'

As she made her way across to the appointed group, Artemis looked round the beautiful room, which was decorated and furnished predominantly in muted reds and pastel pinks.

'Do you live here?' she asked her hostess.

Leila Masters stopped and looked round at her. 'Why do you ask?'

'I love this red,' Artemis replied. 'We had a room this colour at home.'

'Sherry is mad for it. He's mad on anything red, pink, scarlet, what have you.'

They were with the group by the fire now, but Artemis was back in Brougham, in the state bedroom, as it once was. Brougham which was no longer her home, but which now belonged to Hugo. And to Ellie.

She was so busy wondering about them, imagining them in the rooms at Brougham that she didn't catch anyone's names, but then Artemis doubted if anyone caught hers, such was the level of the ever increasing din. Nevertheless, she was soon involved in the conversation, caught up in an argument as to which was the best pack of fox-hounds in the south-west corner. Her fellow guests were what Artemis had come to recognize as typically Anglo-Irish, handsome in an almost mournful kind of way, with a debonair manner born from bravado, a devil-may-care attitude adopted from being residents in an alien land. It went without saying they were all hunting mad.

'I just can't wait, can you?' a slim and tough looking woman in the group asked Artemis, 'until the dahlias are dead, yes?'

'Hurrah hurrah!' the men around her carrolled, echoing Jorrocks as they made their way to dine, 'the dahlias are dead!'

Most of the guests were much older than Artemis and seemed to be friends of Leila Masters rather than her son, who appeared to stand apart from the company rather than be a part of it. Artemis had been watching him during the pre-dinner drinks, moving easily enough from group to group, but never staying very long, listening and laughing at things said to him before soon moving away on and around the assembled company.

'Sometimes I suggest to mother we should dine in the stables,' he said as he sat down at the head of the table next to Artemis. 'Were you with the Barkers or the Brayers?'

'The Barkers, mostly,' Artemis replied. 'But don't worry. I was brought up on it.'

Sheridan leaned back as his soup was served and stared down the table. 'What do you think gets into people when they get on a horse?' he asked. 'Do you see Ursula there? In the dark blue dress? He nodded at a handsome raven-haired woman halfway down the table. 'She lost all her front top teeth one day, riding to the meet. On her horse's head. Banged her in the mouth. But rather than miss anything, she stuffed the teeth in her pocket, hunted all day, and then drove up to Dublin the following morning to get them all replaced.'

'Don't you hunt?' Artemis asked.

'No,' he said. 'Never. But it's not a question of principle. I don't have principles. Principles are too unforgiving.'

Artemis wasn't certain of what exactly her host meant by that. But because he was smiling so engagingly she took it very much as an indication of compassion.

'I'm glad you came,' he said. 'Are you?'

'Yes,' Artemis replied. 'I think I am actually.'

It was true. Once she had conquered her nerves in the car, set foot over the threshold and heard the sound of all the banter and the laughter, she had realized all at once just how lonely she had in fact been. She turned to the man on her right, whose face was the colour of a damson, and engaged him in conversation while Sheridan talked to the thin tough woman who was sitting on his left.

Later, and inevitably, the talk turned to the topic of the moment, Edward and Mrs Simpson.

'She's a perfectly ghastly woman,' the thin tough woman said. 'But then of course she's American. So what does one expect? All Americans are perfectly ghastly. Don't you agree?' The look was across the table to Artemis.

'No,' Artemis said. 'I've been to America and the people I met I liked. Of course unlike you, I didn't meet all the people.'

The thin tough woman stared back at Artemis in silence. Then she bared her upper teeth in an odd but good humoured smile. 'No,' she said. 'I don't suppose you did. Damn good. No I don't suppose you did.'

'I can't be done with him meself,' the damson-faced man beside Artemis rumbled. 'He's such an odd cove. And has some damn' odd chums, too.'

'I think they're both quite dull, personally,' said the thin tough woman. 'I can't imagine they'll last a minute.'

'He can't ride, and that's for certain,' said Artemis's neighbour. 'Saw him decanted twice at the Harkaway.'

'Come to Cork with me on Wednesday,' Sheridan turned to Artemis as the argument ripened, 'and let's have lunch.'

'You want to go all the way into Cork?' Artemis enquired. 'Just for lunch?'

'That depends,' her host replied.

'On what?' Artemis said.

'Whether it's just for lunch.'

'Sorry?'

'Whether it's just for lunch,' her host told her, 'rather depends on what happens at lunch.'

What happened over lunch was that Artemis became convinced she was in love. Having always thought of herself as physically unattractive to men, she found it quite overwhelming to be the subject of such obvious desire. Sheridan Masters could not take his eyes from her. He was early at the restaurant, waiting for her impatiently, a bunch of flowers in one hand and a box of expensive chocolates in the other. He kissed her hand when Artemis arrived, ten minutes late, and held it until they were sat at their corner table, where he suddenly fell silent, before groaning and then mopping his brow with a red silk handkerchief.

'This is absurd,' he said. 'I don't know what is happening to me.'

'Are you unwell?' Artemis asked, picking up the menu.

'Yes,' he replied. 'Very. At least if we were in India I would be diagnosed as being so. Did you know that? That in India they look on love as a sickness?'

Artemis held the gaze that was holding hers, and

although she felt herself badly in need of taking several deep breaths, instead she dropped her eyes and stared at the menu.

'What are you going to eat?' she asked.

'I'm serious,' Sheridan continued, putting a hand on the menu, forcing Artemis to lower it. 'Believe me. This is the last thing I wanted.'

'I agree,' Artemis replied. 'Me too.' There was a silence. 'Perhaps it would be better if I just got up and went.' She put a hand out, reaching for her stick.

'Don't,' he warned her, leaning forward and catching her hand. 'You do and I'll find you, wherever you are.'

Artemis stared back at him, trying to resist his hold on her. 'How can you possibly want the last thing you want?' she asked.

'What I meant was I wasn't prepared for this, Artemis,' he said. 'A flirtation, yes. The moment I saw you I wanted to make love to you. You'd have enjoyed it. We both would have enjoyed it. And that would have been that.'

'I doubt it,' Artemis said as factually as she could, removing her hand.

'You doubt that would have been that?'

'No. I doubt your assumption – or is it presumption? That we both would have enjoyed it.'

But even so, Artemis didn't get up and leave. Instead she picked her menu up again and tried very hard to make sense of the words which swam before her.

'I'd recommend the mulligatawny soup and the game pie,' Sheridan Masters said, also picking up his menu.

After lunch, they walked idly down Main Street, stopping and looking in all the best shop windows.

'I like that hat,' Sheridan announced, pointing to a small dished straw with a polka dot band. 'May I buy it for you?'

'No,' said Artemis.

'And then we'll go back to Caragh Lodge,' he continued, dropping his voice and putting his hand in her's.

'It wouldn't suit me,' Artemis concluded.

'How do you know till you try it?'

'Till I try what?'

'I wonder.'

'I was referring to the hat.'

'Of course. Wasn't I?'

'I don't think so,' Artemis said, removing her hand and walking slowly on.

When she stopped on the street corner and looked back for him, Sheridan had gone. Artemis waited and then crossed the road and walked on, feeling a mixture of relief and disappointment. Moments later she heard footsteps behind her, and then he was once more by her side, carrying a hat box which he thrust at her.

'There!' he said breathlessly. 'If that doesn't suit you, I'll eat it!'

Seeing that Artemis wasn't going to open it in the street, Sheridan took the box back from her and lifted out a little blue hat, made of shiny dark blue straw, shaped like a helmet, with a bunch of mock flowers on the front and a half-veil. Even off, just held in someone's hand, it looked enchanting. Still Artemis made no move, and said nothing. She was totally unprepared for such moments in life and had no way of dealing with them.

Mistaking her silence for stubbornness, rather than helplessness, Sheridan sighed and shaking his head slightly in impatience, put the box on the ground and the hat on Artemis's head. 'Mmmm,' he said thoughtfully, standing back. 'Uh-huh,' before making a slight adjustment. 'Divine. *Très chic*. Yes, very *très chic*.'

His odd choice of words made Artemis smile and her sudden smile made him smile back. She turned and looked at herself in a shop window and saw that the hat was indeed divine, and also very chic. And seeing this was so, and that instead of it looking foolish the hat looked pretty and fashionable, and seeing the look on the face of the man who was looking at her, who was looking as if he was melting, Artemis suddenly and at last in her life felt adored, and wanted and loved, and so she put her arms up round Sheridan's neck and kissed him.

They were married a month later in the little Protestant church of Brinny, in a service conducted by a sweet-faced white-haired rector called the Reverend Noel Arthur, who wore his fishing trousers and shoes under his cassock, and attended by only the bridegroom's immediate family and friends. Artemis neither invited nor told anyone, not even Cousin Rose, not even Dan Sleator, and least of all Ellie and Hugo.

Leila Masters, however, was delighted with the match, and embraced Artemis as a daughter, before announcing she was leaving Shanangarry, since the house was now by rights her son's, to go and live with her brother in America. There was no Mr Masters senior, Sheridan's father having died suddenly the year before.

Cousin Rose heard on the grapevine a week before the ceremony and through sheer persistence finally tracked Artemis down at Caragh Lodge. After congratulating Artemis, she then scolded her roundly for not asking any of her friends to the wedding, and most particularly Hugo and Ellie.

'There's bad luck in it for ye,' she said over the telephone. 'Friendship's not a flower ye can wear on yer sleeve.'

'You're not to say anything about it, please,' Artemis replied. 'I'll tell them in my own time.'

'But why?' Cousin Rose cried. 'Are they not to be included? Were ye born to break people's hearts or what, child?'

'I don't know, Rose,' Artemis said suddenly, and put down the telephone.

They honeymooned in Paris, travelling by the *Golden Arrow*, and arriving at the Gare du Nord mid-afternoon. Besides a somewhat formal kiss after the actual wedding ceremony, there had been no physical contact between Artemis and her new husband. Artemis didn't consider this unusual. In fact it was as much as she'd been led to expect, no more and no less. Nanny had always brought her up to believe that love was something you *learned* to do. First people got married, then they learned how to love each other. Romance was strictly for the poor who needed it. So even though Artemis felt strongly attracted to her tall blond husband, and longed for his embrace and whatever physical adventures this in turn might lead to, she was quite happy to wait and see.

Since their first lunch in Cork, when Artemis had felt certain she was falling in love with Sheridan, and when he'd been so open about his own feelings, without ever actually declaring his love for her outright, there'd been few other overt displays of affection, or references to their emotional state. Instead their relationship had quite simply become a *fait accompli*. When they were out walking, Sheridan would take her arm, when he came to collect her he would bring her flowers, at the end of days spent together they would sit and talk in front of the fire at Shanangarry, either side by side on the sofa, or with Sheridan sitting at Artemis's feet, his arms across her lap. At such times they would talk about the present and the future, which by mutual assumption now seemed to belong to them both, so that when Sheridan arrived one evening to Caragh Lodge to collect Artemis for dinner at Shanangarry and proposed to her as they sat in the window seat overlooking the shadowy lake, it seemed only natural for Artemis to accept.

And despite the doubts she had expressed to Rose Lannigan on the telephone, until the day she was married Artemis never had real cause to regret her decision. Sheridan was the ideal companion: articulate, well informed, attentive and intelligent. It seemed that with the exception of horses, he and Artemis had everything in common, and while there was no passion as yet in their relationship, in her innocence Artemis thought it only a matter of time before this state of affairs was rectified, and that in time that would come quite properly after they were married.

Consummation, however, did not take place on their actual wedding night. The berths on the night train were extremely narrow and the channel crossing was very rough, precluding, it seemed by necessity, any proposed intimacy. At least that was what Artemis thought when she was left alone in the cabin to get undressed, and when Sheridan failed to return by the time Artemis was fast falling asleep. Turning on her side and settling down into an uneasy sleep, Artemis concluded by her husband's continued absence that this night was obviously not to count as the first night of their marriage, and their honeymoon proper would begin as soon as they had arrived in Paris.

From the Gare du Nord, they took a cab straight to their hotel on the Ile St Louis. Through the driver's open window, Artemis savoured the tang of Paris, strong tobacco, garlic and fresh onion, rough wine and fried oil. The late October weather seemed to make the air even more pungent, adding a vapour of autumn and wrapping a faint mist around the city. The hotel was pretty and charming, set around a cobbled courtyard which their balconied room overlooked, and upon which balcony Artemis now stood, drinking in the atmosphere of a city she had always longed to visit and was now doing so under the most perfect of circumstances, with the man she loved.

Sheridan came to her side and put an arm round her waist. 'Ah, Paris,' he sighed. 'A man has no home in Europe save in Paris.'

'But would you give it up for love?'

Sheridan Masters frowned as he stared down into the courtyard where a young waiter had come out of the building to scatter crumbs for the birds.

'*Si le roi m'avait donné Paris, sa grand ville,*' Artemis quoted, '*et qu'il me fallut quitter l'amour de ma vie, je dirais au roi Henri – reprenez votre Paris.*'

'I see. You would rather have love than Paris, yes?'

'Wouldn't you?'

'I'd much rather have both,' Sheridan said, as the young waiter looked up and caught his look. 'At one and the same time.'

They dined out at Maxims, on *Saumon en Gelée à l'Estragon*, washed down with a 1927 Chablis. Afterwards they walked back by the Seine and then across it, watching the *bateaux mouches* gliding under the bridges through dark waters which sparkled with a thousand dancing lights. By the time they'd reached their hotel, Artemis felt at last and for the first time truly happy.

They stood for a long moment on their balcony, without speaking, the stars far above them and the sounds of the city far below. Then Sheridan bent down to whisper in Artemis's ear. 'It's very late. Why don't you go and get ready for bed?'

Artemis turned to him and looked at him, expecting to be held, and to be kissed. Which indeed she was, briefly by one elbow, as her husband leaned a little closer and kissed her on the forehead.

'Go to bed,' he whispered. 'Go on.'

As Artemis sat on the side of her bed taking off her shoes, and then standing to unclasp her silk gown, she felt grateful for her husband's tact. She had honestly been afraid of this moment, of the time when she would finally have to undress in front of him, to stand awkwardly without her stick, lop-sided and a little unsure, while he pretended not to look or to notice. They had talked about her accident and she'd described what had happened, and what the surgeons had had to do to her afterwards. And Sheridan had been understanding and sympathetic. But words were one thing, Artemis thought, as she all but lost her balance trying to pull off her stockings while still standing. Words were one thing, things heard, invisible things, but reality was something seen, images perceived, truths without explanation. And Artemis had been afraid, fearful of what her handsome strong husband would think when he saw the reality of her imperfection.

He must have sensed her disquiet and her anxiety, otherwise why else would he so quietly and discreetly have withdrawn, leaving his new bride to undress herself privately and get into bed in her new peach silk nightgown?

It took a long time before Artemis finally realized, long after midnight, that he was not coming back. At least not to her bed. She woke from a fitful sleep sometime just after four, according to her watch on the table beside her bed, and under the door saw the light in the little sitting room go on. She sat up in bed, afraid to call out, because she knew instinctively that anyone returning to their bedroom on the first night of their marriage did not wish to be asked for reasons, since the reasons must be obvious enough. So instead, Artemis pulled the sheets up tight under her chin and waited.

After a while, not long, just a matter of two perhaps three minutes, the light went out again, and a door opened and closed. Then there was silence. Artemis waited, her heart pounding in her chest, the sheet still pulled up to her face and held clenched in both hands. And then she got up and, taking her stick, went as quietly as she could to the bedroom door and slowly opened it. In the half darkness she could see her husband's discarded clothes, thrown over the back of a chair, with his shoes and socks left lying on the floor, but she could not see her husband.

She could not see him, but she knew where he was, because she could hear him breathing, heavily, deep somnolent exhalations from behind the door opposite her, a little secondary bedroom furnished with just a plain bed and a chair, and designed for a travelling maid or manservant. Not for a husband on the first night of his honeymoon.

But that is where Artemis's husband now was, in the maid's bed, and to judge from the sound of his breathing, not only in bed but in bed and fast asleep.

'Where were you?' Artemis asked him at breakfast.

'I'm so sorry,' he replied, looking up from buttering his croissant. 'Did I wake you?'

'Where were you?'

He glanced up at her. 'In the maid's room.'

Artemis tried a different tack. 'Where did you go?'

'I think we have to get something perfectly clear from the outset.' Sheridan stared at her before wiping a few stray crumbs of croissant from his mouth with his napkin. 'I am not accountable to you.'

Artemis merely stared at him, without expression.

'Because you married me, that does not mean I have to be accountable for everything I do, everything I say, or everywhere I choose to go.'

'I see,' said Artemis after a short pause. 'I only married you. You didn't marry me.'

Sheridan smiled, then poured himself some more coffee. 'I'll try not to wake you again,' he promised.

At a loss quite what to do, Artemis accepted the situation, in the faint hope that Sheridan would soon come up with an explanation for his behaviour. During the day he was a model husband, attentive to all her needs, and taking her wherever she wished to go, which was quite simply everywhere. Together they saw every sight, and although it emerged that Sheridan had been a frequent visitor to Paris, he never bored once, and was always willing to discuss their daily excursions over lunch and dinner, meals which were always taken at the best restaurants. He took his young bride to the opera, to the theatre, and to every exhibition and gallery she wished to see or visit. And then late at night they would walk in some new part of the city, perhaps visiting the *quartier latin* for coffee and cognac, or stroll through Montmartre listening to the dance music filtering out from the busy cafés. In appearance they seemed the model lovers.

But then he would leave her back at the hotel, to go to bed alone. And every night he'd leave her the same way, suggesting it was time for her to go to bed, and then slipping away while Artemis undressed.

At last Artemis summoned up the courage to challenge him directly. 'Look,' she said. 'Is there something wrong with you? Shouldn't we talk?'

Her husband lowered his newspaper and looked across the table at her. 'I don't think so,' he said.

'You don't think what? That there's anything wrong with you?'

'That we need to talk.' Sheridan raised his newspaper and continued to read.

Taking this to mean that he was possibly too embarrassed to discuss whatever problem he had, Artemis fell silent for a while, reading on the front of Sheridan's copy of *La Monde* something about the appointment by the Spanish Insurgents of General Franco as their Chief of State.

'Can't I do anything to help?' she finally enquired, breaking an interminable silence, and summoning up the full quota of her courage.

'In what way?'

'We are *meant* to be married. And apparently, or anyway so I'm told – ' Artemis put down her coffee cup, for fear of spilling the contents. 'I understand,' she began again, 'that there can be well – difficulties. Between men and women. And someone said that they're not always, I don't know. Insurmountable.'

Her husband slowly lowered his paper and stared at her with cold blue eyes. 'That's very kind of you,' he said after a moment, and without a trace of gratitude in his voice, 'but I assure you I have no trouble with my potency, if that's what you're rather clumsily trying to say. None whatsoever. Unlike yourself, my disability is not a visible one. It's a metaphysical one. I am only disabled, you see, in the company of women.'

He went to pick up his newspaper once more, but Artemis stopped him, placing her hand quickly on it.

'Why did you marry me then?' she asked, feeling suddenly frightened and desperately alone.

Sheridan shook his head and removed her hand off his newspaper. 'Please,' he said. 'You're free to do as you choose. You can go where you like, and do as you like, with whomsoever you please. The only proviso is that you must remain my wife.'

'Why?'

'I think I've answered quite enough questions for one day, don't you? You said you wanted to go to the Louvre once more before we left Paris.' Sheridan began to fold his newspaper, prior to getting up from the table, but Artemis picked up her cane, and pushed him hard in the chest, forcing him back down in his seat.

'Suppose I don't want to remain your wife?' she demanded. 'Supposing I leave you? And seek a divorce?'

Her husband looked at her once more with steel-blue eyes, and then pushing the end of her cane from his chest, he rose. 'I wouldn't advise trying to leave,' he said, 'or seeking a divorce. Not under any circumstances.'

For most of the journey back to Ireland they travelled in silence. Artemis tried to read, but the words meant nothing. She tried to find refuge in sleep, but failed, so she spent her time deep in thought, staring at the passing countryside. Occasionally her husband would make some comment about what he was reading, or about something he had seen from the papers, further news about the Spanish Civil War, or the latest about Edward VIII and Mrs Simpson, but these remarks were not intended conversationally, but were made rather as pronouncements, particularly when there was anyone else present in their railway compartment. Otherwise he was as silent as his new young bride.

France passed by, green going brown in autumn, and still bearing the scars of the terrible catastrophe she had hosted for five years. The channel was crossed, its burly brutal seas buffeting the steamer, and then

England, her king dead and her new monarch busy playing the fool. The newspaper hoardings on all the station platforms seemed taken up with this one subject to the total exclusion of everything else.

'As if it mattered,' Artemis said to herself as the boat-train left Euston for Fishguard. 'Europe's about to burn, but all we can do is fiddle about a king's mistress.'

Her husband looked up at her, visibly surprised, as if amazed that she was still alive. 'I wonder what you know about it,' he said. 'Nothing except what you read in the papers.'

Artemis didn't reply, turning instead to another part of *The Times*.

'I know the King,' her husband continued. 'We were in the South of France together. It's not as easy as that.'

'What isn't?'

'It's not a question of just whether or not he should marry Wallace Simpson. He may be the King, but that doesn't mean when he's crowned – '

'If he's crowned,' Artemis interrupted. 'Actually he'd be far better off calling it a day, as far as the crown goes, and going off and living with Mrs Simpson in Germany, where he'd be quite at home.'

Sheridan shot Artemis a look before getting up and opening the door into the corridor. 'Excuse me,' he said.

She curled herself up in the corner of the carriage and again tried to doze, but sleep just wouldn't come. Her mind was too active, too occupied with trying to work out exactly how she had managed to get herself into such an inextricable situation. Because there was no doubt at all that it was entirely her own fault.

It had been hard enough when Ellie had married Hugo, but she had prepared herself for that. She had made a conscious decision to distance herself emotionally from Hugo, because she knew that much as she loved him, he did not love her, which was why she'd decided it was better to give best, rather than live on with false hopes and ridiculously unrealistic expectations.

But then the letter had arrived from Diana, and once again Artemis could make no sense of her emotions. It was only a house, she kept telling herself, hundreds and thousands of times as she had ridden her horse up into the hills to try and sort out the muddle in her head. Brougham was just a house, like any other house. It was just a mass of stones, and stone upon stone, lath and plaster, wood, slate and brick, windows, doors, mouldings, cornices and chimneys, made from inert substances and lifeless materials, so what possible difference could it make who owned it? And why and how could it possibly hurt if its new owners were Hugo and Ellie?

And yet it did hurt. The news had hurt her so much she'd taken to her bed where she lay for days pale, jaundiced, and alone, except for old Mary coming in. She lay there seeing how she'd been made by her father and stepmother to sacrifice Brougham, to sell it for a pittance because of a legal loophole. They had made her give up her home, her mother's home, the home of her ancestors, and it hurt, because although to the eye Brougham might appear to be just a mass of stone upon stone, and wood upon plaster, to the heart it had been transformed by the love of those who'd built it and then lived in it, until the house itself lived, with a soul and a life of its own.

And if the coin had spun differently and fate had decreed it to fall heads up for Artemis, had she had a perfectly even stance and a right leg to match her long and elegant left one, then Hugo might have looked at her the way Artemis had so often seen him looking at Ellie, and Artemis wouldn't have taken him back up to Strand House but kept him as her secret in his red tinker's caravan; or have him tow it up to the lake, her lake, where they would have walked and argued and fished and ridden. It would be her, Artemis, who would be back at Brougham now, restoring the red of the walls and the blue of the walls, and the pale yellows, and the pinks, and the creams and the greens and the greys. And the stables would be full once more of horses, and the wings staffed with servants, and the hunt once again would open its season meeting as before in the shade of the great, double, exterior staircase, and Ellie would be the one to be asked as a guest, to come and stay and admire the great house, her house, Artemis's house and Artemis's rightful home, her beloved Brougham.

And most of all, Artemis would never have rushed into such a foolish marriage with a man about whom she knew absolutely nothing.

She had just fallen finally asleep, when the carriage door clattered noisily open once more, awaking her with a jolt.

'I do apologize,' her husband said, accompanied on his return by a dark-haired supercilious young man. 'I had no idea you were sleeping.' He closed the door again behind the young man, who stood staring at Artemis with ill concealed impudence. 'Good. Now if you'll sit up, I'll introduce you,' Sheridan continued, 'This is – ' He fell silent, all the while looking at Artemis and smiling.

'Ralph,' said the young man.

'This is Ralph,' her husband said. 'We became acquainted in the bar.'

Ralph came and stayed at Shanangarry. Artemis was given a large bedroom with dressing room and bathroom down the west end of the house, while Sheridan slept, washed and dressed in the east end. His guest was given a room next door to his host.

Leila Masters was still in residence on their return from France, but no sooner were they home, than she started to pack.

'As I told you, my dear,' she said to Artemis. 'I'm off to live in America.'

'May I ask you something?' Artemis said, at least happy from being reunited with Brutus, who now sat, as always at her feet.

'When we first met, you and I, and you said you were going to live in America, you also said now that the house was by rights your son's. What did you mean by that? By rights?'

'Family matters,' her mother-in-law smiled at her, patting her hand. 'They really needn't concern you.'

'I'd actually quite like to know,' Artemis insisted.

'You wouldn't, my dear,' Leila Masters sighed.

Artemis took the paw Brutus had suddenly decided to offer her and pushed her fingers into the clefts of the pads below. 'I don't know this man he's brought home, Leila. Sheridan met him on the train.'

'I met his father on a train, you know,' Leila Masters replied. 'And he proposed to me at sea.'

'No,' said Artemis, starting again. 'I don't think you understand.'

'Oh, I understand, my dear,' her mother-in-law said. 'I understand very well. His father was the same you know.'

Artemis looked at her, then let go of the dog's paw. He immediately raised it again. 'No, Brutus, lie down.'

'Would it make any difference if I told you what I meant by the house being rightfully Sheridan's?'

'Probably not.'

'It was difficult, you know, very difficult, giving my assent. I like you so much, you see, Artemis my dear. I liked you the first moment I saw you. If I'd been blessed with a daughter, I'd have wanted her to be like you.'

Artemis pulled at her dog's ears, saying nothing, not even looking at her mother-in-law.

'The family estate, Shanangarry. It isn't just the house, you know. There are shops in Cork. Houses, too. And land. And houses and land up north as well, besides property in England. It's worth a tidy sum. But my husband – well. You must understand my husband was a very conservative man. He was military. And a magistrate. Very conservative indeed.'

There was a silence while Mrs Masters poured them both another half cup of now lukewarm tea.

'The thing is, Artemis dear,' she continued, 'Sheridan is an only child. But his father put a stipulation in his will that he was not to inherit, that the whole estate would pass to his first cousin, with me provided for of course, but the rest of the estate, the grand bulk of it so to speak, Sheridan would see nothing of it unless he married within two years of his father's death.'

'Yes,' Artemis said, 'I see. Except suppose his father had lived until –'

'Forgive me interrupting, my dear,' Leila Masters said. 'But his father knew he was dying. Which is why he redrew his will to this very effect, do you see?'

'I see everything except the point, Leila. What is the point of forcing someone – someone who might not want to get married – into marriage?'

'I think his father thought it might help.' Artemis's mother-in-law looked past her, in embarrassment.

'I don't know what to do,' Artemis confessed.

'Do nothing, Artemis,' Leila Masters advised. 'Sheridan is now very rich. *You* will be very rich. You can do as you like, as long as you stay married. It may seem a little strange to begin with, but if you think about it, my dear, that's how most marriages are these days anyway.'

'I'm sure,' Artemis said, reaching for her cane. 'But I'm also sure it's not the sort of marriage that I'd choose.'

She stood up and, hiding the sudden pain which shot through her right leg, began to walk towards the stairs.

Her mother-in-law rose and hurried after her. 'Don't do anything foolish, Artemis,' she urged. 'After all, an arrangement like this. For someone like –' Then she stopped and dropped her eyes as Artemis turned to stare at her.

'Someone like me should be grateful, shouldn't I, Leila? After all, how many tall, handsome and rich men would marry someone like me?'

'I didn't mean that, my dear.'

'You did, Leila, but what you didn't mean was to hurt me. Besides, it's true. It's a perfectly sensible arrangement.'

From that moment on Artemis determined that it was going to be an arrangement which she was going to work to her best advantage. Once her mother-in-law had sailed for America, and once Sheridan had bored of the shallow and conceited young man he had picked up on the boat-train, Artemis took her husband at his word and did what she liked. She bought herself a brand new Aston Martin, in which she proceeded to terrorize the neighbourhood with her eccentric style of driving, a new wardrobe of clothes, including the most expensive hand-made hunting habit, as much old and beautiful jewellery as she could find in Cork and in Dublin, the kind of fine paintings which she liked and she knew Sheridan did not, and six new horses, two to hunt, and four to ride and race point-to-point. She also commissioned the redecoration of the entire house, with the exception of her husband's bedroom and dressing room, in which she had no interest since she never once entered them.

But whatever she did to the house, she still hated it. So did Brutus. It was sometimes as much as Artemis could do to get her dog to come indoors, even when it was pouring with rain. He would stand in the porch, pulling backwards as soon as Artemis had hold of his collar, grunting and heaving as he tried to escape. If he lost the battle, he would then slink inside and hide under the kitchen table, away from Sheridan, and any of his friends who might be calling.

Sheridan had many friends, none of whom Artemis liked. To a man and a woman they succeeded in making Artemis feel she was very much an outsider. There was something vaguely clannish in their behaviour whenever one or more were met, and if Artemis left their company or rejoined it, she always got the impression of a distinct change of key, of a shift in emphasis. They were not unwelcoming, they were not impolite and they were not offhand. What they were, Artemis decided, was tolerant. They all tolerated her, they endured her company patiently and with good manners, they talked to her on general subjects, and were openly grateful for her hospitality. But all the time she knew they were simply treading water, simply waiting for her to leave.

At first, before she realized that this was what they wished, Artemis assumed the keeping of late hours at Shanangarry to be part of the life she had come to embrace. In Ireland most people rose late and went to bed even later, so that day became night, and night became day. Even hunting was affected by everyone's inability to keep time. In England as a girl Artemis had been drilled to be utterly punctilious when following hounds, arriving early at the Meet and back on time at the end of the day. But in Ireland even if hounds moved off a mere half an hour late, it was usually only to recongregate a couple of miles down the road at the nearest bar, where the next hour was spent in fortifying the inner man before the day's sport began in earnest.

So when her husband's guests stayed late in the evening, Artemis assumed this to be the norm, and as their hostess she would attend to their needs well into the small hours, in spite of her increasing fatigue, for Artemis herself was always up early to supervise morning stables, no matter what time she went to bed. And so it would have continued, with her seeing to her husband's guests until they all finally left, had she not been instructed otherwise.

'There's no need for you to stay up so late,' Sheridan remarked casually to her one night as they were climbing the stairs to go to bed at four o'clock one morning. 'It's different for our guests. Most of them sleep in till lunchtime. So in future, after you've served coffee and we've had a drink, you can go to bed. Why don't you?'

This was Sheridan Masters' way of giving orders, as a question rather than as a directive. Artemis had learned to recognize this, and whenever she was in the mood to aggravate her husband, she would answer his question with a question of her own, which he would answer with another question, and she again with yet another question, until the whole dialogue degenerated into a childish exchange. But with this particular directive, to go to her bed early and leave her husband and his friends to their own devices, Artemis was only too happy to comply.

And once asleep, she had no trouble in staying asleep, thanks to her outdoor life and the wonderful air in the south-west of Ireland. In fact until that night, two weeks before Christmas, Artemis could never remember once waking up from the moment she turned off her bedside light until the moment her alarm clock rang.

But this night, a cold and windy Sunday night, the second Sunday of Advent, she suddenly woke up, and with such a sense of utter terror she would have fled the house there and then.

Had her bedroom door not been locked. From the outside.

Artemis stood staring at the door. The key was gone from the keyhole. And the door was well and truly locked. Sheridan had locked her in. Why lock her in? What had happened, or was happening that he was afraid Artemis might see? And how many times had it happened before? Artemis went to the window to check whether or not that evening's quota of guests had gone, and saw there were still four cars in the drive. And yet no light spilled from any windows in the house, and listening, back against the locked door, Artemis could hear not a sound from anywhere, no voices, no music, no laughter. Just silence. The house was as quiet as the grave.

She stood by the door, her hand still holding the dog by his collar. She wanted to bang on the door and shout and call for help. But she knew no-one would come, because somehow she knew there was no-one out there to hear her, just as she knew when she had been a child at Brougham that all the servants had gone out.

Finally she went back to bed, pulling a trembling Brutus up on to it with her. Moments later, as if at an unseen signal, the dog stopped panting and trembling, and with a sigh and a yawn lay down to sleep. Artemis listened, straining to catch some sound which might explain why the dog had so suddenly found its ease. But the house was still utterly silent.

Although she couldn't find the reason for it, her own terror abated, as quickly as her dog's had done. From feeling quite hopelessly struck with deep panic, Artemis suddenly felt as though a great danger had passed, and that the dark night was over. There was no sign of dawn yet, but nonetheless everything felt inexplicably brighter and lighter. Even the air in her bedroom now seemed to be fresh, when only moments ago it had been stale and had hung heavy, as if no-one had opened a window or door in the room for months.

Artemis settled back down in her bed and stared out of the window. She had left the curtains open so that she could see first light, and she did not lie back and close her eyes until the first rays of the sun had spread glowing red fingers up into the skies, by which time she had finally decided there was very little point in continuing to be civilized, as her mother-in-law liked to have it, about her bizarre and loveless marriage.

'I've been asked to Galway,' Artemis said over breakfast. Her husband was in his dressing gown, shaved, but pale and exhausted. Artemis on the other hand was fully dressed and had made quite sure she looked as though she had slept the whole night through.

'Will you be back for Christmas?'

'That depends whether or not I fall off.'

'Are you going mountain climbing?'

'I've been invited to hunt with the Blazers,' she lied.

'When are you going?'

'This morning.'

'That's rather sudden, isn't it? Even for you?'

'Probably,' Artemis said as she rose. 'Expect me when you see me.'

All the time and for no good reason Artemis expected him to call her back, or to follow her upstairs and relock her in her room, or to come after her in his car as she drove away. But Sheridan did none of these things. Instead she saw him standing at one of his bedroom windows, half hidden by the drapes, watching her all the while as she piled her suitcases into the back of her new car, and her hunting saddle and riding boots, and finally Brutus, who'd been running round and round the car, as impatient as she was to escape.

Finally, with her dog settled beside her, Artemis started her car and drove off down the long straight drive, without another look or a wave to her husband, whom she knew was still standing staring down from his bedroom. But when she reached the main road she turned left, not right, heading south for Strand House and not north for Galway.

'So what the divil was happening,' Cousin Rose asked, 'if he had cause to lock ye in yer room?'

'I can't imagine,' Artemis replied. 'And I don't even want to try.'

'Ach they were probably all getting drunk,' Cousin Rose said, after some thought. 'Ye know men.'

'Absolutely,' Artemis agreed, seeing no point in even attempting to put Cousin Rose on the right path, while remembering how the hackles on her dog's neck had stood right up.

'What about the horses?'

'I'm having Boot boxed down,' Artemis said. 'And I've made arrangements for the others.'

They sat in silence while Tutti refilled their glasses.

'So,' Rose finally said. 'And so what'll ye do now? Until the annulment's through?'

'I don't know,' Artemis replied, with a toss of her blonde hair. 'I think I'd quite like to get a little bit tight actually.'

Porter unstopped the bottle of Veuve Cliquot and poured the first two glasses as always without spilling a drop.

'Happy birthday, my darling,' said Ellie, raising her glass to Hugo. 'To you, and to a wonderful year.'

'The very best year of my life,' Hugo said. 'Thanks to you.'

'Nonsense,' laughed Ellie. 'Thanks to you. To you.' She raised her glass again. 'Hurrah for you.'

'Hurrah for you.'

'Hurrah for us.'

After lunch, when the servants, as Ellie liked to think of it, had vanished back into the walls, she and Hugo walked hand in hand through the house, taking stock of what they had done. Ellie had been surprised how quickly a house once it was left unoccupied could fall into disrepair, until Hugo pointed out that Artemis's father must have done very little to keep it in good order, preferring, as so many of his kind it seemed did, to spend his money on the improvement of hounds rather than house.

'And as for my poor father,' Hugo had explained, 'he hardly had time to do more than scratch the surface.'

So Hugo and Ellie had set to restoring the great house to its glory and had already achieved a considerable amount. The library was finished and furnished, with its shelves once more full of books. The small withdrawing room, repainted a faint yellow, was also furnished again, with elegant Regency sofas and chairs, and two matching Hepplewhite card tables. But the large drawing room was bare, with no furniture, and no paintings on the walls. The saloon needed hardly any embellishment, so magnificent a room was it, with its elaborately carved domed ceiling and its magnificent doorways and decorated arched recesses. Neither did the great hall, with its rows of fluted alabaster monoliths, coved ceiling and three circular skylights. The only items which Hugo and Ellie needed to replace there were the niched statues, which Hugo was in the process of having copied from old photographs.

There was still any amount of work to do upstairs in the main part of the house, but they had managed to furnish and complete one of the main bedrooms, its adjoining dressing rooms and adjacent bathroom for themselves. It was the main bedroom at the top of the grand staircase, with two huge windows overlooking the park. Ellie loved it, with its huge four-poster bed and large comfortable furniture, which included a *chaise-longue* in one window where Ellie used to lie early in the afternoon and look out across the lake, and best of all, a boudoir grand piano which Hugo had installed for her, and which Ellie sometimes would play just before they went to bed.

She played and sung for Hugo that afternoon, a song she'd just learned, called 'I Can't Get Started', while Hugo insisted on slowly removing all her clothes while she played and sang until she sat quite naked and in a fit of laughter at the keyboard.

They made love and then lay silent in each other's arms, Ellie with her head on Hugo's chest, Hugo half propped up on huge pillows, listening to the noise of the log fire in the grate and the February rains lashing against the huge windows, before they both dropped off into a blissful sleep.

'Good heavens,' Ellie suddenly said, waking up.

Hugo stirred under her. 'What?'

'Artemis.'

'What about her?' Hugo stretched out his left arm, upon which Ellie had been lying, to flex away the pins and needles. Ellie was getting out of bed, reaching for her clothes. 'Where are you going, you crazy American woman?' Hugo demanded, looking for his spectacles.

'Quickly, Hugo. Don't you want to see?'

Hugo put his spectacles on and stared at his wife as she struggled into her clothes. 'Have you gone mad?' he asked. 'Or caught a fever? What is there to see? Why are you getting dressed?'

'Hugo – ' Ellie turned back, buttoning up her blouse and tossing back her dark hair. 'You don't seem to understand! Artemis is here!'

Hugo got out of bed and grabbed his dressing gown and joined Ellie at the window. 'What do you mean Ell? Artemis is here?'

Ellie said nothing, just wiped the condensation off the inside of one of the windows with the sleeve of her sweater and peered out into the dusk. Hugo did the same, without an idea of what he was meant to be looking for.

The rain was lashing the windows even harder now, driven by a winter gale, and it was getting darker by the minute.

'There!' Ellie suddenly cried. 'See! I told you!'

She ran out of the room. Hugo peered out of the window and before chasing after Ellie who had a good headstart on him, saw through the downpour a pair of car headlights heading up the drive towards the house.

'How on earth do you know it's Artemis?' he shouted after Ellie, who was now halfway down the stairs.

'I just do! That's all!'

Ellie missed out the last three stairs and skidding across the marbled hall, got to the main doors ahead of Hugo. She flung them open and stood there, pulling her sweater around her while the wind drove the rain and sleet past her into the house. Hugo came to her shoulder, barefoot and in only his wool dressing gown, and stood with his teeth chattering and a hand shielding his eyes against the storm, watching as a car turned in through the main gates and finally pulled up at the foot of the stone staircase.

'If that was Artemis,' Hugo said, 'she'd have knocked down the gates.'

'It's Artemis all right,' Ellie assured him, as a slim woman in a man's trilby and belted camel-hair coat hauled herself out of the driving seat. 'Artemis?' she shouted down the steps and into the rain.

The woman looked up at them briefly, before turning back to fetch a silver topped cane from the car. Past her, from the back of the car and almost knocking her over, a big brown-haired dog leaped out and bounded up the staircase.

'Artemis!' Ellie shouted joyously, running out into the storm. 'Artemis – I just knew it was you!' She reached her before Artemis had even made the first steps. 'Artemis,' she said, smiling at her through the torrential rain.

Artemis smiled back. 'Hullo, Eleanor,' she said.

Hugo waited at the door, freezing half to death, while the two girls embraced and then made their slow way up the staircase.

Artemis stared at him from under her rain sodden hat. 'Hullo, Hugo,' she said.

'Hello, Tom.' Inexplicably Hugo found the sight of the two girls, arm in arm, made his heart sink.

He was asleep when Ellie finally came to bed, or at least he was doing his best to pretend he was.

'Sorry,' Ellie whispered as she eased herself in beside him and felt Hugo stir.

'You know what time it is, don't you?' he asked, keeping his back turned on her.

'Does it matter?' Ellie said. 'We had so much to catch up on.'

'I have to go to London tomorrow, Ellie.'

'I know. That's why you came to bed early, sweetheart.' Ellie kissed him on the back of his head. 'Happy end of birthday.'

Hugo turned and took her in his arms. 'It's not quite over yet,' he said.

13

'Don't you ever draw breath, Ellie?' Hugo eyed Ellie over the top of his glasses and then put down his knife and fork with a pointed sigh. But all Ellie did was just glance at him, put one hand over one of his and carry on talking to Artemis who was sitting opposite her.

'There was too much fat on these cutlets,' Hugo complained, pushing his plate away from him. 'And the soup was cold.'

'OK,' Ellie said, 'I'll have a word with cook,' and then resumed her conversation.

'And stop saying OK.'

'OK. All right! I will.' This time rather than just looking at him affectionately, Ellie flashed him a short but angry glance.

'OK this,' said Hugo, 'OK that. OK, OK, OK.'

Ellie put down her knife and fork.

'Not like that,' Hugo sighed, moving her knife and fork from one side of her plate. 'In the middle if you've finished – '

'I haven't finished, Hugo.'

'In that case then one on either side. *Comme ça.*'

Ellie looked at Artemis then back at Hugo. 'Is something the matter, Hugo?' she asked.

'Ah at last!' Hugo exclaimed. 'At last you've noticed me! You've actually noticed that I'm here! I was beginning to think I must be invisible! But no! You've addressed a remark to me! So I can't be! You can actually see me!'

There was a silence while Ellie bit her lip and Artemis stared at her last lamb cutlet. Then Ellie could contain herself no more and dissolved in a fit of laughter, with her table napkin held firmly to her mouth. Hugo glared at her, his eyes wide with a mixture of dismay and fury, but Ellie just sat with her head bowed, trying her best to muffle her sobs of mirth. Hugo turned to Artemis, but Artemis was still staring down over-earnestly at her lamb cutlet. 'Oh dear God!' Hugo cried, and throwing his napkin on the table. 'Dear God in heaven!' Then he rose and left the room.

'How long is she staying, Ellie?'

'I haven't asked her, Hugo.'

'Isn't it she who should be asking you?'

'Does it matter?'

'I would just like to know how long she is intending to stay.'

'I thought you liked Artemis?'

'Ellie – that is not the point!'

'She hasn't anywhere to go.'

'She has plenty of places to go.'

Ellie sat up in bed and turned on her light. Hugo groaned and pulled the covers over his head.

'You mean she doesn't need people, not really, not if she has connections?'

'I didn't say that, Ellie.'

'If she's privileged, then she doesn't need the love and care and attention of her friends! That's what you mean, don't you! She can just go elsewhere! To some innumerable relative – '

'To one of her innumerable relatives – and no that is not what I meant at all!'

'Of course it is. What the heck. She has no family, she's just lost her home, her husband – '

'He wasn't her husband, Ellie!'

'She was married to him, Hugo! So what does that make him if it doesn't make him her husband!'

'For God's sake, Ellie, whatever he was he certainly wasn't her husband! Not if what Artemis told you is true!'

'Of course it's true, Hugo! Why should she lie about a thing like that?'

'I really don't understand why you need her here!'

'This was once her home, you know, Hugo!'

'Ah!' Hugo pointed a finger at her. 'You feel guilty! You feel guilty because we're living in Artemis's old home!'

'I do not – feel guilty!' Ellie protested.

'Of course you do!' Hugo laughed. 'And you want to make it up to her! Well you won't be able to! You can't make up to Artemis for being Artemis!'

'Don't laugh at me!' Ellie warned, getting out of bed. 'Don't you dare laugh at me!'

Hugo took hold of her wrist and held her back. 'Come on, Ellie,' he reasoned. 'See sense.'

'Let me go, Hugo!' Ellie wrenched herself free and picking up her dressing gown, made for the door.

Hugo took a deep breath and lay back on his pillows. 'Where do you think you're going, Ellie?' he asked, with a sigh.

'You wanted to get some sleep, didn't you!' Ellie called back from the doorway. 'So get some! I'll sleep in the yellow room!'

Hugo was in the main drawing room, with various paints the decorators had left him to try on the walls, when Artemis wandered in with her dog. Hugo said hullo then daubed a wall with the first of the trial colours. Artemis asked him where Ellie was, and Hugo said she was most probably in the kitchens, organizing the staff for the day. But instead of going off in search of her friend, Artemis sat on the ledge of one of the great windows and looked out at what had once, but all too briefly, been hers.

They said nothing to each other for a long time, Hugo continuing to try out all the various colours, while Artemis sat in the window whistling quietly and tunelessly to herself. Hugo did his best not to let the sound bother him while for her part Artemis did her best to resist criticizing Hugo's possible choice of colours for the beautiful room.

Hugo was the first to capitulate. 'If you're going to whistle,' he said, 'couldn't it be something we all know?'

'I didn't know I was whistling,' Artemis replied. 'You should have said.'

'I have just said,' Hugo replied. 'You're the first person I've heard who can actually whistle out of tune.'

'You're not thinking of painting it, are you? In that?' Artemis pointed her stick at a trial patch of pale blue.

'What's wrong with it?'

'It's not right, that's all.'

'You're wrong. Bleu passé is perfectly correct.' Hugo turned his back on Artemis, who had climbed down off the window ledge by now and had made her way over to stare more closely at Hugo's colour experiments.

'Why did you take the paper down?' Artemis asked.

'I didn't.'

'It was eighteenth-century.'

'I don't actually care, Artemis, if it was pre-Christ. I didn't like it. It was too ornate. But I didn't take it down. It fell down.' He turned to her, to emphasize his point with a look. Artemis merely stared back at him, raising both eyebrows.

'Hugo,' she said firmly, 'you cannot paint this room.'

'Yes I can, Artemis,' he replied. 'And if you stay for long enough you'll be able to watch me.'

Artemis looked at him, steadying her gaze, staring right into his eyes. 'I think I'll just go for a walk,' she said finally. 'I thought this would be a mistake.' She turned to go.

Hugo, suddenly and unreasonably infuriated, took hold of her by the shoulders and turned her back to him. 'Where are you off to *now*, Tom?'

'Let go of me, please, Hugo. And don't call me that.'

'Call you what?'

'You know perfectly well. And let go of me.'

'Not until you say where you're going.'

'Please, Hugo. Will you please let go of me.'

'No.'

Artemis fell silent and let herself go limp and unre-
sistant, in an attempt to embarrass him. She stared up
at him, with her eyes wide open, showing nothing but
disinterest. If he let her go, she would fall.

Hugo held her up by both shoulders, aware of what she
was trying to do, and yet helpless himself to do anything.
'Where were you off to, Tom?'

'Does it matter? It's academic, isn't it?'

'Oh for Christ's sake, Artemis!' Hugo felt like shaking
her. 'Stop behaving like such a spoilt brat!'

'You're the one behaving like a spoilt brat, Hugo,'
Artemis said. 'Now will you please let me go.'

'Not until you tell me where you were going!'

Artemis deliberately widened her eyes even further, as
if in amazement, and then suddenly started to laugh.

'You were going to do one of your damned disappearing acts, weren't you?' Hugo began to shout, unable to
resist her provocation any more. 'You were going to keep
the attention on you, the only way you know how! By
taking off and going! And not telling anyone where or
why! You just love doing that, don't you? Doing your
vanishing act! Knowing damned well that the moment
you've disappeared, everyone will be talking about you
even more! And worrying about you even more! And
wondering what they've done this time to hurt you!
While you just take off and enjoy yourself! And do
what you please! What you like! And where you like!
And then you just – you just swan back into people's
lives again out of the blue! As if nothing had happened!
As if you don't give a damn and as if no-one else gives
a damn for you either!'

Artemis was no longer limp in his arms. As he had be-
rated her, her body had stiffened, and now an expression
of real concern and utter astonishment replaced her look
of studied indifference.

Until Hugo kissed her.

He regretted it at once, because as he held her in his arms and kissed her, he found the real Artemis. Gone, as soon as they kissed, was all that toughness and that fierce independence, to be replaced by softness and vulnerability.

'Oh God,' he whispered as they parted. 'God why the hell did I do that?'

'I can't imagine,' Artemis muttered.

'What are you going to do?' he asked, as she finally freed herself and began to back away. 'You're not going, surely?' He ran from where he was standing, round her, intercepting her before she got to the doorway. 'You can't go now.'

'Don't be an idiot.'

'Tom – don't! It won't ever happen again, I promise. And it will only make things worse if you go!'

Artemis turned away from him.

'I shouldn't have done it, I know, and I'm sorry,' Hugo was saying, somewhere in the distance. 'Please, Tom. Please forgive me. You looked – it was just – I'm sorry. I really am. I just couldn't help it.'

She didn't want him to be sorry. She should have done, she knew that perfectly well. She should have slapped his face and told him off. She should have been enraged, outraged and affronted. At least she should have demanded an apology and brought him to his senses by reminding him of what he had endangered by his folly. But instead all Artemis could think of was him holding her once more and kissing her. And because that was all she could think of she despised herself even more deeply than Hugo was at that moment despising himself.

'I was going to leave for Ireland on Sunday,' she said. 'But I think I'd better go tomorrow instead.'

'Don't,' Hugo pleaded. 'You don't have to go. Stay here – please. You must believe me, Artemis. I promise nothing like that will ever happen again.'

The irony, Artemis thought as she tried to ease herself past Hugo in the doorway, was that the real reason for her decision to leave was really because he was making such a promise. If he had told her to stay, because he wanted to hold her again, because he wanted to kiss her, because he wanted to make love to her, then she knew she would have found it much harder to leave than to stay. But because he was admitting it had been a mistake, something done in a moment of rashness, a brief folly, he had now made it impossible for her to remain there.

Hugo rushed after her as she made her way across the hall and towards the stairs, calling for her to wait. At the same moment Ellie came through a pass door from the kitchens.

'Tom!' Hugo was calling urgently. 'Wait a minute, Tom! Please listen to me! Please!'

'What's the matter?' Ellie asked him, appearing out of the shadows and startling him. 'You two aren't having one of your famous rows?'

'Yes,' said Hugo hurriedly. 'And as a result, Artemis is about to perform one of her equally famous disappearing acts.'

'But isn't that just what you wanted, Hugo?'

'Absolutely,' Artemis agreed.

'Look,' said Hugo, taking a deep breath. 'Just listen to me, both of you. I'm very sorry. I'm sorry for the way I behaved. I was behaving – ' He hesitated.

Artemis helped him out. 'Like a spoilt brat?'

'Well said, Artemis,' Ellie agreed. 'You were, too.'

'I know,' said Hugo. 'And I'm sorry.' He turned to Artemis. 'Please forgive me, Tom. Please.'

'Well?' Ellie asked, looking at Artemis who was staring at Hugo. 'Are you going to forgive him?'

'No,' Artemis replied.

'No I don't blame you,' Ellie said. 'I don't think I would either.'

'*Eye*-ther,' Hugo said through clenched teeth, as if scolding a child. 'Eye-ther.'

'I don't forgive you, *eye*-ther,' said Ellie, mockingly. 'I've never seen such spoilt behaviour. OK — so why don't you go back to your painting, Mr Tanner? And leave me to talk Artemis out of rushing off into the blue? Go on.'

Ellie took Artemis's arm and started leading her up the stairs. 'You're crazy if you think you can disappear right now,' she said. 'What about our party tonight?'

Artemis looked back down over the staircase bannisters just once. Hugo was still standing below, staring up at her, the paint dripping slowly from the brush he had in his hand on to the marble floor of the hall.

Later, as she dressed for the party that evening, Artemis tried to attribute her inability to leave to the depth of her affection for Ellie. But the more she stared at her reflection in the mirror, the more she knew she was deceiving herself. There was only one real reason she was staying on at Brougham, and that was to be near Hugo.

Ellie sat her next to him at dinner, opposite an astonishingly pretty girl called Emerald, dressed in an oyster coloured gown with a two-inch-thick choker of huge sheeny pearls at her neck, and next to a most dashing young man called Charles, with dark lanolined hair and a permanently inquisitive expression. Emerald remembered Artemis from when they were both children, as she had often been taken out for a day's hunting when she had come to stay with relatives close by in Malmesbury. Artemis, given Emerald's quite astounding beauty and charming personality, but most of all her proximity to Hugo, found herself absurdly relieved when she learned that Emerald had recently married. Charles Hunter, the dark-haired handsome man on Artemis's right, was a captain in the Hussars, and the son of a general who was sitting on the left of his hostess. Charles Hunter, unlike Emerald, was as yet unmarried.

There were twenty six all told sat down to dinner, including the host and hostess, either side and at the end of a beautifully laid table, set with three superb flower arrangements and four magnificent antique five-sticked silver candelabra. The food and wines were sublime and faultlessly presented and served and the party was so obviously successful that Artemis could only wonder at how someone as socially unversed and apparently unskilled as Ellie could have organized and hosted it.

Thankfully Hugo paid more attention to the girl on his left than he did to Artemis, although he was far too much the perfect gentleman to neglect her. Even so, their conversation was kept deliberately trivial and whenever possible Hugo tried to include the girl on his left and the man on her left, and the young man on Artemis's right. Only once was there any contact between Hugo and Artemis, when Hugo's hand accidentally brushed her's under the tablecloth, and Hugo blushed a deep red. And only once did they find themselves left alone while conversing. It was during pudding, when both their neighbours had simultaneously become deeply involved with both of their neighbours, leaving Artemis marooned with Hugo.

'Tom,' he began.

'Aren't the flowers lovely?' Hugo frowned at her. Artemis continued. 'Nanny always said when stuck for something to say, or the right thing to say,' Artemis glanced at him, 'simply remark on the flowers,' she continued. 'And aren't they simply lovely?'

Hugo smiled, but still tried to catch Artemis's eyes with his. He failed.

'Tell me about the Middle East,' Artemis said, putting her gold spoon down, her food finished, and staring upwards at the ceiling. 'We've never really talked about that, have we?' Then she eyed him. Hugo didn't know whether she was fooling, or being serious.

'I told you. I often went out there with my father,' Hugo replied. 'You remember.'

'No I don't.'

Deciding that Artemis was being deliberately over formal to forestall any intimacy on his part, Hugo told

Artemis all over again about his experiences out east. 'One of my father's many interests,' he recited, 'was archeology.'

The tone of his voice earned Hugo a sharp kick under the table. 'Behave yourself,' Artemis warned.

Hugo glanced at her, and seeing the look in her eyes, started again, but telling it now as if it was the first time. 'My father was very interested in archeology,' he said. 'And so I spent quite a lot of time in Egypt and North Africa, when I was at Oxford.'

'You should never have kissed me,' Artemis said. 'Go on.'

Hugo swallowed and stared at her.

'I said go on,' Artemis repeated.

'In the summer vacs. I think I might have taken it up quite seriously, had my father remained really interested. But while we were in North Africa he discovered an entirely different hobby. Sand.'

'I'd have thought sand was a nuisance rather than a hobby,' Artemis said, at which Hugo laughed. Artemis stared at him. 'That wasn't that funny,' she said.

'I know,' Hugo agreed, looking at her. 'It must have been the way you said it.'

'Said what?'

'That I shouldn't have kissed you.'

She stared back at his stare, outstaring him. 'I'm still waiting to hear how sand can become a hobby,' she reminded him.

'Not sand *per se*,' Hugo replied. 'The movement of sand. Its habits, how, why and where it shifts.'

'That actually sounds quite interesting.'

'It's actually quite fascinating. So much so, I became as obsessed with it as my father was. At the end, he used to take us off into the desert, with no map, no compass, nothing, because he had learned to read the winds and the dunes, and the sand-shifts so well he could read great stretches of the desert as if they were a network of roads.'

'Does it serve any practical use though? Besides — I don't know — to stop one say being stranded at Frinton?' She then looked up at him, poker-faced, catching his eye but this time Hugo didn't laugh. 'I'm being serious, Hugo. What possible actual use can a study of sand be?' Artemis turned to the young man on her right. 'Have you any idea of what possible use a study of sand could be Charles?' she asked.

'As a matter of fact,' Charles replied, 'if one's talking about sand as in the desert, then yes, I think I have.'

Charles Hunter then went on to explain how important it was whenever wars were fought in desert regions to know how to read the prevailing conditions. 'There are no landmarks as such, obviously,' he explained. 'You wake up one morning and there are dunes here.' He placed the salt cellars in a certain way to illustrate his point. 'By the afternoon they could all have been blown away and shifted to here.' Again he moved the cellars. 'East becomes west, and vice versa. An army, unversed in the ways of the desert, becomes disorientated. Yes, of course, true north is still that way, the way the compass points. But imagine being in let's say the Scottish highlands, and the hills and the mountains start to change position around you, daily, sometimes several times daily. You are then at the mercy of your enemy, who by reading the signs knows the future shapes of the shifting landscape.'

'My father used to be able to draw a projection of the next day's lie of the land,' Hugo said, 'by studying the skies, and watching how the sand was shifting.'

'Can you?' the captain enquired.

'I'm not nearly as good as he was,' Hugo admitted, 'but yes. At least I could. My father was a very good teacher, and by the end I think I'd got the hang of it.'

'Then you must talk to my father,' the captain suggested. 'Desert warfare is his particular hobby-horse.'

When the ladies retired and the gentlemen were left alone, the talk became ever more serious and ever more about war. One or two of the older male guests considered the danger from Germany to be greatly exaggerated and seriously believed that Herr Hitler could be easily appeased. Hugo politely discounted such a possibility, despite his elders' insistence that Hitler admired Britain, and in particular the way she ran and controlled such a mighty empire. Hitler, some of his guests insisted, only wanted the best for his nation, and while belligerence would be met with force, appeasement would be welcomed, and there would be peace in all their times.

Hugo, bored of a conversation he had heard round every table at which he had recently dined, privately gained possession of Artemis's discarded table napkin and held it to his face. The scent was a million times more intoxicating than the aroma from his glass of Napoleon brandy.

He was interrupted from his reverie by the arrival of Charles Hunter's father, General Hunter, who pulled a chair up alongside Hugo. 'May I?' he said.

'Of course,' said Hugo.

'Hear you know a thing or two about sand,' General Hunter said, sitting down. 'And deserts.'

'A little,' Hugo replied.

'Good to know,' said the general. 'Sometimes funny things like that come in jolly handy.'

Ellie and Hugo made love that night, as they still did almost every night and Hugo was as astonished as ever at their physical compatibility. All the same, when he first embraced his wife, and held her to him, he was deeply troubled to find that all he could really think of was the sweet memory of Artemis Deverill's pretty little mouth.

14

Ellie insisted that Artemis should live in the Dower House, an idea which met with strenuous opposition from Hugo.

'You seem to forget we are married, Ellie!' Hugo reminded her. 'We're not still all on holiday in Ireland!'

'You mean because we're married,' Ellie said factually, 'we can't all three of us go on liking each other.'

'We can be friends,' Hugo argued. 'Of course! But it has to be a different form of friendship! You and I are man and wife! And well Artemis – Artemis is – ' Hugo foundered. Ellie offered him no help, until all he could offer was just a feeble shrug of his shoulders.

'Artemis is *our* friend,' said Ellie gently. 'And she's lonely.'

'Yes, Ellie! Of course she's our friend! And I'm sure she's lonely. But marriage changes things!'

'I don't see why.'

'Well it does! Look.' Hugo sat down on the bed beside Ellie. 'Look – I can hardly be friends with Artemis the way I was before, now can I?'

'Why can't you?'

'For a start you'd be jealous!'

'Oh Hugo. *Hugo*. Don't be such a child!'

Which was invariably how each argument would end, with Ellie provoking Hugo rather than admitting there was even the slightest possibility of him being right.

For herself, Artemis resisted accepting Ellie's invitation to move into the empty Dower House for as long as she could, but circumstances were against her. Unsurprisingly, she had no real wish to return to Ireland, even though Cousin Rose wrote and said there was a bed permanently made up for her. She told herself that her reluctance to return was because the inexpediency of her hasty marriage might have made her look foolish in everyone's eyes, while knowing full well the real reasons lay elsewhere.

For a start, there was the question of money. Artemis had never had even the slightest idea how to handle the money she had inherited following the sale of Brougham. It was not an enormous sum, but Artemis gave this little or no thought. Instead, whenever she needed money, she simply wrote a cheque, failing to understand that for the cheque to be honoured there had to be money in the bank. As a result, her profligacy, particularly her trip to America and her visits to Europe, had severely dented her resources, so much so that now both her trustees and the bank were writing to her, advising immediate caution.

But more than that, far more than that, and to her shame, Artemis knew that the real reason she did not want to return to Ireland was because it meant she would have to leave Hugo. Since the moment Hugo had kissed her she had behaved in an exemplary fashion, minding that she was never left alone with him and keeping well within the limits of what had previously been, and as far as she was concerned still was, a strictly platonic friendship. For his part Hugo was as good as his word, loving and honouring Ellie as he had always done until that moment of brief betrayal, while keeping the proper distance between himself and Artemis. It was, to all intents and purposes, as if nothing had happened.

Life therefore began inevitably to resume a pattern not totally dissimilar to the one they had all enjoyed in Cork. Once Emerald and her husband Anthony discovered Artemis was staying on, they gave her the run of their stables, and within no time word had spread through the county concerning her equestrian skills, so much so that many of her newly-made friends started to offer her rides in Ladies' races point-to-point. Hugo and Ellie went to the meetings where Artemis rode, and as winter turned to spring, on most Saturdays the three of them went racing regularly, Hugo and Ellie picnicking on the grass or in the back of Hugo's car, while Artemis rode a variety of horses, with varying degrees of success, or, as Artemis liked to joke, with varying degrees of failure, because although out of half a dozen rides she was second twice and third once, victory eluded her.

Most happily, she was finally able to have Boot sent over from Ireland, and he arrived at Brougham personally escorted by Dan Sleator.

'There was no need for you to travel with him, Mr Sleator,' Artemis told him, grateful all the same for his care. 'The horse would have been perfectly all right.'

' 'Twas just as well I was with him,' Dan Sleator replied. ' 'Twas a terrible crossing and all manner of people were sick.'

'Surely horses can't be sick though, can they, Mr Sleator?' Ellie asked.

'My very point exactly, ma'am,' said Dan Sleator.

Dan Sleator had the horse fighting fit and once Boot had enjoyed a few days acclimatization at Brougham, and Artemis had entered him in a choice of races, it was decided to run him in the Ladies' Open at the South and West Wilts. There were several good horses entered, winning horses ridden by winning women, so the unknown horse from Ireland started relatively unfancied.

Once the race was under way, Artemis, who had done her homework, tracked the favourite, a horse called Someone Called and ridden by one of the best female judges of pace, Diana Powers. Four fences from home, with Diana Powers riding her horse astride, compared to Artemis who was riding side-saddle as always, the race looked a foregone conclusion once the favourite was asked to make his move. But Artemis was only biding her time, as she could feel that Boot was full of running, and with two fences left to jump Artemis asked her horse to make his effort. The response was immediate as Boot picked up and jumped past the favourite, taking two lengths off him in the air at the last, to gallop away an easy winner by six lengths.

'Well done,' said Hugo, helping Artemis down from her horse. 'That was simply terrific.'

'Yes well done!' Ellie agreed, patting Boot on the neck. 'He really is the most wonderful horse. And not only that, I've won some money!'

Artemis smiled and having accepted a congratulatory kiss from Ellie, hurried off to weigh in.

'What do you mean, Eleanor Tanner?' Hugo asked. 'You've won some money?'

'I had twenty pounds on him,' Ellie laughed, 'at twenty five to one! Oh my God, that means I've won five hundred pounds!' she ended as the realization suddenly came to her.

Hugo looked at her, at first astounded, and then suspiciously. 'All right. Where did you get the money?'

'From the housekeeping.'

'The money you're given for the housekeeping, Mrs Tanner, is to be spent keeping house, not on gambling.'

'Are you eating badly? Are the servants walking out? Is the house falling round your head?'

'No, but that's not the point.'

'The point is, Hugo, I budget. Some weeks I don't have to spend as much, so it goes in the kitty. And today the kitty went on Artemis and Boot.'

'And what would have happened if he'd lost?'

Ellie smiled. 'I guess I'd just have had to cut a few corners for a week or so.'

Later, as Hugo and Ellie were enjoying their picnic tea, Artemis reappeared, looking preoccupied. Ellie poured her some tea and set down a plate of cucumber sandwiches in front of her. But Artemis didn't touch them. Or drink her tea.

'Someone wants to buy Boot,' she suddenly announced. 'A man with a monocle. He's offered me five hundred pounds.'

'I'm not surprised,' Hugo said, munching a chocolate biscuit. 'That was some performance.'

'That's what this chap who wants to buy him said,' Artemis replied. 'He thinks he might have quite a future.'

'You're not going to sell him though?' Ellie asked. 'You wouldn't even think of selling him, surely?'

'No I wouldn't,' Artemis agreed. 'Never. Not under normal circumstances.'

Both Hugo and Ellie stopped eating to stare at their friend.

'I haven't noticed circumstances becoming abnormal,' Hugo said.

'You didn't get the last letter from my bank,' Artemis replied. 'I'm actually completely broke. Isn't that silly?'

'How much are you actually and completely broke, Tom?' Hugo asked gently. 'Because there's no need to sell the horse. I can lend you the money.'

'I couldn't pay it back, Hugo.'

'Very well, I can give you the money.'

'Yes, Hugo, I'm sure you could,' Artemis said after a moment, which to Ellie seemed like an hour. 'The trouble is I wouldn't take it. If I was a charity, you see, I'd have a flag day.' She gave Hugo a brief but not unfriendly smile, and then started to haul herself up, leaning on Ellie's shoulder.

'Where are you going?' Ellie asked her.

'To talk to the man in the monocle,' Artemis replied. 'I might be able to bump him up a hundred.'

'No,' said Ellie, grabbing hold of Artemis by the hand. 'If you want to sell the horse, fine. And if you want six hundred for him, fine. But you don't sell him to the man in the monocle. You sell him to me.'

Artemis opened her mouth to say something, but Hugo put up his hand. 'You don't have enough, Ellie. You only have five hundred.'

'No, that's right,' Ellie agreed. 'I do only have five hundred.'

Artemis opened her mouth again, but once more Hugo silenced her.

'However,' he said, 'if Artemis wants six hundred for him, I'm willing to lend you the extra hundred.'

'Thank you, darling,' Ellie smiled, putting her hand on his. 'I'll pay you back.'

'How?'

'Out of the housekeeping.'

'Do we have a deal, Tom?' Hugo asked Artemis.

'I'm not sure.'

'If we do,' said Ellie, 'and you sell me the horse, I shall give him straight back to you.'

'Why?'

'Because I don't want him.'

Artemis looked at both of them, then putting a hand on both their shoulders, pulled herself to her feet.

'Now where are you going?' Hugo asked.

'To tell the man with the monocle,' Artemis replied, 'that the horse is sold.'

But the question of the occupancy of the Dower House remained unanswered.

'It's just standing there, empty. And please let's hope it'll be a good few years yet before I'm required to take up residence there.

'It's over half a mile from the main house, Hugo,' Ellie continued. 'It's not as if she'll be living with us, or on top of us. She'll have her own life, an entirely separate existence. You know how independent Artemis is.'

'How can she be totally independent, Ellie?' Hugo asked. 'She has no money. To be independent you need to have money.'

'The idea is for her to buy young horses and bring them on,' Ellie explained. 'We don't use the stables, so there's no reason why Artemis can't keep her horses —'

'What horses? She's going to have to have money to buy horses, Ellie. And money to feed them. And keep them. May I remind you, your friend –'

'Our friend –'

'Artemis is broke, Ellie. Except for the five hundred pounds you gave her –'

'That's enough!' Ellie insisted. 'That's quite enough to buy two or three cheap horses at about fifty pounds each, that's all they'll cost her, she told me.'

'She'd have to furnish the place.'

Ellie felt a little glow inside. She was winning. She was slowly but surely getting there.

For his part Hugo couldn't help hoping he wasn't sounding too agreeable.

'I don't think she should furnish the house, Hugo,' Ellie frowned. 'I think we should. After all, it is ours. So we furnish it, and then rent it to Artemis furnished.'

'We rent it.' Hugo nodded and then shook his head. 'What do we rent it for?'

'As much as she can afford to pay, of course!'

'She can't afford to pay anything, Ellie. She has no money.'

'OK!'

'Can't you even just try to stop saying OK?'

'All right, Hugo! We'll rent it to her for nothing initially, right?'

'And don't say right, either.'

'We'll rent it to her for a penny a week. Until she can afford to pay a proper rent. *OK*?' Ellie bent over and put both arms on the chair in which Hugo was lounging, trapping him under her. He looked up at her. She grinned down at him. 'OK?' she asked again slowly.

Hugo shrugged, as if the whole thing was against his better judgement. 'OK,' he replied. Then he put his hands on Ellie's waist which immediately reduced her to a mass of helpless laughter, allowing Hugo to slip out from under her, lift her up over his shoulder and carry her laughing and struggling to the bed.

'OK,' he said, tearing off his tie and unbuttoning his shirt. 'You want OK, you are going to get OK.'

He didn't even bother to remove her dress, but made love to her as she was, his mouth not leaving hers for a moment, until they lay back exhausted.

'OK?'

'Oh yes,' Ellie sighed, turning and putting an arm across Hugo's chest. 'OK. Sure thing. You bet. OK.'

'It's agreed!' Ellie said to Artemis, looking into her bedroom on her way down before dinner. 'You can have the Dower House! OK?'

Artemis stopped applying a light coat of lipstick to her mouth and looked at Ellie in the dressing table mirror.

'Is that all right?' Hugo asked her, when they were alone for a moment, Ellie having gone with one of the staff to the kitchens to check a detail with Cook. 'I mean if you think it's going to be awkward –'

'I don't see why, Hugo,' Artemis replied not looking at him, 'You'll probably never see me.'

'I hope that's not true.'

Artemis ignored him, and in the ensuing silence carefully sipped her cocktail as if it were her life's work.

'Actually.' Artemis put her half-full glass down carefully and then pushed a lock of blonde hair from her eyes. 'I don't really know quite how to thank you.'

'By forgiving me.'

'Whatever for, Hugo?'

'You know what I mean.' He stared intently at her.

'Oh don't be so wet, Hugo.' Artemis laughed, with genuine astonishment. 'You can be such a child, you know,' she said. 'Such a little boy.'

'Have you forgiven me?'

'There was nothing to forgive you *for*, Hugo,' said Artemis, not laughing any more, just looking at him looking back at her, with anxious and expectant eyes, as Brutus did when waiting for a game. 'If there was anything to forgive you for, Hugo,' she concluded, lowering her voice as she heard Ellie returning, 'I wouldn't have accepted your offer of the Dower House.'

That night, Hugo lay in bed trying to work out what Artemis had meant. Did she mean that she thought nothing of his indiscretion? That the kiss which had sent his senses spinning out of control was nothing but a moment of foolishness, an aberration she had now all but forgotten? Or did she mean that she did not have to forgive it, because it was something she had herself secretly desired?

He turned on his side and punched his pillow up higher under his head in irritation. Why torture himself? He loved Ellie, Ellie was everything to him, his life, his love, his joy. What was he doing even thinking of someone else? Of someone who most probably thought nothing of him, nothing more or nothing less than she did of her Ellie, his wife, the girl so sound asleep by his side.

She was only two, three doors down the dark and moonlit corridor. Ellie slept so soundly, as she always did after they had made love, so all Hugo had to do was get out of bed, tiptoe along the dark oak floor boards, and knock on Artemis's door. He only had to knock on her door to find out.

'Who's that?' Artemis called.

And he whispered his name, 'Hugo.' There was a silence, while somewhere outside an owl called. Then he heard a whispered yes, a yes to tell him to come in, and as he heard that yes he knew then that the kiss had tasted the same to the girl in the moonlight, that it had also sent her senses spinning out of control, leaving her with no hold on herself or her heart.

'What is it?' she was whispering, 'what do you want?'

'I've bought you another kiss,' he said, his hands closed as if over a butterfly. 'Look I've bought you another kiss.' And she smiled at him, sitting half-up in her bed, pushing her blonde hair which had fallen round that beautiful face away from those bright blue cornflower eyes, eyes open

*wide with wonder as he came to her side and naked
slipped himself quietly into her bed.*

Hugo sat up with a gasp, half drowned in sweat, while
Ellie stirred beside him, fumbling for the light.

'Hugo? Hugo – what's the matter?' she asked him.
'Hugo – my God you're soaking! Have you a fever?'

'No, Ellie,' he sighed, lying back on his pillows. 'I
must have been dreaming. Yes. I was. I was having
a nightmare.'

While Ellie fetched Hugo a fresh pyjama jacket and
a towel, along the corridor Artemis lay awake, her dog
asleep at her feet. She too was wondering why she had
said what she had. Their lives weren't some sort of a
game, a deliberately *risqué* after-dinner entertainment
which would be forgotten as soon as the participants
climbed wearily into their beds. There *was* nothing to
forgive him for. If there was, she really wouldn't have
accepted his invitation.

And yet there was everything to forgive him for. And
herself. Artemis sat up angrily and reshaped her pillows.
Brutus growled in his sleep, and Artemis pushed him
crossly with her foot. Of course there was everything to
forgive him for. Why otherwise was she staying?

Ellie lay awake with the sleeping Hugo's hand in
hers and smiled to herself in the darkness. Artemis
was staying. Not only was she staying, she was going
to live at Brougham again. They were all going to
be together once more, Hugo and she in the great
house, and Artemis over the hill in the Dower House.
And Artemis would be able to enjoy Brougham as she
never had been able to before, and soon the misery of
her brief and miserable marriage would be way behind
her.

Artemis was staying, Ellie sighed to herself as sleep
began once more to overcome her. Artemis was staying
and they were all going to be so happy. Now all Ellie
had to do was find that girl.

*   *   *

She found her, with no great difficulty, in a neighbouring village, married and working in a laundry in a nearby town. But her husband, an able bodied man, was at that moment without employment. Ellie immediately offered them both a job at Brougham and Mr and Mrs Kemp could hardly believe their luck.

Not that Ellie needed more help. She wanted Mrs Kemp for a specific purpose, although she would have to create a job for her husband, because Hugo had inherited the house from his father complete with staff, most of whom had been there since the Deverills' day.

Artemis, as Ellie well knew, had been openly curious to see how Ellie would cope with running such a large house and staff, but to her surprise found Ellie managing the task with ease.

'Probably because back home I was a servant to my father and brothers,' Ellie explained. 'Which maybe helps when it comes to understanding your own servants' needs and problems.'

'Brougham is a bit larger, Eleanor,' Artemis said. 'Or maybe you haven't noticed.'

'I noticed,' Ellie grinned. 'But it's only a question of degree. I just remember how it was back home and multiply the experience by about a hundred and twenty.'

And Artemis was impressed. There was no doubt that the staff all liked Ellie and responded to her authority with good grace, whether they were old staff, or new. And there were several new faces around Brougham since Artemis had been forced to sell up. Porter, the butler, had remained, but Cook was new, and there was now no permanent chauffeur, Hugo preferring to drive himself. As yet, of course, there was no nursery staff and several of the kitchen and the house maids were new, the older ones having left when the house was sold probably to get married and raise families of their own. But Coombs the head gardener was still there, as was George Gates the gamekeeper, and Briggs and Hoskins, the two remaining footmen. But best of all, even though when Artemis first arrived back there were no horses as yet in the stables, to her great delight, living in the flat above the stable yard, and a great deal better than he had been when she had last left him, she found Jenkins.

'Mrs Tanner insisted,' he'd explained. 'When her and her husband come here, I called to see if they'd be needin' a groom, and when Mrs Tanner she found out who I was like, even though she's no 'orsewoman, she insisted I come back here, sayin' one day, who knows, she said, one day the stables may all be full again. If only of childun's ponies.'

By the time Artemis moved into the Dower House the stables were a long way short of such a projection. But they were once more in use, for besides Boot, Artemis had bought four new horses, two six-year-olds to be got ready to go point-to-pointing in the next season, and a couple of unbroken two-year-olds whom she intended to break and sell on. They were all cheap horses, the four costing Artemis less than one hundred guineas, but that was of no matter, for to Jenkins a horse was horse, and his yard was alive again.

As for Artemis's new home, it was a house she knew well, for often on their walks if they were caught out when it suddenly rained, Nanny and she would shelter in the then uninhabited Dower House and Artemis would play in and out of all the empty rooms. It was a fine late seventeenth-century house, older than the main house, and in good structural order, needing only redecorating and furnishing before becoming fully habitable.

Artemis plunged herself into the enterprise, determined to restore and furnish the house in the best possible way, something which took up all her time. She drove up and down to London frequently during the week, in search of materials and wallpapers, and scoured the countryside far and near for furnishings. By the end of the summer the house was ready and finished.

Ellie and Hugo were invited to drinks to celebrate the official opening, despite the fact that Artemis had been camping out there since late spring. Ellie had an errand to do first, so she dropped Hugo off at the house before driving to the village.

'It's lovely, Tom,' Hugo said, walking through from drawing room to dining room to study to morning room and back to the drawing room. 'Excellent. Just as one would have expected.'

'What would you like to drink?' Artemis asked, looking in a large cupboard. 'I only have gin.'

'Gin will be fine, thank you,' Hugo replied. 'That red paper in the morning room – '

'I know just what you are going to say,' Artemis interrupted, still pouring his drink. 'So I wouldn't bother.'

'I'm not doubting for a moment that it isn't absolutely correct, Tom.'

'That red is the colour which was here originally.' Artemis handed him a glass which was mostly neat gin. 'That's the last of the tonic, I'm afraid,' she added. 'It's probably flat.'

Hugo tasted his drink. 'Yes, it is,' he agreed. 'And it's not tonic. It's soda.'

'Yes, so it is,' Artemis said, looking at the bottle. 'I should throw it away if I were you and just have gin.'

'It's all right, Tom. I'll stick. It'll all have the same effect. And there's Ellie. No – ' he caught Artemis by the arm just in time. 'No, you're to wait in here.'

'Why?'

'Because Ellie said so.'

The reason became clear to Artemis a moment later when Ellie came through the door.

'Rosie,' said Artemis, staring at the apple-cheeked young woman with short dark curly hair. 'Good heavens.'

'Hullo, Lady Artemis,' Rosie replied, and then she blushed. 'I'm not sure I knows what to say.'

'You're not the only one, Rosie,' said Artemis. 'And who's this?' She stared at Ellie, who was now bringing a man into the room.

'This is my husband, Lady Artemis,' Rosie replied, blushing pink.

'This is Mr Kemp,' Ellie continued. 'Mr Kemp is going to work on the estate, so I thought maybe Rosie could housekeep for you.'

'If that's all right that is,' Rosie added, with a shy smile. 'I mean if that's all the same to you, that is.'

Artemis nodded her agreement. 'I don't see why not,' she said. 'Why not?' She returned her old nursemaid's smile, before walking over to open a large mahogany cupboard. 'So what do you want to drink, Eleanor?' she asked abruptly. 'I've only got gin.'

Outside the gates and walls of Brougham, the world watched uneasily as Hitler, Germany's new self-appointed War Minister, marched into Austria, before turning his attention to Czechoslovakia. By September, after Germany had mobilized her troops and France had called up her reservists, war in Europe seemed increasingly inevitable.

Artemis called in to see Ellie and Hugo on her return from a trip to London one day in late September. She was directed by Porter to the back hall of the house where she found Hugo up a scaffolding which had been erected against the wall of the staircase.

'What ever are you doing up there?' Artemis called.

'Painting a mural!' Hugo called back. 'It's going to cover all this wall! Are you looking for Ellie? Because if you are – '

'It doesn't matter! You'll do!' Artemis replied. 'Do you feel like some coffee? Shall I ring down for some?'

They sat at the foot of the staircase, drinking coffee and eating digestive biscuits which a maid had brought them, while Hugo explained the plans for his mural. Artemis only half-listened.

'I want to know what you think of this Czechoslovakia business,' she asked Hugo, when there was a lull in the conversation. 'I was at a thing with my godmother the other night, and the Coopers, who are friends of hers, they were there. And the Cranbornes. Oh and Hore-Belisha, and all that lot. Shakes Morrison, you know. And they were all getting dreadfully steamed up about this appeasement business. I didn't even know. That Halifax had been working on Hitler privately? A whole lot of them have. Including, hardly surprisingly, my stepmother, Diana's convinced she's a proper fascist. Like so many of these so-called appeasers. They're – what did Diana call them, yes, crypto-fascists. What exactly does that mean, Hugo?'

'Secret fascists,' Hugo told her.

'Yes I know. And apparently any number of them have been sneaking across to Germany,' Artemis continued thoughtfully, 'visiting Hitler on the q.t., hoping I suppose either to keep on the right side of him, just in case, you know. Or to try and talk him out of all this. Can you imagine?'

'I think we'd be surprised at just how many people in this country do have fascist sympathies,' Hugo replied.

'How many of the people we know, you mean,' Artemis retorted. 'Anyway. I think it's dreadful about Czechoslovakia. Duff Cooper said this is one of the most shaming times in our history. Or rather it will be, if we don't fight for them. Did you know there was a march up and down Whitehall the other day, Hugo? There was this huge march, with everyone shouting, "Stand by the Czechs! Chamberlain must go!" '

'Yes, I read about it in *The Times*,' Hugo said.

'I was there. I joined in.'

Hugo washed his paintbrushes off with turpentine and rubbed them clean on an old rag before replying. 'Do you think we should go to war? I mean just on behalf of Czechoslovakia? You think that just twenty years on from the war to end all wars, we should get the rifles down again and go off to war? And that people should sacrifice their children? And the children of their children? Because of a squabble over where to draw the German-Czechoslovak border?'

'Yes,' Artemis replied. 'It's not a question of going to war on Czechoslovakia's account. Any more than it was in 1914. We didn't go to war then for Serbia. Or Belgium. We went to war because one of the things we believe in this country is that no one great power should be allowed to dominate the rest of Europe by brute force.'

'Ah,' said Hugo thoughtfully, taking his glasses off and holding them away from him to stare through them distantly at nothing in particular. 'Yes. Yes I see. *Dulce et decorum est.*'

'I think perhaps sometimes – yes it is,' Artemis agreed, just about remembering her schoolroom Latin. 'It is sometimes a sweet and good thing to die for your country.'

'Would you, Tom?'

'Of course, Hugo. Wouldn't you?'

Hugo simply raised his eyebrows and nodded to himself, as they fell silent at the thought of what could be lying before them.

They were both still sitting for a few seconds in silence on the bottom step of the back staircase when Ellie came through from the kitchens and found them.

'Artemis thinks there's going to be a war,' Hugo told her.

'Oh Artemis, such a pessimist – '

The three of them argued it out over lunch, Artemis provoking Ellie by deliberately misunderstanding her reasons for optimism, and Ellie infuriating Hugo and Artemis with her confident belief that America, simply by arbitration, was influential enough to avert any likelihood of war.

'It isn't as simple as that,' Artemis said.

'Meaning I'm as simple as that,' Ellie countered, 'but this European thing isn't, because nothing European ever is.'

'Look,' said Hugo, trying to restore reason. 'It was a perfectly sound notion of Roosevelt's. There was nothing wrong with the idea in outline. And if he had managed to call the minor European powers to the conference table –'

'If your prime minister hadn't snubbed him!' Ellie exclaimed heatedly.

'Your prime minister, Ellie,' Hugo reminded her. 'You live in England, remember?'

'That's beside the point, Hugo! OK. So let's call him "the" prime minister, OK?'

'OK!' said Hugo.

'If "the" prime minister hadn't snubbed President Roosevelt quite so categorically,' Ellie continued, ignoring the jibe, 'if he had allowed him the opportunity to intervene – I mean he is the president of the United States!'

Hugo looked to Artemis and widened his eyes. Ellie kicked him hard on his shin, under the table.

'God!' said Hugo, clutching at his leg.

'If he had just allowed Roosevelt the chance to get everyone round a table talking, instead of telling the president to go run!' Ellie maintained. 'Saying that any intervention from America at this time would queer his pitch with Mussolini! I mean for God's sake, Mussolini's as big a goddam dictator as Hitler! And all your prime minister could think of –'

'The prime minister, Ellie,' Hugo reminded her, still grimly rubbing his sore shin. 'The prime minister.'

'You can go run, Hugo,' Ellie warned him. 'You know what I'm saying is true! Roosevelt could have averted this war!'

'But we're not *at* war yet, Ellie!' Hugo said.

'I agree with Ellie,' Artemis suddenly announced. 'Chamberlain's not only an idiot, he's a conceited one, too.'

'I suddenly feel Czechoslovak!' Hugo cried. 'Everyone's deserting me!'

'That's not funny, Hugo,' Artemis said.

'No it isn't,' Ellie agreed. 'Not in the slightest.'

'You know what the *on dit*, is don't you?' Artemis put down her knife and fork and drank some water.

'Apparently what the A for Appeasers are hoping is that we promise to go to war on the Czechs' behalf, and then on the q.t. persuade the French that it's not such a good idea after all. And then we pull out as well, piggy-backing on the French.'

'What nonsense,' Hugo laughed. 'That's just café talk. That's not how the English do things.'

'It's exactly how we do things,' Artemis replied. 'That's how we've been doing things for centuries. Really.'

'But if that's the case, Tom,' Hugo argued, 'then there won't be a war.'

'No,' Artemis agreed. 'I don't think there will be. But that doesn't mean I don't think that there shouldn't be.'

They all strolled through the grounds after lunch, through a fine drizzle of rain. No-one said much, they were all three too deeply preoccupied with the events they'd been discussing so heatedly over lunch. Chamberlain at that very moment was on his way back from Germany after his third visit, where he had met Hitler in Munich in the hope of improving the terms proposed to him by the Führer at their earlier meeting in Godesberg. By tea time that afternoon, when they had returned from their walk, Hugo tuned in the wireless and the three of them learned that the prime minister had landed at Heston with a signed agreement in hand, assuring the British people and the world at large that there was to be no war, and peace for their time.

Hugo was delighted and giving a boyish whoop for joy, dashed off to find Porter to send him to the cellars for his best bottle of champagne. While he was gone, Artemis got up and went to look out of one of the huge windows, across a parkland already turning autumnal.

After a moment, Ellie threw a log on the fire and sat back in her chair with a sigh. 'Thank God,' she said. 'After all that.'

'Don't speak too soon,' Artemis said. 'It's only a scrap of paper.'

'Aren't you ever optimistic about anything?' Ellie asked her. 'The four powers have all signed! There is going to be no war!'

'Not for the moment, Eleanor. No.'

'You heard your prime minister, Artemis! Come on! It's peace! Guaranteed peace! They saw Hitler down! And it's peace! Peace for our time!'

'It's peace for the time *being*, Eleanor.'

'What is it? You want there to be a war?'

'That's the very last thing I *want*.'

'Because if there was a war, you know what would happen, don't you?'

'Yes, I do. Do you?'

'You bet I do.'

'Exactly.'

Hugo arrived back at that moment, accompanied by Porter bearing a bottle of vintage Krug. As he came in, he was met with a silence.

'So what's the matter with you two?' he grinned. 'Don't you feel like a party?'

'I'll say,' Ellie said, putting out of her mind the image of Hugo in uniform.

Artemis stared at Hugo, who in her mind had become just a cross on yet another grave. 'Blast,' she exclaimed, suddenly picking up her stick. 'Sorry. I forgot to feed Brutus.'

Ellie discovered what had happened before Christmas and after the initial shock, decided to say nothing to Hugo. Instead, she bought an extra present and placed it under the tree with a special card attached. She then continued busying herself helping Hugo as if nothing was out of the ordinary.

The house was almost finished. In the short time Hugo's father had owned it, he had managed to find and buy some fine paintings, and a certain amount of the right furniture, but Hugo had determined on making the house his and Ellie's, rather than a memorial to times past. Happily Ellie and Hugo shared exactly the same tastes, despite their very different backgrounds, and the end result, due to Ellie's sense of homeliness and Hugo's classically trained eye, was a house which combined a sense of history with a feeling for comfort, and one that welcomed rather than overwhelmed its guests. All the important rooms were furnished without pomposity. Instead visitors got the impression of unity, of a sense of perfect order, as if the eighteenth century had been conjoined quite seamlessly with the twentieth. And at Hugo's insistence, all the rooms were used whenever possible, such as when their friends were gathered for one of their increasingly popular parties, when endless treasure hunts or protracted games of sardines and hide and seek were played all over the house, or when Ellie and Hugo were alone together and decided that Pelmanism was even harder to play when the cards were laid out over the entire marble floor of the great hall.

Sometimes the games were more intimate, as when Hugo would dismiss the Porter and the footmen and make Ellie pretend she was visiting royalty, sitting her at the huge dining table all by herself, while he attended to her needs and served her dinner as if he was a footman. Ellie could never get very far into these particular evenings without becoming quite helpless with laughter, particularly since Hugo played it all so seriously, managing to ignore the muffled sound of laughter while he bowed and scraped before her, backing out of the drawing room to leave Ellie to drink her champagne alone before dining, and then making her eat her food while he stood rigidly behind her against the wall, never uttering one word, unless in character.

She would then be led by candlelight to be put to bed alone in the state bedroom, which once again boasted a superb handcarved wooden fourposter. The first couple of times they had played this game, by the time they reached the bedroom Ellie had been begging for mercy, so helpless had been her laughter. But even then Hugo had ignored her, and disappeared to leave her to undress and get into bed alone, only to reappear under cover of dark sometime later and slip into the bed with her and make passionate, glorious love to her. By then all laughter was forgotten as Ellie thrilled to Hugo's wonderful love-making, and to the notion of his mischievous fantasy.

And then all would be laughter again as Hugo would leap out of bed, and back in his footman's character, would charge around the state bedroom with only an eiderdown wrapped round him shouting that he, modest Jack Smith the footman, had ravished the queen or princess of whatever country Ellie was meant to be ruling that night.

Which was how Hugo came to be given a Christmas present that year from Queen Hecuba of Heligoland, with a card that wished the season's greetings to her most loyal subject, with her majesty's deepest gratitude for what they had managed to make on the occasion of her last visit.

Inside the wrappings was a baby's silver rattle.

15

The house had been full at Christmas, full of friends and relatives, and the children of friends and relatives. Rather than going to London which had been her original plan, to stay with her godmother, Artemis had instead been persuaded to invite Diana Lanchester up to Brougham to celebrate the festival with Hugo and Ellie and their house guests. And once she had accepted the invitation, Artemis was, as Hugo used to joke to Ellie behind the closed doors of their bedroom, no end of a help.

'Here goes,' she announced grimly, at the beginning of December, 'I know I'm going to be told to M Y, but there used to be certain traditions here at Christmas.'

Hugo deliberately left a long silence while he continued to sign the Christmas cards Ellie was handing on to him. Ellie also kept silent, aware of her part in the good natured provocation of their friend.

'It doesn't matter,' Artemis finally resolved, throwing a rolled up ball of newspaper across the room for Brutus to fetch.

'For instance,' Hugo said, not looking up.

'Good dog,' said Artemis, as Brutus slithered back across the floor to her feet, bringing half the Persian carpet with him.

'If you want to play games with that dog,' Ellie sighed, 'might not the corridor be a better place?'

'For instance?' Hugo repeated, now looking Artemis in the eye.

'Sorry?' Artemis said.

'Didn't you just say something? Something about I don't know – ' Hugo looked to Ellie.

Ellie continued signing her cards, explaining that she can't have been listening. Artemis rolled up another large ball of newspaper. 'For instance,' she said. 'We used to have the choir here. On Christmas Eve. To sing carols.' Then she threw the ball of newspaper, but this time at Hugo, hitting him on the head. 'And the Hunt always used to meet here on Boxing Day.'

'How about a pantomime?' Hugo suggested. 'There's always a dip after Boxing Day, before New Year's Eve, so let's organize a pantomime.'

'I don't even know what a pantomime is,' Ellie complained.

'Oh of course the Yanks don't have them, do they?' Artemis asked Hugo. 'What on earth do they do with their brats at Christmas?'

'They don't have Christmas, Tom,' Hugo grinned. 'They have Yule.'

'And suspenders for braces,' said Artemis.

'And pants for trousers,' added Hugo.

'I can learn,' Ellie shrugged. 'It can't be that difficult. If you Limeys can do it, so can us Yanks.'

'We Yanks, Ellie,' Hugo said, tongue in cheek. 'Please. Not us.'

And learn she did, the way Ellie always set about learning anything, diligently and assiduously. She read everything she could about pantomime, its theory, its history and its practice, and she even managed to get hold of some film of a traditional British panto, which Hugo would run for her whenever asked on his film projector. For days before Christmas the house would echo with Ellie rehearsing her lines, and slapping her thighs as she went hither and thither to bedroom and bathroom.

'I say, Puss!' she would cry, for it had finally been agreed they should perform *Dick Whittington*, or more correctly Hugo Tanner's version of it. 'And now to London!'

Hugo wrote the whole show in two days flat, including the music, and all the household were roped in; Porter,

Cook, the maids and the footmen. Ellie played the title role and played it to the manor born, her beautiful legs shown off in fine hose and leather high boots. Hugo played the cat, and Artemis played Long Jean Silver, Dick Whittington's pirate girlfriend, an invention of Hugo's, and a necessary one too, since Artemis had flatly refused to appear onstage at any cost.

'We need someone to play the pirate,' Hugo said in a moment of inspiration.

'There isn't a pirate in *Dick Whittington*,' Artemis said.

'In pantomime anybody can be in anything,' Hugo corrected her. 'And in my Dick Whittington there is this absolutely beautiful pirate girl, and she's Long John Silver's daughter, so she has only got one leg.'

'That isn't logical,' Artemis argued. 'Because her father had one leg doesn't mean his daughter would have one.'

'Yes it does,' Hugo said. 'He bequeathed it to her.'

Artemis couldn't help laughing, as always with Hugo. And as Ellie knew, once you got Artemis to laugh, she would agree to almost anything. And so against all odds Hugo got her to appear onstage.

The pantomime, performed initially for the benefit of their guests, and then at Hugo's instigation also for the entertainment of the estate workers and the villagers, was a huge success, prompting Artemis to remark that they had initiated yet another tradition.

'You know the trouble with traditions,' Hugo said in reply. 'You have to uphold them.'

'Not according to *The Summing Up* which I've just finished reading,' said Artemis. 'Somerset Maugham says tradition's a guide, not a jailer.'

'Remove not the ancient landmark which the fathers have set!' said Hugo, putting on a Biblical voice and waving an admonishing finger in the air.

'And let the dead govern the living?' Artemis asked. 'I don't think so.'

And so they wandered off down one of Brougham's long corridors, deep in conversation, while Ellie followed slowly on behind, left out for a moment, and finding herself jealous of Hugo and Artemis's companionship. It wasn't just their intellectual compatibility, because Ellie had always and readily given Artemis best in that field with no great concern, but more the fact that Artemis could make Hugo laugh, really laugh, out loud, and sometimes uncontrollably. While Ellie didn't seem to be able to, at least not in the same way.

No, she argued with herself, ever more glumly as she trailed further and further behind the couple ahead, that wasn't strictly true. She could make her husband laugh, but only either through deliberate foolishness, like when they were playing games, or in their more intimate moments, as when they were making love. Ellie might captivate Hugo, she might beguile him, delight and enthral him, but she didn't amuse him, she couldn't divert and entertain him with her wit and by her observations, not the way Artemis could. Artemis was droll and obtuse, with a fine, dry wit. Artemis made Hugo laugh. And that made Ellie jealous. And when she realized that was what it made her, Ellie was appalled.

So was Hugo when she told him.

'But I can't help it,' Ellie said. 'Everywhere I look — what do I see? You and Artemis. You and Artemis talking. You and Artemis arguing. You and Artemis teasing each other. And joking. And laughing. Damn it, you spend half the time laughing!'

'You'd rather we were quarrelling?' Hugo asked, removing his front collar stud. 'Listen — I was jealous of Artemis when she arrived here out of the blue, and you two did nothing but behave like a couple of giggling little schoolgirls — '

'We did nothing of the sort!' Ellie followed Hugo through into his dressing room, peeling off her shoes and throwing them behind her. 'You were the one who acted childishly! You sulked like a spoilt six-year-old!'

'And you gave me a rare old wigging,' Hugo replied. 'And quite right, too. And that's what I should give you now. Because you've got absolutely *nothing* to be jealous about!'

'You mean that you had? Ellie asked, looking deliberately over-astonished.

'Meaning that I love you,' Hugo said.

'No you don't,' Ellie replied, foolishly, senselessly, ridiculously.

'OK I don't,' Hugo shrugged, pulling on his pyjamas and walking back barefoot to the bedroom.

'If you did!' Ellie shouted after him, before following on. 'If you did, you wouldn't find her so goddam funny! She only has to raise an eyebrow, or say it's raining and you fall off your chair laughing!'

Hugo said nothing, seeming to pay her no attention, as he picked a book up from a table, examined the spine and then got into bed to read.

'Hugo – I'm talking to you, damn it!'

'No you're not, Ellie. You're shouting.' He looked up at her over his glasses. 'I don't like being shouted at.'

'And I don't like being made to look a fool!'

Hugo gave her another glum look, and then turned on his side, leaning on one elbow as he opened his book.

Ellie leaned over him, took hold of the book, and threw it away against the wall. 'I'm talking to you, Hugo Tanner!'

'You know, if you weren't pregnant, Ellie, do you know what I'd do?' Hugo asked her, leaving the question unanswered.

'If I wasn't pregnant, Hugo!' Ellie suddenly sank to the bed, and put her hands to her face. 'If I wasn't pregnant,' she said, in a muffled voice, 'I wouldn't be behaving like this.' Then she threw her arms around Hugo's neck and sobbed on his shoulder. Hugo laughed, in relief, and hugged her, and kissed her, and stroked her hair, and kissed her again, and laughed.

'You know I love you.'

'Yes I know you do,' she answered. 'I guess I just didn't realize what a jealous person I was. Not until now, anyway.'

'I guess,' Hugo said, lightly mocking her, 'I guess none of us do. But zen,' he continued, changing his accent from American to German, 'where zair is nein jealousy, zair is nein luff.'

Ellie sat back, and wiping her tears away with the back of her hand, smiled. 'And do you know the worst thing, Hugo?' she said. 'The worst thing in the whole world when you're jealous is the sound of the people you're jealous of laughing.'

She laughed and then she began to cry again, at one and the same time.

Artemis was jealous as well. Not of Ellie, at least not of Ellie with Hugo, but of Ellie and her unborn baby. Before Ellie had become pregnant it seemed to Artemis that life had returned to how it had always been between the three of them, carefree and casual, the threat of war serving only to heighten their fellowship rather than threaten it. If there was such a thing as a perfect triangular relationship, then the three of them most surely enjoyed it, remaining, it seemed to Artemis, even-sided and absolutely balanced. Never once was she aware that her association with Hugo could be construed as being anything other than utterly platonic, and had she entertained even the slightest of suspicions that she might be making Ellie feel jealous, she would have decamped from Brougham immediately. Subterfuge and flirtation had no part in Artemis's armoury, and she would quite literally rather have died than be the cause of Ellie's jealous misery.

Such noble sentiments, however, could not prevent Artemis herself from becoming almost obsessively jealous of Ellie and her recent conception. It was not that Artemis wished that she herself could be pregnant, far from it. Artemis was appalled by the state of gestation and not even particularly attracted by the idea of babies.

Children she tolerated because at least she could relate to children, but infants frightened and appalled her. What she resented wasn't Ellie's pregnancy itself, but the fact that the conception of a child must inevitably alter the nature of their three-cornered friendship. Artemis could only guess at the wonder of maternity, although her dead mother's letter had given her an indication of its strengths and determinations, but instinctively she knew enough to realize that as the child grew in Ellie's womb and its time came to be born, and when Ellie actually did give birth, Ellie's love would be for her child, and for her husband, and Artemis would become a friend like any other, no longer an intimate.

There would be no more rows and arguments, no more mad games and crazy capers, midnight swims in the lake, or fancy dress dinners with Hugo one end of the great table dressed as Boadicea, and Brutus the other end dressed in a child's sailor suit, and Ellie and Artemis blacked up as minstrels, while Porter and the footmen served them their food without any of them once cracking a smile. No more soapbox car racing along the subterranean passageways, with Hugo and Ellie taking on half the county, no more late-night sessions of Hugo's patented card game, Non-Strip Poker, whereby the losers instead of disrobing had to put on more clothes, and everyone ended up looking like dirigibles. No more youthful follies, no more elaborate practical jokes, no more uncluttered fun. Hugo would become a father, and Ellie a mother, and Artemis would become as she had already been invited to become a godmother, and fathers and mothers and godmothers were not expected to go on cutting capers.

So although Christmas had been, as agreed by all, great fun, when the bell of Brougham rang out the last minutes of 1938, Artemis wanted time to stop exactly where it was, on the last chime of midnight, and the New Year never to be rung in. There was a dread feeling in her heart, a sense of inexplicable regret, and it wasn't due to just the possibility of a war. As the great bell in the tower rang out the last of the dying year, Artemis knew that if she was being honest, her feeling of doom and despondency was entirely due to the conception of Ellie's child. For with the promise of young life they themselves were no longer really young. Hugo and Ellie and Artemis had finally spent the last of their youth.

Artemis found herself dancing in Charles Hunter's arms. They had often danced and Charles, either due to Hugo's private tuition, or from a gentlemanly instinct, had understood at once how best to manage her. And Artemis had been grateful, as grateful as she was for his attentions and his friendship. They had hit it off from the moment they had sat down next to each other at dinner the night they first met, and besides proving to be good company, and a good dancer, Charles Hunter was also a fine horseman. He and Artemis hunted together regularly, so much so that friends and acquaintances it seemed had already earmarked them as a couple.

Artemis was perfectly well aware that the dashing soldier was in love with her, but did nothing either to discourage or encourage him. He was attractive, light-hearted, caring and courageous, and therefore the ideal escort. He was also in the Army which meant that he was not always around, so Artemis could spend as much time as she was allowed with Ellie and Hugo without it ever appearing scandalous, which it most certainly was not, indiscreet, which it most definitely was not, nor an imposition, which it hopefully was not. And then when Charles was on leave in the country they would go hunting, or if Artemis was in town they would go out dining and dancing. Ellie thoroughly approved, but Hugo said nothing. Neither did Artemis.

And now they were dancing once more, as the balloons showered down on them and the streamers unfurled over them, and mock stardust fell and glittered all over them. The last strains of 'Auld Lang Syne' had died away and the band was playing a slow foxtrot, which along with the mood and the food and the drink was making Charles Hunter feel even more romantic than ever. So he held Artemis to him ever more closely and buried his face in her hair, muttering things to her which thanks to their proximity to the band Artemis could not hear.

Artemis wouldn't have heard anyway, so busy was she watching the couple in the middle of the dancefloor, the beautiful slender brown haired young woman in a white and gold gown who was being kissed gently but extensively by a handsome fair-haired man in glasses. They were standing, almost dancing, but not quite, beneath the revolving mirrored ball Hugo had ordered to be installed for the party, lit by the multi-coloured flicker of the lights playing on it, a beautiful image from a wondrous dream, dappled in splashing colours, blue and red, pinks, bright white, and greens. They kissed oblivious to the world, without heed to anyone, Hugo turning Ellie slowly round and round to the liquid sound of a solo clarinet.

Artemis looked away, surprised at the sudden white heat in her veins. She looked away from the lovers and back at the man in whose arms she was, who was now looking at her adoringly. Artemis half-opened her lips, to draw a slight breath, to gasp slightly in astonishment at her feelings, but Charles took the shape of her pretty mouth as an invitation to kiss her, which he did, softly and sweetly.

But all Artemis could see was Hugo. And Hugo and Ellie. And Hugo kissing Ellie. She knew Charles was kissing her, but it was as though her lips were senseless and her senses numb. All the time he kissed her, her eyes were open, watching Hugo, who was close to them now. And then Hugo opened his eyes, quite suddenly, and found himself staring into Artemis's own bright blue and very wide eyes.

Which she closed at once, and far too late.

Charles stopped kissing her, and held her slightly away from him. 'Artemis,' he said, out of breath, as if he'd been running. 'Artemis – '

'It's a terrible name, isn't it?' she said. 'I don't think it's at all possible to say it romantically, do you?'

Charles smiled and put a hand up to brush her hair gently from her eye. 'You know I love you, don't you?' he said.

'Yes,' said Artemis.

'Then will you marry me?' he asked.

'I think I'd better,' Artemis replied.

'What? What did you say?'

The band had started to play again, louder, a quick-step. Artemis put her hand back on his shoulder. 'I said — ' she shouted, 'I think I'd better!'

'Why?' the perplexed Charles shouted back, the trumpeter blasting in his ear. 'Why on earth do you think you'd better?'

'Because — ' Artemis yelled, 'I think it's better I marry you than not!'

She kissed him, sweetly, briefly, and smiled, turning her back on Hugo and Ellie and quite deliberately danced away from them.

Charles called on Artemis early the following evening.

'You weren't out today,' she remarked, pulling off her hunting coat. 'I shouldn't worry, you didn't miss much.'

'I felt a little fragile,' Charles replied. 'Didn't you?'

'Not at all,' Artemis said. 'Have some gin.'

She pushed the decanter towards her visitor, who collapsed in a chair, still holding the decanter and a glass, and then barefooted she stood in front of the fire, staring at him while she shook her blonde hair from its net.

'You looked frightfully bleached,' she told him. 'Didn't you get to bed at all?'

Charles Hunter sighed and explained that after he had escorted Artemis to the Dower House, he had foolishly returned to Brougham instead of going straight home and got rather involved with Hugo and the diehards in a game of Getting Round The Room Without Touching The Floor.

'Which room?' Artemis asked. 'Some are a great deal easier than others.'

'The library.'

'That's the easiest of them all. It's just shelves.'

'And two windows,' Charles said grimly, taking the top off the decanter and pouring himself some gin. 'You can't get from the shelves into the bay and on to the window ledge on the first one, and you can't get from the radiator on the other one on to the ledge likewise.'

'Hugo can.'

'Hugo was the stakeholder. Hugo wasn't playing. But even if he had been, it still isn't possible.'

'Yes it is. I've done it.' Artemis padded barefoot over to her drinks cupboard and looked for the squash bottle. 'Only thing is you need a walking stick,' she said over her shoulder.

Charles thought about it, as Artemis poured herself a soft drink, and then curled up in the large armchair by the fire. 'I give up,' he said finally.

'I hook my stick on to the top of the architrave, in the middle,' Artemis explained. 'It's a good wide moulding, you see, so you can get a decent whatever, purchase. Anyway, I lean out from the shelves on the left, hook my stick in the middle of the moulding, and then swing across and on to the shelves the other side.'

'Brilliant,' said Charles, lost in admiration. 'Well done. Yes. Anyway,' he continued after a moment, 'look, about last night.'

'The saloon's the only one of the major rooms which can't be got round.' Artemis quickly continued, tucking her legs up even further under her. 'It's a cakewalk as far as the doors, because of the way the chairs and sofas are placed against the walls, but there's absolutely no way across the doors because they're double. And the architrave's about twenty foot high.'

'I'm sure. Anyway.' Charles put down his glass, anxious to change the subject.

'Unless you sit on one of the chairs by the pillars and sort of wiggle-waggle it over, you know,' Artemis continued blithely. 'Sort of jumping it to the other chair. But then that's not really allowed. At least not under Hugo's code of rules.'

'Artemis.' Charles got up and started to walk over to where Artemis was sitting, looking as if he intended to perch on the arm of her chair. Artemis got herself up quickly before he could do so and went to pick up his glass.

'Drink?' she asked.

She couldn't avoid him this time, because he moved too quickly for her, catching her by one arm.

'About last night,' he said.

'Yes,' said Artemis, 'wasn't it fun?'

'I proposed to you, remember?'

'Yes.'

'And you accepted. I think.' Charles turned her round to him, but Artemis said nothing. She just looked at him directly, her head cocked slightly to one side. 'I meant what I said, Artemis,' Charles continued, realizing Artemis was in one of her unforthcoming moods. 'Did you?'

'What did I say, Charles? Can you remember?'

'I know what you said, Artemis. I'm just not sure what you meant.'

'Didn't I say yes?' Artemis asked, wide-eyeing him.

'No.' Charles shook his head and smiled at her, her deliberate elusion only making him love her all the more. 'What you actually said was that you suppose you had better.'

'Have another drink,' Artemis said, freeing herself. 'I'm going to have one.' She fetched the decanter and poured them both a gin. She gave Charles his neat, and poured lemon squash into her own, topping it up with water. 'Happy New Year,' she said, briefly holding up her glass.

Charles put his drink down untouched and followed Artemis as she strolled over to the fire where she stood with her back to him, staring down into the flames. He put both his hands on her shoulders, but felt her stiffen and resist his touch. So rather than try and turn her to him, he left her alone to stare into the fire while he went to pour some bitters and water into his gin. He swilled the drink round and then half-drained it.

'Sorry,' Artemis suddenly said from the fireplace, still without turning round.

'Meaning sorry you don't think that you'd better? That you'd better not marry me?' Charles enquired, unable fully to conceal his disappointment.

'No. Meaning sorry but I think I'd just like a little bit more time,' Artemis replied, 'If you don't mind.'

'How much time do you want?'

'I don't know actually. Sorry.'

Charles put his empty glass down and looked at the girl who was still staring down at the fire, with her head bent so that the tumble of her blonde hair obscured the expression on her face, which Charles was unable to read from any angle as he walked across to her, to put both his hands on her slender waist. Again he felt her resist his touch, but this time she also verbally rejected him.

'No, Charles,' she said, 'please don't. Not just now.'

'I don't think you understand, Artemis,' he replied. 'I happen to love you.'

'I know you do, Charles.'

'But you don't love me.'

'I don't know, Charles. I really don't.'

'Which is why you want more time?'

'Probably.'

She was doing her best to resist him, but was finding it hard. It would be all too easy to allow him to take her in his arms, and to hold her and kiss her, and she would be grateful to him, because just at this moment what she needed more than anything else was for someone to hold her, and to tell her they loved her. But it would be too easy and it would be wrong, because Artemis knew if Charles took her in his arms and asked her again to marry him, she would say yes, she would agree to marry him, but not because she loved him as he said he loved her, but because Artemis knew that if she did not marry him she might end up destroying the happiness of two people whom she really did love.

So instead of agreeing or refusing, she prevaricated, asking for more time, which she really didn't need. In her heart Artemis knew she should accept Charles Hunter's proposal of marriage unconditionally, since he'd take her away from Brougham, and from Hugo, defusing a potentially dangerous situation. But this wasn't her heart which was speaking now. This was her alter ego, her other side, her dark side.

Charles Hunter, however, took her request for more time at its face value. He had been brought up to understand that marriage was something into which people should not enter lightly, and when all things were considered, although Artemis and he had enjoyed a warm and companionable relationship, until he'd kissed her the previous night, there had been no intimacy whatsoever. The nearest Charles and Artemis came to physical contact was when he helped her down from her hunter. And yet after one kiss at a New Year's Eve Ball he had proposed marriage to her, and in the cold light of day such a suggestion can only have seemed hasty and impulsive.

So he respected Artemis's request and left her, after telling her he was returning to London that night, and that he would wait for her answer, however long it took her finally to make up her mind. Artemis did not see him to the door. She stayed exactly where she was by the fireplace. She did not even go to the window to watch his car vanish into the winter evening. Instead, despising herself for her guile and her false-heartedness, and fearful of the reason she was allowing herself to be propelled along a path she knew to be treacherous, she slowly spilled her drink on to the flaming logs in the grate. The flames spluttered and seethed and the fire hissed back up at her, as if passing judgement on her behaviour.

She said nothing of the matter to her godmother when they dined together later that evening, in fact she did very little talking at all. There was no need, because Diana was in top form, telling her goddaughter about Unity Mitford's absurd passion for Hitler, and of Artemis's stepmother's increasing involvement with Oswald Mosley and the British Fascist party.

'She'll end up dangling off a lamppost, darling, mark my words. Even if we do go to war, and the Germans invade us, that little lot's not going to be safe for a moment. The first people Herr Hitler will get rid of will be his pathetic fellow-travellers.'

'How will you stand, Diana?' Artemis asked. 'If there is a war —'

'Which there will be, darling, whatever the papers say.'

'Suppose the Germans did invade us. What would you do?'

Diana toyed with her food for a moment and then put down her fork. 'I'd shoot myself, sweetie. Wouldn't you? Actually, I've already bought a gun.'

'I'd shoot myself, too,' Artemis replied. 'After I'd shot my horses and my dog.'

'Well of course. Vita Nicolson's got pills in her dressing case.' Diana drank some more of her whisky, which she had been steadily imbibing throughout dinner, before continuing. 'Have you seen any of these privately circulated newspapers?' she asked. 'I don't suppose you have. Not down here, anyway. There are quite a few doing the rounds, you know, because a lot of us don't quite believe what the Press are telling us. We feel we're being lulled into a false sense of security. Particularly, you'll be glad to hear, us girls. I was having dinner with Duff the other night, and he told me of the twelve happily married couples he and Diana know, every one of them were divided over what happened at Munich. And in every case it was the men who supported Chamberlain and the women who were opposed to him. Which is why if we do go to war – '

'When we do, Diana, according to you.'

'When we go to war, darling, thank you, when we do go to war that's the very reason we shall prevail. Because the women in this country have a sight more sense than the men. We don't believe for a moment in this ridiculous peace, and if women were in power the country wouldn't be sitting around twiddling its thumbs. We'd be re-arming. And getting ready to blow the pants off Jerry.'

'If or when there is a war,' Artemis said ruefully, 'I don't suppose I'll be of much use.'

'Nonsense,' Diana answered. 'You can drive, can't you?'

'Well of course,' Artemis replied. 'Although I don't suppose Hugo would agree.'

'Really?' Diana eyed Artemis as she drained her whisky. 'What about Charles? Would Charles also disagree?'

Artemis pushed herself up on the arms of her chair and suggested that they move through to the drawing room. 'Let's sit by the fire,' she said. 'And have some coffee.'

Rosie brought through a tray of coffee and built up the fire with more logs. Artemis refilled her godmother's whisky glass, and also helped herself to a drink. They small-talked while Rosie fussed round them, poured their coffee and drew the curtains as tight as she could against the January night, before leaving them alone. For a while they sat in silence, Diana sipping at her whisky and Artemis idly stirring her coffee.

'Is there something you want to talk about, darling?' Diana finally asked.

'No,' said Artemis. 'Should there be?'

'It must sometimes get a bit frustrating. Living by yourself. Without anybody to chew the cud with.'

'Not at all actually. I've got Brutus. And Rosie.'

'In that order.'

'Brutus doesn't have opinions.' Artemis leaned forward, to push a tumbling log back up on to the fire with the poker. 'You live alone, Diana,' she said.

'Not stuck away in the country like you I don't,' Diana replied.

'I know masses of people, Diana. You know how it is when you hunt and things. And anyway, if I really want to talk, there's always —'

'Yes?' Diana broke the silence. Artemis just shrugged, leaving it to Diana to say, 'there's always Hugo and Ellie.'

'Yes,' said Artemis.

'How's Charles?' Diana asked. 'I like Charles.'

'I know,' Artemis replied. 'Everyone likes Charles.'

'Do you like Charles?'

'Yes.'

Diana drained her coffee, which she'd allowed to get cold, and poured herself some more. 'Wish I'd had a Charles in my life,' she said, spooning some crystals of sugar into her cup.

'Absolutely,' Artemis vaguely agreed. She put down her coffee cup, but made no move to refill it. Instead she studiously looked at her wristwatch before staring briefly at the fire. 'I think I'm going to bed now,' she announced finally.

'All right, darling,' Diana agreed affably. 'You do as you please. I think I'll stay up for a while and read. This fire's much too good to leave.'

Artemis stood up. 'Good night then.'

'Good night, darling.' Diana offered up her face to be kissed. Artemis bent over her and kissed her on the cheek. Diana caught hold of her hand. 'Just one little word of advice though, darling,' she said. 'I'm allowed that, I think, as your godmother, even though you are over twenty one. Believe me, in married life, two's company and three really is none.'

Artemis sat down. She stared at the fire, at the ceiling, at her feet, at the nails on her fingers, at the fire again, and finally back at the ceiling, before exhaling a sigh that was more telling than any words could ever be.

'I think you should marry Charles,' Diana said gently. 'Don't you?'

It mattered not that she didn't love him, what mattered it seemed was that Artemis had to be married, as if the ceremony of being wed would finally exorcise her feelings for Hugo. Besides, as Diana had kept assuring her through the long night, some of the very best and most successful marriages were made between people who were not passionately in love with each other, but who simply liked each other as friends, and even more importantly had things in common, which lovers who were just lovers rarely did. Of all the most successful marriages she knew of in London, none she told Artemis, had been the result of love affairs.

'And as I'm sure you're more than well aware of, darling,' she added, trying to lighten the atmosphere, 'love's an ideal thing, and marriage a real thing. And a confusion of the real with the ideal never goes unpunished.'

'I'm sure there's something in what you say, Diana,' she said at last. 'But then who knows. Perhaps the war will solve it all for us, Diana. Perhaps we'll all be killed and that will simply be that.'

By March, Ellie was five months pregnant and Artemis could hardly bear to look at her. She had become, as so many mothers-to-be can become, even more beautiful since conceiving, and the size she had now reached made her look endearing rather than cumbersome. Hugo fussed around her, fetching and carrying, his mind on nothing else.

Artemis observed from afar, rather than near, taking Diana's advice and making sure to plough a lone furrow.

While she remained unengaged to Charles Hunter, she nonetheless was seen everywhere with him, on both sporting and social engagements, and on the two occasions she had been invited to dine at Brougham, Charles had been her escort and Artemis, due to Ellie's placement, had been seated in the middle of the table, well away from her host. All told, by the middle of March, Artemis had not spent one moment alone in conversation with either of her two friends.

To compensate for this, and to try and counter the feeling of almost uncontrollable jealousy Artemis experienced every time she thought about Ellie's baby, or, from her car, saw Ellie being helped solicitously by Hugo up the front steps of Brougham, or spied Ellie out walking slowly in the park in a March wind, stopping to bend and pick some daffodils with increasing difficulty, Artemis bought a proven race mare due to foal in April. The mare was a big, bonny and good tempered bay, who had already produced a decent colt who the previous season had won as a two-year-old, picking up his maiden, and towards the end of the season a good Stakes race. Artemis was thrilled with her purchase which, because it had been bought at an executor's sale, she had managed to get relatively cheaply. In affording it the fact that she had also managed to win on one of the point-to-point horses she had bought the year before, and sell it on at a profit helped considerably.

The mare became the new focus of Artemis's attention and she fussed over it as Hugo fussed over Ellie. Jenkins thought the mare a nice sort of animal, but couldn't help being surprised and a little amused at the way Artemis, who was normally so self-contained, worried over her.

'You'll pardon my sayin' so, your ladyship,' he said one morning, 'but it's like you was havin' the foal yourself.'

Artemis patted the mare on the rump and smiled. 'Horses and all animals really,' she said as she left the yard, 'they're much more sensible than we are, Jenkins. Once the baby's weaned, that's it.'

And so once more life at Brougham settled down and seemed as serene as life did generally in England. The Government assured the Press who passed it on to the people that the international outlook was positively serene, and *Punch* published a cartoon which depicted John Bull waking from a nightmare, which was labelled 'Danger of War' and seen to be floating out of the window. On exactly the same day *Punch* was published the Germans marched into Prague, placed Czechoslovakia under 'protection' and renounced her non-aggression pact with Poland. The prime minister responded by announcing that the guarantee Britain had made to protect Czechoslovakia's frontiers was no longer valid.

Upon reading this, Hugo threw his copy of *The Times* to the floor. 'Am I a belligerent person, Ellie?' he asked his wife across the breakfast table. 'I'm not belligerent, am I? Yet the things we're being expected to believe. The lies.'

'What's the connection with whether or not you're belligerent?' Ellie wanted to know, and somewhat anxiously. 'You're not going to rush off and join up, are you? I mean not yet?' She put a hand to her growing stomach, instinctively.

'If there's a war,' Hugo replied, getting up from the table, 'if there is a war, I can't wait to be called up. Of course I shall enlist.'

'What about your eyes?' Ellie asked hopefully. 'You said yourself – '

'I don't know, Ell,' Hugo said, pacing the room. 'I'm not actually that blind. Not blind enough to be turned down.'

Ellie picked up her newspaper and frowned at the front page. 'It says here,' she folded her paper over and tapped it, as if it was a tablet from the mountains. 'It says the German annexation of Czechoslovakia doesn't necessarily mean war. In fact far from it.'

'That's just what I'm saying!'

'It says as long as we keep negotiating with Germany — '

'They don't want to negotiate with us, Ellie! They never have done!'

'Just listen for one minute will you, Hugo?' Ellie eyed him over her newspaper. 'Everyone's negotiating. Your prime minister and Lord Halifax have even been to Rome. President Roosevelt has demanded assurances from Hitler and from Mussolini that they won't — '

'What will you do, Ellie?' Hugo suddenly interrupted Ellie, coming to sit down close beside her and to take her hands in his. 'Supposing there is a war, a European war, and America stays at home. And doesn't fight. What will you do?'

'Hugo my darling,' Ellie leaned over a little, far enough to kiss him softly on the mouth. 'What do you mean — what will I do? You know what I'll do. What else? I'll put on my gas mask, and my tin helmet, and take up my pitchfork, and I'll line up on the cliffs at wherever it is — '

'Dover.'

'Right. I'll be right there in line on the cliff tops of Dover along with the rest of us women.'

'It's going to happen, Ell,' Hugo said. 'Forget all this rubbish in the newspapers. I can feel it in my heart. The earth's moving. I can hear the feet marching. And the rifles being cocked. We're going to have to fight this Fascist pig.' He took Ellie's hands and placed them on her stomach. Then he placed his on top of hers, and stared at their unseen child. 'We're going to have to fight this lunatic for him, or her. For all the hims or hers unborn everywhere. To make sure the world is still a little bit of a good and decent place to live in.'

They made love before they bathed and got dressed for the day, tender love, slow love, full of lingering kisses and caresses, and smiles and sighs. And then as Hugo lay in the bath, seeing images in his mind he had never dreamed he would see, Ellie buried her face in her pillow and wept, because she knew from the way things were now and from the way that things were going to be that Hugo was no longer just hers.

That evening a band on the wireless played 'Falling In Love With Love' and when it had finished, Ellie sat at the piano and played it straight off, having only heard it once.

'I don't know how you do that. How did you learn to do that?' Hugo wanted to know.

'Isn't necessity the mother of invention?' she replied. 'I had to learn things when I heard them. We could never afford sheet music.'

She played the song through again and as she did, she remembered herself as a little girl, sitting in Madame's parlour, on a round piano stool covered in dark red velvet, a stool that spun round and round in front of a rosewood upright piano, inlaid with gleaming brass and embellished with two candleholders. Madame had taught her the rudiments of music, the keys, the intervals, the harmonies, but the ability to hear and learn was born in Ellie. She wondered often as she sat and played whether or not her mother had been a pianist. Or her grandmother. Somewhere someone in her family had been musical, but now she would never find out, for her father never returned her letters.

'Let's ask Artemis to dinner tomorrow,' Ellie suggested when she had stopped playing. 'We haven't seen her for ages.'

'She hasn't seen us,' Hugo replied from behind his newspaper. 'She has a house of her own remember? We've only ever been asked there once.'

'You know Artemis,' Ellie laughed. 'She prefers dogs and horses to human beings. I'll telephone her now.' Ellie moved to the telephone as Hugo folded over the next page of *The Times*.

'Charles is in London,' he said.

'So?' Ellie had the phone off the hook and ready. 'Are you going to ask her by herself?'

'I'm going to have to, Hugo, if Charles is in London.'
Ellie tapped the bar of the receiver, to call the operator.

'No, wait a minute, Ellie,' Hugo said suddenly. Ellie
looked back at him, her finger on the bar, killing the
call. 'Do you think this is a good idea?'

Ellie laughed, and then shook her head. 'You're right,'
she teased. 'What a terrible idea, asking your best friend
to dinner.'

She put through the telephone call and waited for
Artemis to answer.

'I must say she's been very elusive of late, even for
Artemis,' said Hugo.

'OK,' Ellie replied. 'So let's find out why.'

It was a disaster. From the moment Hugo opened the
front door, wearing his newly acquired gas mask, to
greet an Artemis who had already had too much to drink,
the evening was calamitous. Before dinner Hugo, in an
absurd but gallant attempt to put Artemis at ease, drank
far too much far too quickly, and was all but incoherent
by the time they sat down to eat. Ellie, who wasn't
drinking at all because of her pregnancy, found herself
involuntarily excluded from subsequent proceedings and
had to sit and suffer in silence while Hugo drank himself
from a state of incoherent intoxication to a coherent
one, in which he found everything he said extremely
important, and every joke he made funny. But he was
talking to himself and laughing solo at his own jokes,
because Artemis seemed to pay no attention to him
whatsoever, nor to Ellie. But then Artemis could hardly
be blamed altogether for Ellie was so dumbfounded she
couldn't think of anything to say to either of them. She
was also alone in her sobriety.

From the outset, Hugo and Artemis seemed, for some
unknown reason, intent on becoming drunk. Artemis
offended only by her inebriation, since her conversation
consisted of single words or short phrases of assent
and agreement. Whatever was said to her she would

answer with 'absolutely' or 'why not' or 'well done', or sometimes just quite simply 'quite'. Ellie enquired and probed and questioned and pumped and queried, but Artemis just stone-walled, either shrugging if asked a direct question, or not-knowing when asked an indirect one. So Ellie finally gave up, realizing that Artemis was up to what Hugo facetiously described as one of her little pranks.

Unfortunately Hugo was far too well stewed to be able to read the writing on the wall. On to the vintage port by now, he had stopped being argumentative or jocular, and had now become sentimental. Ellie made several attempts to leave the table and to take Artemis with her, but they both ignored her, Hugo flapping a hand at her to sit back down and Artemis simply turning away from her to try and focus on Hugo.

'Just sit down, Ellie,' Hugo kept telling her, until Ellie gave up and sat down and stayed sitting down, 'just sit down. Sit down and listen, because I want to tell you something. All of you. Both of you. This is something I want us all to hear. Something *very* important, for us all to hear, do you hear?'

'Don't you think you've had enough?' Ellie asked as the port was passed from Hugo to Artemis and back to Hugo once more, and which made Artemis laugh. 'I don't see what's so funny,' she said.

'You wouldn't,' Artemis replied, before draining her port.

Ellie could have slapped her. She felt like leaning over the table and shaking Artemis by the shoulders, and boxing her ears before giving her another darned good shake. Not just for being drunk, but for managing to be so drunk and still remaining so fascinating. Not a hair nor a stitch was out of place, and her lip-sticked mouth was still as pretty and as perfect as ever. Neither did she slur her words. She just became a little more carefully articulate, waiting a split second before answering, before pronouncing her answer lucidly and clearly, albeit often with an involuntary hyphenation –

'Abs-olutely,'

'Terr-ibly funny,'

'Simp-ly tragic.' Her reactions were slower, too, but still just as telling. Instead of shooting Ellie one of her usual darting glances, or suddenly raising her eyebrows and widening her bright blue eyes, she would carefully brush a flick of blonde hair away from one eye, then blink, and then look round at Ellie with a gaze deep and bland. And then she would blink once more and run her hair away from both sides of her perfectly oval face, before turning her attentions back to Hugo.

'Isn't anybody going to listen to what I have to say?' Hugo asked, although neither of the two women had said a thing in the meanwhile. 'You really have to listen, really, because I may never get the chance to say what I'm going to say to you both. The way things are, I might never get the chance to say this to either of you ever again. And so I'm going to say it now.'

Ellie's blood ran cold. She knew what Hugo was going to say, she could see it in his eyes as he looked slowly from one to the other of them, frowning suddenly, and with his head wobbling very slightly as he tried to keep them both in focus. Ellie tried to get up but Hugo had thought about this and he grabbed hold of her wrist, as he did of Artemis.

'Ow,' said Artemis. 'You idiot.'

'Sssshhh,' said Hugo. 'You have both got to listen. Because. You have. You both have got both to listen. Right.'

'Ow!' said Artemis again, as his grip tightened on her wrist.

'Ssshhhhh!' Hugo hushed again. 'You know what I'm going to say and I know what I'm going to say, and you know what I'm going to say. But it doesn't matter. Because it hasn't been said before, has it. Not by you. Not by me. And not by you.' Unable to let them go,

Hugo could only identify who he meant by nodding at them, a simple act which he was finding more and more difficult. 'There's going to be a war,' he announced.

'Hugo,' said Ellie, her mouth getting rather small.

'Sssshhhhh!' hushed Hugo, louder and longer. 'I know what I'm talking about. There's going to be a war! And when and if there is – ! Well. You tell me. You tell me what's going to happen. God. Really. You tell me. But before it happens. Before as they say – before the barroon. Baroon. Bal-loon. Before the balloon goes up, you've got to listen to what I have to say.'

'Hugo – ' Ellie warned, with a little more urgency, trying to tug her arm away.

'Carry on,' said Artemis. 'We're list-ening.'

'I love you, Ellie.' Hugo focused on his wife, barely. He frowned at her, harder. 'I do,' he said, 'God you know how I do. God I love you.'

Ellie said nothing, too mortified with embarrassment in front of the three silent servants who were standing, backs against the wall.

'I love you, Ellie, and – ' Hugo turned his head slowly round to Artemis. 'And I love you too, Artemis. I do. I love you too, and I love you both. I do. Both of you.' He looked slowly from one to the other, with a look on his face which was half puzzled frown and half ridiculous grin. Both the women stared back at him, but neither was smiling.

'That's it,' Hugo said, letting go of their wrists. 'It had to be said. Someone had to say it. So that's it. I've said it, and there it is. I love you. I love you both.'

Artemis lined him up at the end of her vision, just as the spitfires would soon train their sights on the Messerschmitts, and once she had his face clearly aligned she picked up a glass of wine and threw the contents right at him.

Ellie got to her feet and left the room, as did Artemis a moment later. But Ellie went straight upstairs to her room, while Artemis weaved across the hall and limped out into the night.

Hugo was left at the table, his face and hair awash with claret. 'Good God,' he said. 'Good God.' And then he made an attempt to rise, pushing his chair back and grabbing at the table. Porter stepped forward and caught him, just in time.

Artemis never made it home, at least not by car. She missed the bridge entirely and rolled very slowly into the edge of the lake where she sat for ten minutes wondering where she was and what had happened. Then she opened her door and fell straight out into the dark water, losing her precious silver topped cane.

'Damn,' she swore. 'Bugger. Bugger, damn and bugger.'

Above her the lights shone out from Hugo and Ellie's bedroom, but Artemis was oblivious to them and to the raised voices which floated out across the park as she searched on her hands and knees at the water's edge for her stick, without which she knew she could never get home.

Hugo had expected, in his drunkenness, to find Ellie in bed, curled up and possibly weeping, although for the life of him, as he staggered into the bedroom, he could not imagine why. Why should Artemis have thrown her wine at him? Why should Ellie have walked out like that? All he had done was to tell them that he loved them. So what on earth could all the fuss have been about?

The door slammed shut behind him as he crossed the threshold and someone kicked him barefooted but hard on his backside, knocking him slithering and sliding across the polished wood floor. He cried out, but too late, for as he tried to pull himself up on to the bed, whoever it was kicked him again, and then started to pull his hair ferociously, so hard that his head was jerked back and he found himself staring upside down at the furious face of Ellie.

'Ellie?' he mumbled. 'Ellie – '

She pulled his hair harder and his head further backwards, and shouted at him through her tears. 'You idiot!' she yelled. 'You stupid, dumb idiot!'

'What did I do?' Hugo shouted back, his own eyes beginning to water from the pain in his scalp.

'What did you do?' Ellie yelled at him. 'What do men ever do! Except open their great, dumb mouths!'

Hugo managed to get his hands to her hands, which were still holding his hair, and grab them, so that he could turn himself to her without her pulling at him any more. They remained like that for a moment, Ellie out of breath and staring furiously at him through her tears, while Hugo, his face contorted with pain and his hands clasped on top of his head, stared back up at her.

'Please,' he said finally. 'Ellie — you're hurting.'

'This is nothing to what I was planning to do!' came the reply. 'Listen, Hugo. Now you listen to me. If I wasn't pregnant — '

'My God, Ellie!' Hugo gasped. 'What are you doing? You're pregnant!'

Ellie let go at once, staring at him wild-eyed. 'If anything happens to the baby, Hugo!' she warned him.

'Nothing's going to happen to the baby, Ell, honestly, really,' Hugo had hold of her and was steering her gently round to the bed. 'Now just listen — '

'You must be joking!' Ellie retorted. 'That's the last time I listen to you!' She sat down on the edge of the bed, suddenly frowning, both hands clutching her stomach.

'Are you all right, Ell?'

'I'm fine. Don't worry about me, I'm fine.' She sat still for a while, just trying to relax and breathe regularly and deeply. 'I'm just fine,' she said. 'No thanks to you.'

'Do you want me to call the doctor?'

'I want you to go to hell!' Ellie hissed.

Hugo tried to gather his thoughts, but although his brain was clearing, he was still too addled to remember the exact order of events, or precisely what he said. 'What did I say?' he asked. 'I'm drunk. You don't want to take any notice of anything anybody says when they're drunk.'

'Is that so?'

'That is so.' Hugo nodded. 'That is so.'

'So what about in *vino veritas* or whatever?'

'What about it?'

'Exactly, Hugo. What about it?' Ellie turned to him and grabbed one of his little fingers, pulling it back.

'Ow,' Hugo said. 'Ow.'

'Are you in love with Artemis?' Ellie demanded.

'Did I say that?' Hugo felt a hot blush starting somewhere under his arms and down round his feet, and spreading rapidly all over him. 'I didn't say. Did I say that?'

'Answer me!' Ellie yelled. 'Or I'll break your goddam pinkie!'

'What's a goddam pinkie?' Hugo enquired.

'This!' And Ellie pulled his finger back some more.

'Don't do that!' Hugo shouted. 'That really hurts!'

'Are you in love with Artemis!'

'No I am not in love with Artemis! Why should I be in love with Artemis!'

'Because — you dumb great idiot — because you said you loved her!'

'That's different!'

'What's so different?'

'I love Artemis, but I'm not in love with her! I love her as a friend! The way you do! You love Artemis, don't you?'

'I did,' Ellie said, releasing the pressure on Hugo's finger. 'Now I'm not so sure.'

'Why?' Hugo wrenched his finger away and rubbed it, his tongue stuck in his cheek like a little boy.

'Why do you think?' Ellie asked. 'Because she's in love with you.'

'Oh don't talk such rubbish,' Hugo sighed. 'You love Artemis, Artemis loves you, I love Artemis, maybe Artemis loves me — '

'You bet she loves you.'

Hugo turned to Ellie, sober enough now to read her tone right. 'I love you, Ellie,' he said, putting his arm round her waist. 'You know I love you. I love you and that's what matters. There might be six or sixty or six hundred people out there – which there aren't. But there might be. Who might be in love with me. But that doesn't matter. It wouldn't matter how many there were. What matters is who I love. And I love you. That's what matters. I love you, and you love me.'

'What about Artemis?' Ellie rested her weary head on Hugo's shoulder.

'When I said I loved you both, if that's what I said –' Hugo replied.

'That's what you said all right,' Ellie sighed.

'I meant it. I do love you both. As friends. I love some of my male friends. William. I love William.'

'You don't go around telling William you love him.'

'That's different.'

'No it isn't.'

'Yes it is. I love William, but that's different.'

'OK,' said Ellie with a grin. 'If you love William, you make sure you tell him next time you see him.'

Hugo looked at her and smiled back. Then he kissed her. 'I love you,' he said.

'And I love you,' she said.

'And we both love Artemis.'

'OK. We both love Artemis. I'm just not too sure how she feels about me right at this moment.'

Hugo suddenly put a finger to his lips and pointed to the doorway, under which was seeping a slow trickle of water. Ellie frowned, but keeping his finger to his lips Hugo got up and did his best to tiptoe in as straight a line as possible over to the door, which he then flung open.

Artemis was standing there, soaking wet from the lake. She looked at Hugo, blinked then looked past him at Ellie. 'Hullo,' she said.

'Hi,' said Ellie.

'How long have you been out there?' Hugo asked.

Artemis shrugged. 'Long enough,' she said.

'What's the problem?'

Artemis shrugged again. 'Life,' she said. 'I suppose.'

'I thought you'd gone home, Tom.'

'The car decided it wanted a swim.' Artemis smiled for the first time that night. 'And I've lost my bloody stick.'

Hugo caught her just before she fell.

Ellie was the only one of them who knew precisely what had been said. Artemis remembered getting drunk and the reasons for getting drunk, but that was all. When she woke the next morning and saw the groundsmen pulling her car from the edge of the lake, she realized something unusual must have occurred, but all Ellie would say when pressed was that everyone had drunk too much.

'Did you drink too much?' Artemis asked. 'No, you're not drinking because of the baby, so you must remember what happened.'

'Sure,' Ellie said, smiling only briefly. 'You and Hugo got sauced.'

'Then that's not everyone,' Artemis argued.

'From where I was sitting it was everyone,' Ellie replied, and then went, leaving Artemis to finish her breakfast and to ponder alone.

Hugo was still in bed, lying on his front, occasionally groaning into the mattress. Ellie drew the curtains and then went over to the bed and pulled the covers off the inert form.

'What happened?' Hugo moaned.

'It's time to get up,' Ellie replied.

'What happened last night?'

'I'd rather not talk about it.'

'Ellie?' Hugo turned round but she was gone. 'What happened?' he asked himself, turning his face back down to the mattress. 'What did I do?'

Artemis was still sitting at the table when Hugo came down for breakfast. He came to a standstill when he saw her, and stood speechlessly for a moment behind her back, forgetful suddenly of everything that had happened. At that moment he could not even remember catching her as she had fallen and carrying her along the corridor to a spare room.

'Artemis?' he said.

She looked round briefly, knowing perfectly well who it was. Then she turned back again and picked up her black coffee. 'Don't tell me you don't remember anything either?'

'Not a lot,' Hugo admitted. 'No.' Hugo sat down at the table, opposite Artemis, who was staring into her coffee cup. He put his head in his hands. 'But whatever,' he said, 'I think we're in trouble.'

The housekeeper told Artemis Mrs Tanner was in the east wing, somewhere up on the nursery floor. Artemis made her way across the great hall, into the wing and up the long twist of stairs, to a land she had not visited for a decade, a place high above the meddlesome world of the grown-ups, where at the end of every day Nanny had waited with relief that at last it was six o'clock and she could start putting her charge to bed.

She paused as she reached the top of the stairs and looked down the nursery corridor. The paint was still the same, brown woodwork and cream walls, and the smell was just the same, lino, and soap, disinfectant and furniture polish. There was no sense of time up here, not like there was in the grown up world, where the chariot was always, it seemed, hurrying nearer and nearer. Up here it seemed to be just one long and eternal childhood.

And a sun-filled one, too. Artemis had all but forgotten how bright and sunny the nurseries were, compared with the shadowy coolness of the formal world below. All the nursery bedrooms faced due east, so when it was fine weather everyone got up with the sun, and since all the playrooms and sitting rooms were on the west side of the wing, tea and story-time were sunlit as well. Artemis felt a sudden sad longing to return to that world, as she stood in the morning sunshine in one of the empty maid's bedrooms. It had all been so secure up here, so far from real harm's way.

Ellie was in Artemis's bedroom, sitting with her back to the door on the edge of the single bed, which was still covered with Artemis's old yellow eiderdown, the corners of which she used to suck every night as she fell asleep.

'Hullo,' Artemis said. Ellie looked round, surprised. 'Mrs Blythe said I'd find you here.'

'You know, I haven't really been up here since I don't know when,' Ellie said, turning away again. 'Since we were married, I guess.'

'No. Well,' said Artemis, leaning back on the doorpost, 'there'd not be a lot of point.'

'Weren't you dreadfully lonely up here?'

'Why? You could hardly be lonely. It was crawling with staff.'

'Numbers have nothing to do with loneliness.' Ellie got up and started opening and shutting cupboards and pulling out and pushing in drawers, all of which were empty. 'It must have been absurd.'

Artemis remained silent, considering it to be more prudent under the circumstances, despite the fact that Ellie's quite categorical conclusion had immediately put her on the defensive.

'I'm certainly not going to stick any baby of mine away up here,' Ellie continued. 'As if it was some sort of freak of nature.'

'Really?' Artemis asked curiously. 'What does Hugo think?'

'You mean to say you haven't discussed it with him?' Ellie's eyes flashed as she looked briefly at Artemis, before walking past her out of the bedroom. Artemis again remained silent, refusing to be drawn. Instead she counted up to ten before following Ellie across the corridor and into the main playroom.

'Something seems to be bothering you, Eleanor,' Artemis said casually, having summoned up the courage. 'I can't imagine what.'

'Ask Hugo.'

'Hugo hasn't a clue.'

'So you've come up here to find out, yes? Or rather you've been sent up here.'

'No,' Artemis replied. 'No-one sent me here.'

Ellie turned on Artemis and stared at her. 'Do you know how drunk you were last night?' she asked.

'I think you mean tight,' Artemis replied.

'OK,' Ellie said. 'Do you know how tight you were?'

'I haven't a clue.'

'OK. So let me tell you. You were tight. Boy were you tight. You were stinko. And so was Hugo.'

'So?' Artemis shrugged.

'You arrived tight!'

'So?'

'You don't normally arrive tight!'

'You don't normally – ' Artemis stopped, changing her mind mid-sentence.

'I don't normally what?' Ellie demanded.

'It doesn't matter.'

'You know how mad that makes me, Artemis! When you don't answer!'

'It really doesn't matter, Eleanor. Really.'

'My God – who let you get away with this? I mean it! Who in hell allowed you to grow up like this! As if other people didn't matter! As if you can just walk all over them if and when you damn well feel like it! I really would like to get hold of that nanny of yours. She must have done this to you. Because oh boy, oh boy, I never met anyone in my whole life who just – who just rail-roads people the way you do!'

'I got tight, Eleanor,' Artemis replied, 'because I wanted to.'

'You got drunk simply because you felt like it?'

'Tight,' said Artemis. 'Yes.'

'Yes,' said Ellie, 'that figures.'

'Well? So what? Did I do anything?'

'What do you mean?'

'Did. I. Do. Anything.'

'Like? Such as?'

'Was I sick? Did I fight you? Did I hit anybody? Did I break any furniture? Did I set fire to the curtains? Stop me when I'm getting warm. Did I throw glasses at the wall?'

'This isn't funny, Artemis. This isn't a game.' Ellie walked past her again, and Artemis followed, her stick tapping on the polished wooden floor.

'So what did I do, Eleanor? Besides getting tight!' Artemis called after Ellie, who was walking far too quickly for her.

Ellie then stopped way ahead of Artemis, down the far end of the corridor, and turned to face her. 'You made a goddam fool of yourself, Artemis!' Ellie called back. 'That's what you did!'

'All right. I apologize for that. But if I made a fool of myself, isn't that rather my concern?'

'No it damn well isn't!' Ellie yelled. 'You made Hugo make a fool of himself, too! And in front of the staff!' Ellie started on her way downstairs, but Artemis called after her, to try and stop her.

'Ellie?' she called. 'Eleanor!' She walked as fast as she could to the top of the staircase, and as she did, she saw Ellie's face looking at her from floor level through the bannisters.

'I really have nothing more to say to you, Artemis,' she said. 'Nothing whatsoever.'

'I want to know why I was responsible for Hugo making a fool of himself,' Artemis said.

'Because you were drunk.' Ellie glared at her up through the bannisters. 'Hugo only got drunk to keep you company. So as you wouldn't feel – I don't know. Disgraced,

I guess. Hugo got drunk because he's a gentleman. Pity you didn't act a bit more like a lady.'

'You still haven't told me what I'm supposed to have done.'

Ellie eyed her long and hard and then walked back up to the top of the stairs. 'First you tell me something I want to know,' she said. 'Do you love Hugo?' she asked.

The words echoed round and round in her head, as if she was down a well and Ellie was calling to her. Did she love Hugo. Did she love Hugo. And then she was falling deeper into the well, spiralling headlong into darkness, but slowly as if in a dream. Except now she could feel Ellie's hands take both her shoulders, holding her upright as her legs buckled beneath her.

'What is it? Are you OK? Artemis?'

She mustn't faint, she knew she mustn't. It would look so foolish if she fainted, as though Ellie had thrown open a door and found her with Hugo. So she closed her eyes tight, breathed in and breathed out, and clung on to the silver top of her cane, to try and take her weight off Ellie. 'I suppose I must still be a bit tight,' she heard herself saying. 'I suddenly went rather giddy.'

Ellie led her back along the corridor, away from the stairs, and into a room where she sat her on a bed. Then she stood back and watched her, while Artemis, averting her eyes, waited for her head to stop swimming. Her hands and feet were ice cold, and yet she could feel the dampness of her brow and a trickle of perspiration running between her breasts and on down her stomach.

'Sorry,' she said suddenly. 'I really think I must still be a bit tight.'

'You reckon that's what it is?'

'I can't remember what you said,' Artemis stalled, wiping her brow dry with her fingertips. 'Or what you asked.'

'I asked you if you loved Hugo,' Ellie said evenly.

This time Artemis was quite prepared for it. She tossed her hair back from her eyes and looked steadily back at Ellie. 'Of course I do.'

Ellie was as unprepared for Artemis's answer as Artemis had been initially for Ellie's question. She had expected a flat denial, or a flash of temper, or even a mocking laugh in return. Instead she'd got the answer she'd least expected, and it left her speechless.

'Look,' Artemis said, carefully monitoring Ellie's reaction. 'If you insist on asking this sort of question, you have to be ready to hear the truth.'

Ellie, still silent, sat down in an old green wicker chair and leaning forward, half-hid her face in one hand. 'I should never have asked you.'

'I don't suppose you should,' Artemis agreed. 'At least not if you didn't want to hear the truth. But then perhaps you asked because you already knew the truth.'

Ellie sighed, leaning backwards and now putting both her hands to her face. 'Does Hugo love you?'

'Of course not,' Artemis retorted, clicking her tongue. 'Don't be such an idiot.'

Ellie took her hands away from her eyes and looked across at Artemis, whom she saw had taken a gold compact of loose powder from her bag and was now carefully dusting her face with a small feathered puff.

'If Hugo loved me,' Artemis said, stopping briefly to glance up at Ellie, 'I'd hardly have told you what I've just told you.' She returned her compact to her handbag. 'My feelings, Ellie, are neither here nor there. You love Hugo and Hugo loves you. As you must know. So that's that. Quite frankly, I can't imagine any woman meeting Hugo and not falling in love with him. He's what every woman wants. And you've got him. So there.' Artemis looked at Ellie, defying her not to laugh. Ellie couldn't laugh, but she managed a smile, as Artemis deliberately widened the look in her eyes.

'How can you bear it?' Ellie wondered after a moment. 'Being here. Being around. If that's how you feel.'

'Simply because it would be a great deal worse not being here,' Artemis replied. 'Anyway, I'm used to it now. When I found out in Ireland, I mean how I felt, as it were, I just thought this is ridiculous, and that was that. And then I thought – '

'Hold on. Whoa,' said Ellie. 'What was so ridiculous?'

'I thought I don't see any real reason why we can't still be friends,' Artemis concluded.

'What was so ridiculous?'

'I don't remember.'

'Artemis – '

'It doesn't matter.'

'You thought it was ridiculous to expect Hugo to fall in love with you?'

'Why should I think that? Don't be an idiot.'

'You're the one who's an idiot,' Ellie said, and fell to silence.

'If you'd rather I didn't stay around,' Artemis added, 'I'll understand. I mean I don't mind.'

'I would. I'd mind like hell.'

Artemis clasped her hands together in her lap and bent her head over them thoughtfully, putting her two thumbs together side by side. After a moment, Ellie put a cool hand over them and they both sat in silence, with nothing more to say to each other, while the morning sun slipped from the room and cast them slowly into shade.

1939

16

Except within the confines of the great estate of Brougham, where relationships were calm, elsewhere peace reigned uneasily. At the beginning of the year the view of the majority of people concerning the possibility of a war had been hypothetical. War as an if. If there is a war, people said, not when. But by April, after the German invasion of the Sudetenland and Italy's occupation of Albania it then became a matter of when war broke out, and this was reflected by the government finally bowing to the pressure brought to bear on it by its more realistic members, stepping up preparations for the now surely inevitable conflict. It passed a new Civil Defence Act and finally introduced conscription, against the opposition of both the Appeasers and the Labour party.

Nevertheless, there was still more than a faint air of unreality about the impending crisis. Even the issue of thirty eight million gas masks the previous year, a greatly increased army recruiting drive and the publication of a series of ominous pamphlets advising on the protection of the nation's homesteads failed to bring home the reality. Town and Parish Hall demonstrations of how to cope with the aftermath of gas attacks, air raids and even with invasion itself were inclined to be treated light-heartedly, while classes attending instructional lectures for first aid reportedly collapsed in laughter as legs dropped off ancient dummies and volunteers were gagged into total silence by the bandaging of over enthusiastic volunteers. At the fire-fighting classes the pupils' fight was more to control their mirth rather than possible conflagrations, as they were shown how to douse small domestic fires with bedpans, and as enthusiastic girl fire-fighters kept falling down before they could reach the extinguishers due to having forgotten to cut the strings which tied their new wellington boots together. Even graphically illustrated lectures on how to treat broken bones and severed arteries were greeted with good-natured barracking and wisecracks, as if there was simply no likelihood at all of anyone inflicting such appalling injuries on a civilian population.

For a while Artemis, Ellie and Hugo were all to a greater or lesser degree infected with similar such optimism and unaccountable light-heartedness. Artemis birthed her mare in April, and temporarily forgot the outside world, watching in wonder as the beautiful bay filly, barely a week old, cantered and bucked and squealed around the carefully prepared nursery paddocks. Hugo continued with the painting of his mural, depicting life at Brougham, while Ellie grew larger with her child and calmer as its birth date in July approached. In the lengthening summer evenings, Hugo and Ellie would sit out on the lawns behind the house where Artemis herself had once played as a child, and Hugo would lie Ellie down on her back, and in time honoured way, put his hands on her stomach to feel the life inside her. At the same time of day Artemis and Jenkins would lead the mare and foal into their stable and stand together watching as the filly settled into the straw for the night with her mother standing guard over her.

And then one day Hugo put away his paints and went to London, without Ellie, and without telling her why. When she awoke to find him already gone, with just a note on his pillow to say he should be back for dinner, and if not, he would telephone her, she knew he had gone to enlist.

Ellie knew it to have been the subject of Hugo's conversations with Charles Hunter, for whenever Charles came down to visit Artemis, he would call in to see Hugo and Ellie before returning to his regiment. They would have tea or a cocktail, and then Hugo, on the invention of some pretext or other, would take Charles off to the library where they would remain cloistered until Charles finally had to leave. Hugo and Ellie would then dine together, but nothing would be said.

She had once asked to know the particular nature of these conversations, but Hugo had answered with deliberate vagueness and immediately switched subjects. And Ellie had never pursued the matter further, simply because she was trying to delay a moment which she knew must come, the moment when Hugo decided he must join up.

'How?' Artemis had asked her, as Ellie sat out in Artemis's garden, watching her deadhead the borders and prune the sweet scented old rose bushes. 'And as what? Hugo's hardly front line material, not with those weak eyes of his. So he certainly won't be flying any aircraft. Or captaining any ships.'

'It doesn't matter. You know Hugo. He'll find something.'

'Yes,' Artemis stopped for a moment to think. 'Yes you're right. He will find something, the idiot. Something incredibly stupid.'

Ellie knew that by incredibly stupid Artemis had meant, quite naturally, the very opposite.

Hugo was away for over two days. He telephoned Ellie on both evenings and said he was unavoidably delayed, but that he would return as soon as possible.

'Where are you exactly? Suppose I need you? I don't even know where you are.'

Hugo told her to leave any message at his club and they would guarantee to pass it on to him at once. Apart from that, all he would say was that he loved her, and that she was to take the greatest care of herself.

When he did return, unable to stand the suspense any longer, Ellie confronted him.

'I told you ages ago I couldn't stand idle, Ell,' he said, wandering ahead of her into the room they had made their private sitting room. 'But then I knew there was a chance they might spin me for my eyes, so rather than that I went to see Charles's old man.'

'You mean you were recommended to go and see Charles's father.' Ellie could hardly bear to look at him he was so beautiful, his slender elegant figure draped over the old rug-covered sofa. 'That's what you've been cloistering yourself away with Charles about. I knew it.'

'Of course you did.'

It seemed that Hugo, desperate to do something other than push a pen or be sidelined into administration when war broke out, which was all he supposed they would let someone like him with such poor eyesight do, had mentioned his unease to Charles who had taken it further. Hence Hugo's visit to London, and his meetings with General Sir George Hunter, DSO, MC.

'Yes? And?'.

'He thinks he can find me something useful to do,' Hugo replied, stretching his arms out up above his fair head.

'What exactly?'

'I can't say, I'm afraid, Ell. Not because I don't know, but because I can't.'

'Artemis said you'd find something stupid.'

'Sorry?' Hugo turned to look at her sideways on. 'Has she been talking to Charles?'

'No.' Ellie lowered herself down very slowly into an armchair, letting out a deep sigh. 'By stupid she meant foolhardy. Or heroic, I suppose you'd say. I mean I take it if you can't talk about it, it must have something to do with military intelligence. Or whatever.'

'Ellie, my darling,' Hugo smiled, and held the smile, looking at her tenderly. 'If you only knew how much I loved you.'

The plan had been for Ellie to have the baby at a nursing home in London, and for her to move down and stay in the family house with Hugo the week before it was due. But Diana Lanchester on her last visit to the Dower House had told Artemis all the latest news and rumours, which included a real fear in certain government circles of a 'knock-out blow from the air', aimed at London, with the intention of paralysing the country. So it was therefore decided that Ellie should not travel to the capital, but should be delivered at a nursing home on the outskirts of Bath.

Artemis rang and asked if she could visit before Ellie left Brougham? 'Or rather before we both do,' she said on the telephone.

'So where are you going?'

'I'll tell you over a drink.'

'Tell me first where you've been,' Ellie said after Artemis with Brutus in tow had arrived, and they'd settled into Ellie's little sitting room, which Hugo had rechristened the ladies' sulking room. 'I gather you've been away.'

'I've joined the ARP,' Artemis said, trying to find room on the sofa beside her large dog. 'And I've joined the WVS. And I've had a hysterical time. You see, there aren't all that many women who can drive, you know.'

'I know,' said Ellie with a smile. 'I happen to be best friends with one who can't.'

Artemis ignored her and continued. 'If you think about it, which I admit I hadn't, it makes sense, you see. Because there aren't that many women with their own cars, are there? Anyway. I've been on a course in Swindon, being taught by the chap who owns the taxi service how to tow trailers containing or rather how to tow trailers which *will* contain stretchers. On racks. Sort of home-made ambulances, if you see what I mean. And it's an absolute nightmare when you have to back, or reverse, or whatever you call it. Because the wretched bit with all the stretchers, you see, it goes the other way. I kept getting frightfully stuck. And then we were all sent up to Burnham Beeches, to learn how to drive in the dark. I nearly died. First of all we all had to drive in gas masks, do you see, on just our sidelights in total darkness. You know, about two in the morning. Can you imagine? My gas mask kept steaming up, and I drove into God knows how many trees. I do wish you'd listen.'

Artemis had to stop, while Ellie tried to bring her laughter under control. She wiped her eyes on her handkerchief, and bit hard on her lip. 'Sorry,' she said weakly. 'I really am sorry.'

'It gets worse,' Artemis warned. 'Because after we'd all been driving around in our steamed-up gas masks, they then had this special test, as a kind of *pièce de résistance*. And we all had to do it. In twos. You each started out at either end of the woods, do you see. I mean miles away from each other. Then you had to drive, without any lights at all, mind. Not even your sidelights. You had to drive along this desperately wiggly sort of road, towards each other in pitch darkness, the point being you had finally to pass each other safely, without stopping. And without crashing. Honestly, I got so nervous about the whole business because I thought I mean knowing me, I thought I was bound to crash head-on with my opposite number, and I mean they all take it terribly seriously. You get badges and things. And a certificate. Anyway. I just couldn't face it, so I ducked off the road and drove through the woods and got completely and utterly lost.'

Ellie wasn't laughing now. She was just staring at Artemis with an odd expression.

'I told you it wasn't funny,' Artemis said, picking up her drink.

'It's not that,' Ellie said rather quietly. 'Is your car outside?'

'Yes,' said Artemis. 'Why?'

'I think I've started.'

'I thought you weren't due for a week,' Artemis yelled as she swung her car out through the main gates of the estate.

'The baby obviously has other ideas,' Ellie groaned, lying as far back in her seat as she could and staring

382

at a rain-laden sky. 'Don't you think we should have the roof up?'

'We haven't the time! It takes ages!'

'Oh my God!' Ellie called out in despair. 'Oh my God!'

'I hope you know the way!' Artemis yelled, as she took a sharp left-hand corner on the right-hand side.

'I haven't the faintest idea!' Ellie gasped as another agonizing pain took her breath away. 'Just head for Bath!'

'Of all the stupid times for Hugo to be in London!' This time Artemis took a right-handed corner on the left-side and for a while ran along the neatly trimmed verge. 'What the hell does he think he's doing down in London!'

'What in hell do you think you're doing up on the grass?' Ellie yelled back. 'God only knows what you must be like in the dark! And in a gas mask!'

The Aston Martin came to a standstill on the top of a hill outside Cold Ashton, still some eight miles short of Bath.

'What's the matter?' Ellie asked, unable to keep the hysteria from her voice. 'Why have we stopped?'

'I don't know,' Artemis frowned, pressing and repressing the ignition button to no avail. 'It seems to have gone out.'

'Why?' said Ellie, her voice rising. 'Why?'

'How should I know!' Artemis shouted, getting out. 'I hate cars!'

Five minutes later, a large black Austin six-cylinder pulled up in answer to Artemis's distress signals, and a good-looking well-dressed middle-aged man, wearing a dark blue suit and his regimental tie got out to offer his assistance. Artemis explained the situation and he at once agreed to carry the two women post haste to the nursing home, with whose location he was happily familiar. Together with Artemis he laid Ellie carefully on the back seat, tucked under a travelling rug, with his rolled up jacket under her head, and then proceeded to drive quickly and expertly towards Bath.

'Ready for the war?' he enquired.

'Absolutely,' Artemis replied, her mind on other matters.

'Damn business,' the driver replied. 'Ridiculous really.'

'Quite,' said Artemis, turning round in her seat to watch Ellie, who smiled back at her.

'No it really is the most damnable business,' the driver continued, shifting gear. 'Let's face it, anybody who's anybody in this country, they've got no argument with Hitler.'

Artemis made to turn back to the driver to engage him in argument, but reading her intention, Ellie held tight to Artemis's hand and frowned at her to remain silent.

'No,' the man continued, 'we've got no quarrel with Herr Hitler. And neither has he with us. He admires us. He does. And frankly, the people who know a thing or two over here, they admire Herr Hitler in return. It's these wretched radicals who can't wait to spill blood. Boothby. Sandys. Churchill. Hore-Belisha and Duff Cooper's little lot. Jew-lovers, the lot of them.'

Hearing this and sensing Artemis stiffen, Ellie tried desperately to hold on to her friend's hand. But Artemis had got it free and had turned her sole attention to the driver.

'Artemis – ' Ellie began, but too late.

'I don't think I can have heard you right,' Artemis said, in the clipped way she spoke when angry. 'At least I hope I didn't.'

The man turned and glanced at her for a moment, and then smiled, brushing the left-hand corner of his moustache upwards with his index finger. 'That's what it's all about, young woman,' he replied. 'No two ways about it. The Jews.'

'What about the Jews?'

'If the radicals get their way, don't you see? All our young men – your young men, your husbands, your boyfriends, whatever. My sons. One's friends' sons. One's friends, damn it. What'll they be fighting for? A lot of blasted Jews.' He smiled as he spoke, as if such a thing was beyond comprehension, and then he shook his head ruefully.

'Artemis –' Ellie started, but Artemis ignored her, and drew a deep breath.

'You don't think much of the Jews, obviously,' she said. 'Even though Christ was one.'

'What did you say?' the man asked.

'I said Jesus Christ was a Jew,' Artemis replied. 'Remember?'

'I don't see what that's got to do with it,' he said. 'No, Hitler's got the right idea all right. Good lord, they're everywhere! I was dining at the Savoy last night and the place was crawling with Jews! When you think what the blighters get up to – and then we're expected to go to war to save the silk shirts on their backs! Dear me. Oh dear me. Don't you sometimes wonder what this world of ours is coming to?'

'Only when I meet people like you,' Artemis said.

Ellie lay back and shut her eyes knowing there was nothing she could do now.

The man slowed down the car. 'What did you say?' he asked.

'I said,' Artemis sighed, 'only when I meet people like you.'

The car now ground to a complete halt. 'You think the yiddisher are worth fighting over, do you?'

'What I think is you'd better catch the first boat to Germany before it's too late.'

'You're a Jew!' the man said suddenly. 'Is that what it is?'

'Of course,' Artemis lied. 'Couldn't you tell?'

The man's complexion changed visibly, turning a deep and angry red. 'I've a good mind to kick you out here and let you damn well walk,' he said.

'I would hardly call yours a good mind,' replied Artemis.

There was a groan from Ellie in the back, a sign of her utter dismay. Fortunately the driver mistook it for a sign of imminent birth, and rather than be forced to act the midwife, re-engaged gear and drove on.

No-one spoke another word until the car had turned into the drive of the designated nursing home and had pulled up outside the main entrance.

'Just remember,' the driver said as he pulled on the handbrake, 'when this war breaks out, it'll be due to you Jews. And no-one else.'

To Ellie's horror, Artemis turned to the man as if she was prepared to argue. Since her pains were coming now every two or three minutes, Ellie let herself out the back of the car and staggered in to the nursing home. Fifty five minutes later, and fortunately with no complications whatsoever, she was delivered of an eight-pound baby boy. His skin was wrinkly pink, he had Hugo's fair hair, and Ellie's dark brown eyes.

'Well done,' said Artemis, leaning down to kiss Ellie's forehead. 'Jolly good for you.'

'You're crazy,' Ellie replied, taking her hand. 'You know that? You are. You're completely nuts.'

This time there was no cheering, not as there had been in 1914 when flags had been unfurled and the streets had echoed with cheers and hurrahs, as a nation in its innocence decided it was time to teach the bosche a short, sharp lesson. This time war came in on thunderclouds, as violent storms swept across the country after a hot and sunny Saturday, as if presaging years of death and destruction ahead. That night the country lay in darkness, blacked out by the new regulations, the only illumination for those hurrying back to their homes from a day at the seaside in darkened railway carriages being the constant flashes of lightning.

'You could see the same thing on everyone's faces,' Hugo whispered to Ellie, as they sat side by side in their darkened bedroom, watching the storm. 'As I drove down the Strand, all you could see was this extraordinary look. This look of sort of contempt. And — and disillusion.'

'What's going to happen?' Ellie whispered back, moving even closer to Hugo after another clap of thunder had pealed right overhead.

'I don't know,' Hugo replied. 'With this fool of a prime minister probably nothing. I mean it's two days now since Germany invaded Poland. And he still won't declare war.'

Half an hour later, Ellie got up and went to feed James Michael Hugo Tanner, who was sleeping in Ellie's dressing room which she had now made his nursery. While she was gone, Hugo also got up and went and stood at the window, watching the lightning flicker over the landscape, and listening to the rumble of the thunder as the storm passed, a dress rehearsal for the air raids which soon must come, he thought, bringing death by blast and fire from the skies.

The morning was bright, clear and refreshing, the storms having dispelled the sultriness of the night. Hugo and Ellie were both up at sunrise, which that fateful Sunday was at a quarter past six, and on the first news bulletin at seven o'clock they heard that there had still been no response from Hitler to Britain's ultimatum that he should withdraw from Poland. Unable to eat any breakfast, they took their coffee outside to the terrace at the back of the house where they sat saying very little and staring at nothing in particular.

Artemis rang at a quarter to eight and asked if she could come up to the house, and Ellie agreed at once. Somehow they all knew that any minute the country would be at war. Artemis arrived ten minutes later with a battery radio to which they could listen outside, and on the next bulletin they learned of the destruction of German tanks and planes by the Poles.

'Wishful thinking, I'm afraid,' Hugo said. 'This time Goliath wins.'

Two hours later it was announced that the prime minister would speak to the nation at eleven-fifteen. In the meantime, while the population held its breath, they could listen to a selection of music ranging from *Princess Ida*, to 'The Passionate Shepherd' sung by Parry Jones, and then to a recorded talk entitled 'Making The Most of Tinned Foods'.

'I don't think so, do you?' Artemis asked, switching the radio set off. 'I'd rather listen to the birds.'

'Eleven-fifteen,' Hugo mused. 'Damn. Right in the middle of Matins.'

Hugo went to church every Sunday when he was at Brougham, because living in the great house it was expected of him. Everyone from the estate worshipped in the beautiful little church which was part of the house, as did those from the village, a tradition which had its roots long before the present house had been built. So Hugo had felt it incumbent upon himself, as the latest owner of Brougham, to continue the tradition. Ellie, however, never accompanied him, the only time that she had been in a church since taking her vow as a child being the occasion of her marriage.

But she volunteered quite spontaneously to go with Hugo this day, as did Artemis, whose idea it was to take her battery radio with them so that the prime minister's message could be broadcast to the attendant congregation.

'Most enterprising,' the Reverend Slater said as Hugo explained their intentions. 'I was about to send my daughter home so that she could bring us the news, but this is much more enterprising altogether.'

Just before the broadcast was due, the vicar made an announcement, and the people gathered in the thirteenth-century church sat down in their pews, alongside their boxed gas masks which they all had religiously brought with them, to await the news of their country's fate. Two minutes later their ageing prime minister read his bulletin over the air sadly, with an air of resignation:

I am speaking to you, from the cabinet room at number ten Downing Street. This morning, the British Ambassador in Berlin handed the German government a final note, stating that unless the British government heard from them by eleven o'clock that they were prepared at once to withdraw their troops from Poland, a state of war would exist between us. I have to tell you now that no such undertaking has been received, and that consequently this country is at war with Germany . . . The situation in which no word given by Germany's ruler could be trusted and no people or country could feel itself safe, has become intolerable. Now we have resolved to finish it . . . May God bless you all. May he defend the right, for it is evil things that we shall be fighting against — brute force, bad faith, injustice, oppression and persecution; and against them I am certain right will prevail.

The national anthem followed and everyone stood up. One or two of the congregation began to sing the words, but they were soon drowned out by a howl of anguished crying from the back of the church. The curious turned round to stare at whoever it was, while the more polite faced the altar, or held their children tightly to their sides to stifle their curiosity.

Artemis recognized who was crying instinctively and went at once to take the young woman outside and into the fresh September air.

Rosie's face was blotched red. 'I'm so sorry, your ladyship!' she sobbed as Artemis led her to a wooden seat in the graveyard. 'It's not me, you see! I'm not crying for me! It's 'cos like we're 'avin' a baby, see!'

'It's all right, Rosie,' Artemis said, sitting her down. 'You'll be quite safe down here. In the country.'

'No, your ladyship!' Rosie gasped, trying her best to stem the flood of tears, 'it's Jack, see! He's joinin' up! An' 'e's goin' to get isself killed!'

They sat and watched the congregation file out of church. Some of the men, those in their middle- or late-twenties, were walking taller now, with their shoulders back, as if their purpose had finally been decided for them, while the older men looked introspective or thoughtful. And then there were the boys, young lads of fifteen or sixteen, some hoping the war would be a quick thing, and others that it would last until they were old enough to go and fight themselves. They were followed or accompanied by their women; wives, mothers, sisters. Some of them with faces quite ashen from the shock while others wept into their handkerchieves, their heads half-turned away in grief, as if they were already mourners at a loved one's funeral. All of them held on to the hands or the arms of their menfolk, as if uncertain of how much longer they had to love them and enjoy their company.

Hugo was the last to leave the church with the vicar. He had stood and talked to those he knew and those he half-knew and to those who were strangers, a word here, a smile, a nod, or just a hand on an arm. And now, as Ellie talked to one of their farmer's wives, he stood momentarily alone, gazing up into the clear blue of the midday sky, as if that was where their salvation lay.

There were just the three of them for lunch, Hugo, Ellie and Artemis. Charles had been intending to come down for the weekend, but events had overtaken him and he telephoned Artemis the night before to say all leave had been cancelled.

'Have you any idea what's happening?' she had asked him when they had spoken. 'When the balloon goes up, where will they send you?'

'I don't know,' he laughed, 'and if I did, I certainly wouldn't be allowed to tell you.'

There was a short silence, during which neither of them could think of what to say. Charles broke it. 'You know what I'm going to ask?'

'Of course.'

'Well?'

'If I say yes now, you'll think I'm only doing so because – well. You know.'

'I don't care. Just please say you'll marry me.'

'I can't, Charles.'

'Why not?'

'You know why not.'

'I don't care, Artemis. I love you, that's all that matters. So please say you'll marry me.'

'I can't, Charles.'

'It doesn't matter that you don't love me.'

'It does to me, Charles.'

'Why? Don't you realize I could be sent abroad any moment?' Artemis remained silent. 'Artemis, darling,' Charles said. 'Please. Please say you'll marry me.'

'Charles,' Artemis replied after a moment. 'Charles if you want me to come up to London, and stay with you, I will. But I won't marry you. I'm sorry.'

'Why not?'

'Why do you think? It would be silly.'

Charles thought about it, and then laughed. 'That's why I love you, Artemis,' he said. 'You're right. It would be silly. Damn silly.'

'If I married Charles,' Artemis explained to Ellie and Hugo, 'and I don't know,' she shrugged, 'say the war's over in six months. A year. Less. And he doesn't get killed. Then we're stuck with each other.'

'You mean you're stuck with him,' Hugo said, picking at his food.

'You can be just as stuck with somebody you love who doesn't love you as you can with somebody you don't love who loves you. If you see what I mean.'

'Sure,' said Ellie. 'I do.'

'I don't,' Hugo frowned. 'But I admire your principles, Tom.'

Apart from that diversion, the talk was all exigency plans. Hugo had already made arrangements for all the art treasures and the fine furniture to be sealed away deep in the vaults which ran below the house. Ellie said that she couldn't see the point because if the Germans invaded, they'd certainly find anything hidden around the estate, but Hugo told her that was not the object of the exercise. He was adopting a more optimistic point of view, namely that there would be no invasion, but if the war was a long one, houses such as Brougham would be requisitioned for other purposes, just as they had been during the last war, and so it would not be sensible to leave the place furnished as it was.

'And supposing you're wrong?' Ellie asked. 'Supposing there is an invasion?'

'You want to talk about that now?'

'Certainly,' Ellie said. 'And then I must go and feed James Michael.'

This was the first Artemis had heard about Ellie's feeding methods. 'You're not actually feeding it yourself?' she asked.

'Him,' Ellie replied. 'And yes, of course I am. And do try not to look quite so disgusted.'

Artemis stared at her, then looked at Hugo, and then back at Ellie. 'Really?' she said, still unable to believe it. 'And you're going to go on feeding it?'

'Him,' Ellie sighed. 'And yes, I am. And now can we go on with what we were talking about?'

'Good God,' Artemis said, half to herself. 'How weird.'

Ellie turned to Hugo and reminded him of her question. Hugo paused for a moment, drumming his fingers on the dining table. 'It's not as easy as that,' he said finally. 'I mean for a start, you're an American, and whatever warning noises Mr Roosevelt has made this year and last, the feeling is that it's a case of once bitten. You know. America feels it won the last war and saved the world, and never got thanked for it.'

'Nonsense.'

'Seriously, Ell. That's what I've been told. They haven't even been paid back the money they lent us. It's not that America is unsympathetic – far from it. They'll want us to win. But — or at least as they tell me — they don't quite see why they should sacrifice their young men at the altar of the British Empire.'

'Let's leave that aside for the moment. I'm married to an Englishman, and I live in England, I now feel English.'

'Then,' said Hugo, looking at her in the eye, 'in that case they'll probably line you up against the wall and shoot you with the rest of us.'

'No,' said Artemis firmly. 'Rather than that, I vote we all shoot each other.'

'We can't *all* shoot each other, Tom,' Hugo said. 'Ellie shoots you, I shoot Ellie, who shoots me?'

'I shoot you, as you shoot Ellie, as Ellie shoots me,' Artemis sighed, as if Hugo was missing out on what two and two made. 'Look.' She made her hand into a mock gun and held it up, index finger pointing barrel-like at Hugo's head. 'Go on,' she instructed Hugo and then Ellie. 'And you. Go on.'

The three of them sat there, an index finger pointed at each other's heads.

'One, two, three,' Artemis counted. 'Bang.'

'One, two, three — bang,' said Hugo thoughtfully, his finger still pointed at Ellie's temple. Then he lowered it. 'Surely it would be much easier just to shoot ourselves?' he asked.

'What about James?'

'I'd shoot my horses,' Artemis put in. 'And Brutus.'

'I'm talking about my baby.'

'And I'm talking about my horses, and my dog,' said Artemis.

Ellie looked blankly at Artemis and then got up and left the table. Hugo sighed a deep sigh and shook his head at Artemis as he rose to go after his wife.

'No,' said Artemis.

'I hope you're not forbidding me to go after my wife, Tom,' Hugo said.

'Yes I am,' Artemis replied, reaching for her stick. 'It's about time I learned to pick up my own pieces.'

By the time Artemis had followed on upstairs, Ellie was already in the nursery preparing to feed her baby.

'I shouldn't come in if I were you,' she said to Artemis. 'You'll probably be sick.'

'Why don't you have a wet nurse?' Artemis asked, standing in the doorway. 'Or bottle feed, like everyone else?'

'Either come in or out,' Ellie said, ignoring the question. 'Don't just stand there in the doorway.'

'Where's your nanny?' Artemis asked, shutting the door behind her and going to look through into the other rooms.

'I sent her home,' Ellie said, 'on Thursday. Her family live on the coast, in a place called Hornsea – would that be right?'

'Probably.' Artemis now wandered over to the windows, keeping her back firmly turned on Ellie and her baby.

'Apparently Hornsea could be a likely target if there's to be a surprise attack,' Ellie continued. 'And Nanny was very worried about her parents.' She fell to silence, her head bowed. Artemis could see the reflection of the mother and baby in the window, reminding her of a painting she had seen, of a girl in a pale red dress just as Ellie was now wearing, bent tenderly and lovingly over the child at her breast. She stared at the image, unable to take her eyes off it.

'Did you want something?'

'Yes,' Artemis replied. 'I came up to say sorry for being so stupid. For saying what I said. But I'm not sorry.'

'That's nothing new. Tell me something I don't know,' said Ellie absently. She hadn't looked up, so she was unaware that Artemis was actually staring directly at her and the baby.

'I mean I'm not sorry I was so rude. And so stupid,' Artemis continued, 'because if I hadn't been, I wouldn't have had to come up here to apologize.'

'And?' Ellie now looked up and saw the expression on Artemis's face.

'Would it be all right? Or rather would it be "OK"? You know – if after you've finished I held Jamie?'

After the initial alarms and excursions of the first weekend of war, when four barrage balloons caught fire at Portsmouth after being struck by lightning, causing the inhabitants to believe the invasion had already begun, and the deliberate false alarm organized by the government to test London's population to the air raid warning system, in Britain nothing warlike occurred at all. There was no invasion, or even hint of it. Neither were there any air raids, nor gas attacks. The only indications that the country was at war were at sea, where from the very beginning the fighting was ruthless. Before September was out, the Germans had torpedoed and sunk the British aircraft carrier HMS *Courageous*. Which was why initially Hugo resolutely refused Ellie permission to go to America.

In late October, out of the blue, Ellie had received a letter from her father, the first he'd written to her since she had emigrated. That was the first shock. The second was that it had not been sent from Westfield Drive but from an altogether smarter part of Boston, on the right side of the tracks. The third shock was the worst and was the reason why Ellie was determined to recross the Atlantic. Madame Gautier was seriously ill and was asking for her.

Ellie reasoned that since America was neutral, if she travelled on an American ship, she would be in no danger. But Hugo opposed the idea vigorously, particularly since Ellie intended taking the baby with her.

'Madame Gautier was like a mother to me, Hugo,' Ellie argued. 'She was also my best friend. She's told my father she won't die happy unless she sees me.'

But Hugo wouldn't relent and showed no signs of so doing, until one day towards the end of October he returned from one of his trips to London in a very different frame of mind.

'You can go to America, Ellie,' he told her the same evening, as they sat in the little sitting room in front of the fire, 'but only conditionally. If the war worsens, which everyone thinks it must, you have to stay in America, and that's an order. You and Jamie stay there until it's safe to come home.'

'I see,' Ellie said. 'And what about you?'

'They've found me something to do, at last, and I'm not going to be able to spend much more time up here at Brougham. So you might as well take your trip now, while you can.'

'There's something else, isn't there?' Ellie put an arm around his neck and kissed the side of his face. 'You can't fool me.'

'I'm being sent abroad, Ellie, but I'm not sure when. It might even be next week. And I can't say where.'

'Do you know?'

Hugo nodded.

'What are you doing, Hugo? Can't you tell me?'

'Not really, Ell. All I can tell you is it's advisory.'

'Is that the official word for spying?'

'No, Ell,' Hugo smiled. 'I promise I'm not going to be a spy.' He threw another log on to the fire and stared into it for a while, falling silent. 'The other condition, Ellie,' he said finally, 'the second condition is that if anything happens to me, if I get killed, you're to stay in America.'

Ellie prodded the fire with the poker. 'I'm not so sure I want to go now. Maybe I'll stay here after all.'

'No,' and by his tone Ellie knew he meant no. 'There's talk of an invasion either at the end of the year, or the beginning of next. So I'd rather you went now, while nothing is going on, than try and get out when things have got really bad.'

'I don't want to go, Hugo. I mean it.'

'You must go, Ellie. For Jamie. Now. You must.'

'But what will I do without you, Hugo?'

'What will any of us do, Ellie?' Hugo sighed, holding her hand. 'The whole world's about to go up in flames, what can any of us do?'

They held each other all night, never letting go for one moment. Outside the skies were dark but quiet, silent except for the screech of distant owls.

'The cherry trees bend over, and are shedding
On the old road where all that passed are dead,
Their petals, strewing the grass as for a wedding
This early May morn when there is none to wed.'

As Ellie lay beside him, Hugo whispered the poem quietly to her, but only once he was sure she was asleep.

'I'm going to be driving somebody in the government,' Artemis stared down at Ellie's dozing baby.

'I hope they know what they're letting themselves in for,' Ellie answered, circling the bedroom once more on the look-out for anything forgotten. 'I'd have said it would be safer for them to hike it, rather than have you drive them. Bombs and all.'

'Do babies always dribble like this?' Artemis asked, carefully wiping Jamie's mouth with her handkerchief.

'Don't ask me,' Ellie smiled, 'this is my first, remember?'

She seemed to have packed everything, as there was nothing more she could find which she imagined she might need for her stay in America. So after one last look at the room, Ellie snapped her suitcases shut and fastened the straps.

'You're very much the democrat, aren't you?' Artemis teased. 'Rosie even packs my sponge bag.'

Ellie rang the bell for Porter to come and fetch her luggage before coming to sit on the window seat beside Artemis. 'I wish you were coming with us,' Ellie said.

'Yes,' said Artemis. 'I do, too. But England needs me,' she added, poker-faced.

'Like heck. You'll do more damage driving round London than the entire German Army.'

The baby in Artemis's arms awoke for a moment, stared at the face above it, caught Artemis's lip in one small pink hand, and gave a happy gurgle.

'I didn't tell you,' Artemis said, for want of something to say. 'At one of these ARP classes apparently, according to a friend in London who's learning to be a warden, Rachel Durden-Jones. You met her, remember? Anyway, she was at this class where they had this gramophone record of exploding bombs. And because there were all these women present, they turned the volume down so that the bombs wouldn't sound so loud.'

Ellie smiled, and sat down to brush her hair in front of her mirror.

'Oh and they spun me by the way,' Artemis continued, 'for any voluntary ambulance work, and the such like. Usual thing. My mobility problem. You know. Luckily Diana got me this job driving HM's MPs about the place.' She gave a little shrug and then added as an afterthought, 'Could be interesting, I suppose.'

Porter knocked on the half-open bedroom door and Ellie asked him to carry her luggage downstairs.

'I start on Monday,' Artemis said, as they followed the butler down the stairs and across the marbled hall, with Ellie now carrying her own baby. 'Jenks is going to look after Brutus. I suppose one will just have to get back down here whenever possible.'

The two women stood on top of the stone staircase outside while Ellie took a last look at her home. Nanny, back from her visit to Hornsea, was now hurrying across from the east wing, a suitcase in one hand and a large brown paper parcel under her other arm, which when she reached the waiting car she gave to Jenkins, who was waiting to drive them.

'All the men have gone, I suppose,' Artemis wondered out aloud, as Jenkins started to pile all the luggage into the estate Humber and Nanny hurried up the steps to take charge of the baby. 'Gone, or just about to go.'

Ellie kissed James Michael and then handed him over to his nurse. 'I'm afraid so,' she said. 'We had a card from Roger and Paul. They're waiting to go over to France.'

'Roger and Paul?' Artemis frowned, trying to give faces to the names.

'Our two footmen,' Ellie answered. 'Roger and Paul.'

'Porter won't go,' Artemis said, 'because of course he must be over the age. What is it? Forty one or something, isn't it?'

'That's right,' Ellie agreed. 'No Porter won't be called up.'

'No,' Artemis nodded. 'And neither of course will you, Jenks. Thank heavens.'

'Morning, ma'am,' Jenkins said to Ellie, holding open the car door. ' 'Fraid the weather's gone.'

It had begun to rain again, a cold and heavy rain which swept across the parkland in grey drifts. Ever since that fateful first Sunday of September it seemed to have done nothing but rain.

'I don't think I'll come to the station,' Artemis said looking past Ellie. 'I'm not very good at stations.'

'Neither am I,' said Ellie.

'We'd better say goodbye here then.'

'We'd better.'

Artemis brushed a stray lock of blonde hair from over one blue eye and looked at Ellie. 'Well,' she said. 'Goodbye.'

Ellie didn't reply leaving Artemis to take the initiative.

After a moment, Artemis rather formally kissed Ellie on both cheeks. 'Write if you have time,' she said gravely.

'Of course I will,' Ellie replied. ' 'Bye, Tom.'

It was the first time Ellie has used Hugo's nickname for Artemis, and for a moment it caught Artemis off guard. She hesitated and stared at Ellie, not knowing what to say. And then she collected herself and flashed Ellie a smile.

'Cheerio,' she said, before turning and walking away from the car, jabbing her stick into the gravel.

Hugo was waiting for Ellie at Paddington. She kissed him, then took his arm, while Nanny followed on with the baby.

There was an army staff car waiting for them, with a uniformed girl driver, who stood smartly to attention as she opened the car door for the party. Ellie was impressed.

'They certainly haven't signed you up just to push a pen, have they?' she said as she got into the back of the car.

'Not exactly,' Hugo said, climbing in beside her, as Nanny and her charge were put in the front. 'How was the journey?'

'Fine.'

The car was to take them across London to Waterloo station, where Ellie, Nanny and Jamie were to catch the boat-train to Southampton. Ellie, never letting go of Hugo's hand for one moment, asked him if it was still impossible for him to accompany them to the docks, and he told her that hard as he had tried, he only had an hour's leave from duty.

She had so much she wanted to say to Hugo that she ended up saying nothing at all. Instead she just sat gripping his hand like a child, looking out of her window at a city prepared for war, sandbagged and shuttered, its citizens going about their daily business with their gas mask boxes slung over their arms.

'Things aren't too bad up here at all,' Hugo assured her. 'Actually, to tell the truth you'd hardly know there was a war on. The feeling is it'll all be over in six months, though some of us aren't at all sure what Chamberlain's masterplan is exactly.' He smiled. 'There's an official pamphlet going the rounds, which explains that we don't have to defeat the Nazis on land – all we've got to do is prevent them defeating us. There's so little happening, they can hardly sell a newspaper at the moment.'

Their car was held up for a moment behind a bus which was waiting to make a right turn. Hugo attracted Ellie's attention to a newsvendor on the corner of Trafalgar Square. 'That's old Tommy, see?' he said. 'He's a right card. Sells more papers to the unsuspecting than – than I don't know. He caught me yesterday. And you know how? He shouts "Germans in . . . read all about! Germans in . . . read all about it!" And after you've bought the paper and can't find a thing in it about wherever it is Germany's meant to have invaded, and you ask him – you say where are the Germans now, Tommy? He says Berlin, guv'nor. Where they've always been.'

'Not according to the village milkman,' Ellie replied. 'That's not how he sees it at all. Cook says he's been busy going round telling everyone that Romford would it be? And Chatham, and some other big dockland, that they've all been razed to the ground by bombing, and that the government's hushed it all up, of course.'

'Of course,' laughed Hugo.

'And that there's already a shortage of timber,' Ellie continued, 'because they've had to make so many coffins.'

'And not just coffins, Mrs Tanner,' Nanny reminded her from her seat in front. 'But also the racks to store them.'

'You don't believe such nonsense, surely?' Hugo asked them. 'That's just scaremongering.'

'I don't know what to believe any more, Hugo,' Ellie replied. 'No that's not true,' she corrected herself. 'I just find it all unbelievable.'

Through the car windscreen she could see the barrage balloons floating in the sky, held to earth by their mooring ropes. Hugo pointed out that the two visible hanging over Chelsea were nicknamed Flossie and Blossom, while the ones which could now be seen as they crossed the river, rising in the sky above County Hall had been named The Bishop of London and Herbert Morrison by the House of Commons.

'I guess I'll never really understand the English,' Ellie said. 'I suppose the idea is to joke Hitler out of this war.'

'If only,' Hugo replied. 'If only.'

At Waterloo they sat alone in the car while the driver unloaded the luggage, and Nanny walked discreetly up and down the station forecourt, with their sleeping baby in her arms. The station was thronged with parties of children being evacuated to the country, their names and destinations on labels attached to their coat buttons or strung round their necks, and their gas masks slung behind them. Trains drew out, slowly, creaking and billowing sooty smoke, leaving parents and relatives staring in forlorn disbelief at their departing offspring and wondering where or when they would be reunited.

Hugo kissed Ellie, long and tenderly, while Nanny looked away. And then he kissed her again. Afterwards, he removed his spectacles and polished them on the end of his tie while they lapsed into silence.

'Where shall I write?' Ellie finally asked. 'London I guess.'

'Write to Eaton Square, and write often,' Hugo replied, holding his glasses up to the light. 'But if it's urgent, if there's an emergency, use that number I gave you.'

'Whose number is it?' Hugo had given her an address and a number in Whitehall.

'It doesn't matter, Ell,' he said. 'It'll reach me, that's all.'

Ellie pulled on her gloves, and buttoned them carefully. 'I take it what you're doing is dangerous,' she said, 'otherwise, knowing you, you wouldn't be doing it.'

'Not really,' said Hugo. 'It's just something that's got to be done. Anyway, if what everyone is saying is true, that it won't last much beyond the New Year, then I might not have to do whatever it is I might have to do.' He put his glasses back on and smiled at her.

Ellie put her hands to his cheeks and kissed him again. 'I love you, Hugo,' she told him in a low voice. 'I always have. From the moment I first saw you come up the drive at Strand House I've loved you, and I shall love you until the day I die.'

'And I love you too, Ellie,' Hugo told her, and then whispered, 'I have spread my dreams under your feet. So tread softly.'

'I shall,' Ellie held his hand tightly to her. 'I shall.'

The porter had found her a window seat and put the luggage in the guard's van. Following Ellie's instructions, Nanny sat with her back to the engine and settled the still sleeping baby into the carrycot beside her. Ellie stood at the window of the carriage and made small talk to Hugo, who kept looking anxiously down the platform to the front of the train in case it should draw out early. In Ellie's compartment was a four-year-old boy who was being evacuated, it seemed, to America, but the reality was lost on him as he kept urging his father who had come to see him off, and who was hovering in the corridor till the last possible moment, to come and sit down beside him. The train was crowded, even in the first class carriages, and as Ellie stood at the window a seemingly endless line of soldiers and sailors kept squeezing past her.

And then came the sound they had all been dreading, the sharp blast on the railway guard's whistle and the final slamming shut of the doors. The train grunted and moved backwards before it started to go forwards, throwing Ellie off her balance so she had to grab the brass top of the lowered window. In doing so, for a moment she lost hold of Hugo's hand, and then of Hugo himself as he suddenly became engulfed by a throng of parents and friends and relatives and sweethearts who had all come to wish their children and friends and husbands and lovers goodbye.

Ellie, grasping the window tightly, leaned out as far as she dared, and suddenly Hugo emerged from the crowd most of which was now moving to keep up with the train. He thew his hand out and Ellie just managed to catch hold of it briefly, for a moment, before the train gave another jerk as it gathered speed, and severed their connection.

She wanted to call to him, to shout out a final affirmation of her love, but he was going, he was becoming just a face in the crowd, another hand waving.

'Hugo!' she shouted. 'Hugo!'

But he couldn't hear her. He saw her wave and he saw that she was calling, but he couldn't hear what. Running still, thrusting his way through the crowd of people, some calling their farewells, while others slowed down to a walk and just gazed in stupefaction, Hugo suddenly burst clear of the field only to find he was running out of platform. He got to her just in time, before the platform became a ramp, and then gravel and then rails. She had one kid gloved hand to her mouth.

'I love you, Ellie!' he shouted. 'It won't be long!'

She was about to shout something back, when the wind suddenly whipped her hat from her head, tossing it up in the smoke filled air and out on to the tracks. And then she was gone, hidden in a thick puff of white as the train gathered speed past an incoming train. And when the smoke cleared the departing train had snaked round a bend, taking Ellie from his view.

But at his feet, down the ramp, in the gravel, by the lines which were taking her away, lay her hat, a little dark-blue hat, a Paris hat, with a tiny veil on the front and a small red feather on the back.

Ellie pushed the window back up and squeezing past a couple of soldiers who were standing smoking in the corridor, returned to her compartment. Her heart was breaking, but so too was the little boy's, now unhappily abandoned by his father and sitting in the seat next to Ellie's while the tears ran down his face. Ellie at once began to try and comfort him, as at that moment his need seemed even greater than her own.

'Where's your hat, Mrs Tanner?' Nanny asked, and Ellie put her hand involuntarily to her head. She hadn't even noticed it had gone. As she had gone now from Hugo, who stood alone at the end of the slowly emptying platform, staring down the line, turning the brim of her little blue hat round through his fingers.

There was no band on the quayside this time, and there were no streamers. There was just a sense of desolation and melancholy on board as the liner was tugged slowly out into the Channel from the barrage-ballooned port.

'Do you reckon those things do any good?' a stout middle-aged American woman asked Ellie as they stood watching the coast line of England recede.

'My husband says they're rather like the gas masks,' Ellie replied. 'Rather than necessarily being any good, what they do is show we're good and ready.'

'I notice you say "we",' the woman replied. 'You think Roosevelt's going to drag us into this one, too?'

'I hope so,' said Ellie. 'It's not just Hitler we're fighting, you know.'

'Come now,' said Ellie's fellow countrywoman. 'Germany's not going to pose Uncle Sam any problems. And besides, all the British seem to want is to make peace with Adolf, not war.'

'You've heard what the Germans are doing to the Jews, surely?' Ellie asked.

'Sure I have,' the woman replied. 'And what did we Americans do? At least we withdrew our man from Berlin in protest. And what did the British do?' She laughed. 'They signed an agreement with Hitler!'

Ellie could see the woman's point. The British government's obsession with appeasement had lost them a lot of points in America, as her brother Patsy had pointed out in his occasional letters to her. And although most Americans hoped Britain would defeat Germany, the country's cause was not a popular one.

'I think those things are kind of cute,' Ellie's neighbour said, switching subjects, as the barrage balloons caught the last of the day's sunlight. 'They're like great big fish up there, wouldn't you say? Like giant shiny silvery fish. It's as if England's giving a great big party.'

'I say!' one small boy said to another as they passed behind Ellie. 'Wouldn't it be fun if we were torpedoed!'

They were not torpedoed. But there was a scare, for at one point after two days at sea the ship suddenly started zig-zagging at top speed.

'Steward?' an American gentleman called as he noticed the change in the ship's navigation. 'What exactly's going on here? What is it? A submarine?'

'No, sir,' the steward answered calmly, collecting any empty glasses. 'Just a beam sea.'

But his reassurance fell on deaf ears as the ship's tacking manoeuvres became more desperate, and the passengers in the lounge where Ellie was sitting reading lapsed into an ominous silence.

'To hell with this!' the gentleman passenger finally protested. 'This is an outrage! We're flying the Stars and Stripes! And not only that – this is a passenger liner!'

'So was the *Athenia*,' another voice reminded them all of the passenger boat which had been torpedoed only the day after the outbreak of hostilities. 'And she's rusting up nicely on the bottom somewhere off Ireland now.'

Strangely, Ellie felt no fear. It suddenly seemed pointless to be afraid, because now there was danger everywhere and for everybody. She felt desperately sad she was no longer home and with Hugo, and she felt fear lest anything should happen to James. But for herself, she felt no terror. While the ship fled from the unseen danger beneath it, Ellie simply put down the book she was reading and prayed.

After a seemingly endless three hours, the ship slowed its speed and began once more to sail in a straight line, head-on into seas which were fast becoming much rougher. Ellie retired to her cabin, not because she felt sick, but because it seemed everyone else was starting to do so. By evening they were in the throes of a force-eight gale, which lasted until they sailed into the shelter of the American coast two and a half days later.

As Ellie was setting foot back on her homeland, Hugo was leaving his by plane for North Africa, in the company of two of General Hunter's personal staff and two of General Wavell's. They were to land first at Gibraltar, and then on to Cairo, where they would learn the purpose of their visit.

One of General Hunter's officers, a Major Timothy Curling, sat next to Hugo on the flight out.

'You just along for the ride?' he enquired, offering Hugo a cigarette which was declined.

'More or less,' said Hugo.

'What are you, old chap? A boffin?'

'Not really, no.'

The young officer frowned. 'Must have some sort of claim to fame,' he said.

'Sand,' said Hugo. 'I suppose.'

'Sand?' Curling's frown deepened even more. 'As in castles, you mean?'

'As in deserts,' Hugo replied. 'My father was an expert, but unfortunately he's dead and I got custody of the knowledge.'

'Yes,' Curling said. 'Could well come in handy. If, as the top brass seem to imagine, Mussolini brings Italy into the war. Could well come in handy.'

'So I imagine,' Hugo replied. 'Hence my free weekend in Egypt.'

Tim Curling smiled and drew deeply on his cigarette. 'Personally speaking, old chap,' he said, 'the only sand I reckon we'll all be seeing is the stuff we'll all being lying out on quite peacefully next summer along the dear old South Coast.'

Artemis was living with Diana Lanchester in her large Bayswater flat. Not that she had a great deal of time to do much living since it seemed she spent her every waking hour driving important members of the government from the House to meetings in Whitehall and back again to the House. And she had little time off, because although most people seemed to believe that the war on land was at an impasse, and that peace was just around the corner, there was constant activity in Whitehall, what with meetings between the top brass and the government leaders, and the prime minister and his cabinet ministers.

Although the public was already being warned that careless talk could cost lives, the perpetrators of the propaganda seemed to consider themselves immune, and talked quite freely in front of Artemis when she was driving them to and fro as if she was not there.

Many ministers expressed the concern that Chamberlain was not interested in fighting Germany at all, but was really only anxious to have a crack at Russia, since he and many like him considered that Communism posed a far greater threat to world peace than Fascism. Others, returning after meetings with the military, talked with astonishment at the unreality of High Command's proposed offensives at Germany, which, with the absurdly limited resources the Allied governments had at their disposal, they had no possibility whatsoever of achieving. From her seat up front, Artemis heard of plans for striking at the Ruhr through Belgium, or attacking Germany's rear flank through Scandinavia, or her remote eastern flank from Greece and the Balkans, or even for attacking Russia's great oilfields in the Caucasus, and thus cutting off the Germans' only supply of petrol.

'Pipe dreams,' one of Artemis's passengers once remarked with some feeling. 'Collective fantasies. These people are living in a dream world.'

'I quite agree,' said his companion. 'We should be thinking how to best defend this island against what's now got to be certain attack. Instead of talking all this well-off nonsense.'

The truth of this remark was brought home one evening to Artemis when on her way back to Bayswater the air was suddenly split with the banshee wail of air raid sirens. For a moment everyone around her stood stock still, as if unable to believe their ears, and then suddenly a panic set in and Artemis found herself in the middle of a jostling and running crowd, fighting their collective way to the nearest shelter. Unable to keep up with the mob, Artemis was knocked to the side, off the pavement proper and on to the road, losing her stick in the process. No-one paid her any attention, as they were all too concerned with seeking sanctuary. Some glanced fleetingly up at the skies above them but most just hurried heads down as fast as they could into the makeshift shelter below a large department store.

Artemis was one of the last down the steps which she had to negotiate carefully, one at a time. A man passed her, and seeing that he was carrying her silver topped stick, she called out to him. But he failed to stop, disappearing into the crowd which had already settled into place, either seated on slatted benches or standing against the walls, staring upwards at the ceiling as if it were a part of the sky.

'It'll be another false alarm, don't you worry,' a man next to Artemis announced to all and sundry as the crowd waited in near silence. 'The only casualties in this bleedin' war are the poor baskets gettin' knocked down in the black-out.'

Ten minutes later the all clear sounded, and with a mass sigh of relief, everyone began to make their way above ground once more. But while they had been waiting, Artemis had at last found the man who had her walking stick, and had made her way across to him. He was sitting on a bench at the far end of the basement trying his best to prise the silver top off.

'That's mine, thank you,' she said, standing in front of him.

'Yeah?' He looked up, a young sallow-faced man with a black pencil moustache.

'Yes,' said Artemis and held out her hand.

'There's no name on it,' the man said, after giving it a cursory look.

'There's a crest though,' Artemis said, 'which you'll find matches this.' She showed him her signet ring.

The thief eyed her, taking in her lop-sided gait, and as the shelter began to clear, got up and made a run for it, pushing Artemis to one side so that she fell across the bench. Seeing what was happening, a large man in a collarless shirt, his work trousers hitched round his belly with a thick leather belt, caught the thief by the scruff of the neck and lifted him up on his tiptoes.

'Drop it, son,' he said. 'There's a good boy.'

The large man returned Artemis her stick. 'Steal the froth off your beer, that sort would,' he said, nodding after the disappearing figure. 'Makes you wonder who we're fightin' for.'

The cab driver found the address with no difficulty.

'This is a good neighbourhood,' he said over his shoulder to Ellie, never taking his eyes off the road. 'Nice.'

'It's number 1219,' Ellie said, looking at a line of smart suburban houses, with their manicured lawns and washed motor cars, and wondering how her father now came to be living here.

'I got you, lady,' the driver said. 'Number 1219.'

There were two cars parked outside number 1219, one of them, a pale yellow saloon, looking brand spanking new. The cab-driver whistled. 'Hey!' he said. 'Nice! A new Chrysler Imperial! *Very* nice!' He moved his gum to the other side of his mouth and opened Ellie's door by just reaching out behind him with his arm. 'One dollar ninety, lady,' he said, and then as Ellie looked for the money in her purse, he reappraised the Chrysler. 'Oh yes ma'am. That is very nice indeed.'

A black maid opened the front door. 'Who shall I say please, ma'am?' she asked.

'Mrs Tanner,' Ellie said, taken aback one more step. 'Mrs Eleanor Tanner. Mr Milligan's daughter.'

The maid shut the door behind Ellie and beamed. 'Why of course!' she said. 'Miss Eleanor! Why I have heard so much about you! Please follow me through here now, and I'll go tell your daddy that you're here! I don't think he was imagining you would be here till this *evening*!'

The maid led Ellie through into a comfortable and well-furnished sitting room, so different from the home in which Ellie had been born and reared that she thought she had to be dreaming. There was a three piece suite of furniture, a nest of occasional tables, a small white grand piano which was covered with photographs of 'the Broth', and even a glass fronted bookcase, full of good looking books. More than that, the whole room was close carpeted and decorated with a pretty floral wallpaper.

'You must be just dying for some refreshment, Miss Eleanor,' the maid said, plumping up some cushions in a chair for her. 'After such a *journey*. What can I fetch you now? Some coffee? A hot chocolate? Or would you like some tea like your daddy likes? A nice strong cup of tea?'

Ellie decided on tea and then sat down to wait for her father who, it appeared, was on the telephone in his den.

'Are any of my brothers around?' Ellie asked, before the maid finally departed back to the kitchen.

'Why bless you no, Miss Eleanor. All your brothers, except young Patsy of course, all your brothers they is off working as usual.'

'Do they still work for my father?'

'Oh yes, Miss Eleanor, they sure do. And they's all doing so *well*!'

Ellie could see that from the photographs, which she examined when the maid had gone. She knew Dermot had married, because Patsy had told her that much at least in his letters. Her new sister-in-law was blonde and enthusiastic looking, with broad shoulders and large

411

breasts. She was grinning rather than smiling and holding on to Dermot's arm as if she was never going to let go, now that he had vowed himself to her until death did them part. Mike and Fergal were not yet married, but there were new photographs of them as well, smart suited and with their dark hair fashionably brilliantined down. Their pictures flanked the one of Dermot and his bride, and there was no doubt about it they were a fine looking bunch.

No new picture of Patsy graced the white piano, nor indeed of Eleanor. There was just the same old tired yellow snapshot there had always been, the one taken of them aged ten and eleven respectively, in their Sunday best, standing together back to back because it was the last picture on the roll of film.

'Eleanor?' said a voice behind her. 'Is it you?'

'Hullo, Pa,' Ellie replied, putting down the cheaply framed photograph and turning round. Her father stood in the doorway, looking more handsome than she'd remembered him, a fact she decided must be more to do with the fine suit he had on, and the way his now almost white hair was so well cut, rather than to any actual change in his countenance.

'I never thought you'd come,' he said. 'Never.' He nodded at her in such a way as to make Ellie uncertain of whether it was in welcome, or because she herself had visibly changed. Ellie smiled by way of reply.

'And so where's this famous grandchild of mine?' Her father now walked into the room, passing Ellie by to stand in front of the fireplace, hands folded behind his back. 'You said on the telephone you were bringing the child.'

'He's at the hotel, Pa,' Ellie explained. 'He's caught a bit of a cold.'

Patrick Milligan clicked his tongue and shook his head as if the cold could have been avoided. 'A cold indeed. That won't do at all. A cold. Fancy.'

The maid came back in with a tray of tea and set it out in silence. Ellie sat down while the maid poured the tea.

'You've said nothing about the new house,' her father said after the maid had been dismissed. 'Sure I might just as well never have moved.'

'I was waiting for you to tell me,' Ellie replied, slipping back easily into the old game of cat and mouse.

'It's a fine house,' her father announced. 'The sort of house a man can be proud of. Particularly when it's a house he has earned through the sweat on his brow.' Here he gave a look, which was intended to be telling, but which Ellie stone-walled with a polite smile. She was determined on silence, remembering how it always provoked her father into telling.

'It hasn't been easy,' he continued, when he had failed to get the anticipated rise. 'But then the virtue of honest labour is that it is always finally rewarded. And this house is a monument, a testimony to the labour of your father and of your three eldest brothers, fine men, every one of them.'

Ellie had no need to ask of Patsy. She knew from his frequent letters that he was going from strength to strength in Hollywood, no longer now working as a stand-in and stunt man but as a junior assistant producer.

'This house is a monument to industry,' her father sighed. 'Industry, and nouse.'

'You're still building then?' Ellie asked, unable quite to contain her curiosity.

'In a manner of speaking,' her father replied. 'In a manner of speaking. But tell me something.' He put his teacup on the mantel behind him, then fixed her with a steady gaze as he switched the conversation. 'Tell me, what do you make of the war then? Particularly you, as an American. The feeling here, if it's any interest to you, is the whole thing is a result of the bully-boy tactics the English and the French adopted with the Germans in 1918, at Versailles.'

'Yes,' Ellie agreed, anxious not to get embroiled into an argument about the war, but only to discover how Madame was, since after all this was the purpose of her visit. 'Yes, I've heard all that.'

'Ah,' said her father with a nod. 'You've heard all that, have you?'

'Hugo says people have short memories, particularly certain Americans.'

'Really? Is that really so?' Her father nodded once more, but this time not in agreement.

'He says,' Ellie continued, 'that a lot of Americans seem to forget their own President Wilson was the principal author of the Treaty of Versailles.'

'Their own president,' her father picked up. '*Their* own president. Uh huh. Uh huh.'

There followed a silence, during which Patrick Milligan stared up at the ceiling. 'Myself,' he finally announced, 'and this may sound strange coming from an Irishman, but myself – I hope that we – America that is, I mean by we I mean America – yes I hope we do get into the war.'

'Why do you hope that?' Ellie asked, her curiosity again getting the better of her. 'It doesn't seem at all like you.'

'Because,' her father replied with a smile, 'it'd be good for business.'

Ellie frowned. War and the building trade seemed hardly compatible, and she was about to say so when her father held up his hand.

'Don't you want to see Madame?' he enquired. 'After all, that's the only reason you're here, isn't it?'

Ellie agreed, ignoring the inference, pulling on her gloves and straightening her hat.

'Fine,' said her father. 'Then come along.'

Nothing was said on the journey regarding Madame's health or condition. All that Ellie was told was that Madame's health, which apparently had never been strong, had suddenly and rapidly deteriorated, and since they were not driving out towards Westfield Drive, Ellie assumed that their destination must be the hospital. For the last part of the journey her father lapsed into total silence.

But instead of a hospital, the car pulled up at a sidewalk outside a nondescript building. Her father picked his hat off the back seat, adjusted it in the mirror and then opened his door.

'Where are we?' Ellie asked suddenly, bending down to try and see exactly outside which shop or building they were parked.

'We're going to see Madame,' her father replied, before leading the way into the sombre building, where they were greeted by a dark-suited man with grey eyes and oddly transparent skin.

'Mr Milligan,' he murmured, with a slow bow. 'And this will be?' He turned his pale grey eyes to look at Ellie.

'This is my daughter, Mr Saul. Mrs – ' Her father paused just long enough to make it sound as if he was searching for her name. 'Mrs Tanner,' he said.

Mr Saul gave Ellie his hand and even through her leather glove Ellie could feel its undue warmth. 'Mrs Tanner,' he slowly bowed and turned to show them the way.

The casket was of deeply polished oak, lined with quilted white silk. Madame was dressed in a gown of her favourite colour, red, and in her perfectly manicured hands rested a garland of flowers. She looked, quite simply, as if she slept, but only lightly, as though the slightest of noises would awaken her and bring her back to life.

Mr Saul took two steps back, expressing as he did his opinion that Madame Gautier looked at peace and quite beautifully so. Ellie's father sighed deeply as he gazed down on the dead woman, pursing his mouth in sadness and slowly shaking his head.

'Requiescat in pace,' he whispered. 'And may God love you always.'

Outside it had begun to snow, large perfect flakes which fell straight to earth in the windless conditions.

'Why didn't you tell me?' Ellie asked her father in a trembling voice when they stood once more outside the funeral parlour.

'You didn't ask,' he replied.

'I did. I asked you how she was.'

'And I told you how she was. I said she was mortally ill, and so she was.'

'You didn't tell me she was *dead*!'

'No?' her father asked, turning his collar up against the cold. 'No I don't suppose I did.'

They drove back through town in silence, Ellie sitting huddled in the corner of her seat, with her coat pulled tightly around her.

'You look just like your mother,' her father said with an accusing glance, finally breaking the silence.

'When did it happen?' she demanded, watching the frozen rain settle on the rooftops. 'When did she die?'

'Ten days ago. At five past one in the morning. She just slipped away.'

'Ten *days* ago?'

'Ten days ago.' Patrick Milligan nodded and then wiped the inside of the screen with the back of his gloved hand.

'You should have told me,' Ellie said, looking out of the window, unable to face her father. 'Why didn't you tell me?'

'Because you wouldn't have come, Eleanor.'

'Of course I would.'

'Indeed you would not. And you know it.'

Her father was right, but Ellie wouldn't admit it. She *would* never have come over. Never, not at this time, risking her baby's life and her own, leaving Hugo to fly off God alone knew where, leaving her beloved home, leaving her life. She would have stayed in Brougham, with her baby, waiting for her husband to come back, as other women all over England were doing, waiting for their men, waiting for the war to end, waiting for peace. And *then* she would have come.

'I won't forgive you this,' Ellie said in a low voice. 'Ever.'

'Mmmm?' said her father, pretending not to have heard. 'Let's have some lunch.' He pulled the car over to stop outside a plum colour painted restaurant with steamed up windows. 'I could do with some food. And a drink.'

Ellie followed him into the warmth of the restaurant, in a haze, still numb with the shock. The place was full of people, all eating and drinking as if nothing had happened, or worse, as if nothing was happening. Ellie suddenly wanted to put them all to rights and tell them that something had happened, that someone unique had just died and was now lying embalmed in a casket, dressed and made up to look as if her life had been a cakewalk. And she wanted to tell them that other things were happening, too. That a world was going to war, and that young men, every one of them someone's son, were about to lay down their lives so that all of them could still sit and drink cocktails, and eat beefsteaks, and shout to each other at the tops of their voices.

And then it all went dark.

'She's had a bit of a shock,' she heard her father saying, somewhere in the distance. 'Bring some brandy.'

Someone lifted her and sat her down in a booth curtained off from the main room, while someone else wiped her forehead with a linen napkin soaked in cold water.

'What happened?' she asked, trying to bring her surroundings back into focus.

Her father was by her side, one arm round her shoulder, half propping her up. 'You fainted,' her father replied. ' 'Twas the heat most likely. Coming in from the cold into this heat.'

A waiter arrived with two glasses and a bottle of brandy. Her father poured Ellie a shot, which he held first to her nose for her to inhale and then to her mouth to sip. Ellie took the glass and eased herself away from him. As she did, her father poured himself half a tumbler, which he all but drank in one.

'I'm sorry,' Ellie muttered, reaching into her purse for a handkerchief. 'I don't know what came over me.'

'Probably some sort of shock,' her father sighed. 'You were losing your colour in the car.'

He drained his glass and called a waiter in to the booth to take an order. Ellie wanted nothing, but Patrick Milligan insisted on ordering her some thin hot soup and a little fish, before instructing the waiter to bring him chicken broth and a ten-ounce steak.

When the waiter had gone, Patrick Milligan tugged the curtain tight shut and poured some more brandy. 'You know what Madame used to say?' he asked. 'She used to say what is life without death. What is life without death? Death has to be there, she said, waiting for us at the end of the walk. Or else we wouldn't see the flowers and we'd never hear the birds.' He gave a laugh, as if what he had said was just bar room banter, while Ellie stared at him. 'I should have told you, of course,' he finally admitted. 'The poor woman — God rest her — when I wrote to you to say she was ill, she was already comatose. But I knew you thought a lot of her. And so I thought you'd want to pay your respects. Before she was consigned to the earth.'

He looked at her, over the rim of his glass, his eyes hard and unforgiving, while Ellie stared evenly back. For a while, neither of them spoke. Then her father took a deep draught of his brandy and wiping his mouth on the back of his hand, reached in his pocket for a cigarette.

'God help us,' her father said, tapping out a Lucky Strike. 'Sure God help us all.'

The waiter brought their first course and set it before them. But neither of them ate. Ellie sat staring at the table cloth while her father smoked his way through his cigarette.

'I wonder why,' Ellie said, more as a thought than a question.

'What do you wonder?' Patrick Milligan ground his cigarette out and looked back at his daughter. 'What now?'

'I wonder why couldn't you love me, Pa. You're capable enough of love. You love your "broth". Fergal and Dermot and Michael. So why not us? Patsy and me? I wonder why you couldn't love us two?'

Her father sighed, as if the question she had asked him was a foolish one, and then poured another shot of brandy which he downed in one. 'Sure Patsy was meant to be a girl,' he said, lighting another cigarette. 'And you weren't meant to be at all. It's an impossible thing, loving mistakes. Particularly when they're not of your making.'

'If you loved our mother the way you always said you did,' Ellie retorted, 'you'd have loved Patsy and I.'

Her father's face hardened at this, and leaning across the table, he pushed his face close to his daughter's. 'Don't you ever dare!' he said. 'Don't you ever dare say I never loved your mother! I loved her all right! The point is she never loved me!'

Ellie stared at her father, hardly able to believe her ears. All this time she'd believed and still did believe that when her mother died giving birth to her, her father's happiness had died with her. 'Of course she loved you,' she heard herself protesting faintly, as if in the distance. 'You're just saying this now, just to make it all worse.'

But her father shook his head, and clenched his two hands into great fists. 'I have no reason for lying,' he said. 'I worshipped your mother. There was nothing – nothing I wouldn't have done for her. But it made no difference. I wasn't the man she loved. The man she loved was dead, drowned back in Ireland. And I was second fiddle. She was a good mother to her children. And a good wife to me. But there was no love in her heart. Then – then you were born and God took her. He took her from me.

Away to the next world, to be reunited with the man she really loved, leaving you, Eleanor. Leaving you in her place.' He brushed the cigarette ash off the front of his jacket, before looking back up at his daughter, his dark eyes still full of fury.

Ellie buttoned up her coat and rose from the table. 'I can't stay here,' she said. 'Would you mind if we went now?'

They drove back slowly through the ever deepening snow. As he turned the car into the avenue where he now lived, Patrick Milligan glanced at his daughter who was sitting as far away from him as she could, against the passenger door, her coat held tightly around her.

'Don't you want to know about Madame?'

'What else is there to know?' Ellie replied, watching the snow as it settled on the branches of the trees.

'Didn't you ever wonder about me and her?'

'I used to wonder why you hated her so much.'

They were outside the new house now and her father was swinging the car off the road and into the parking space in front of the garage which someone had already cleared of snow. Patrick Milligan shut the engine off and then ran his gloved hands round the ebony white steering wheel. 'I didn't hate her, Eleanor,' he said. 'Madame and I were lovers.'

Ellie wanted to laugh. It was the most shocking thing she had ever heard. 'Don't be silly,' she said, unable to stop the smile spreading. 'Don't be so ridiculous.'

'Oh I'm sure it seems silly to you, Miss high and mighty,' her father replied. 'I'm sure you find the idea ridiculous. But it happens to be the truth.' He was no longer looking at her. Instead he stared out into the snow, tapping his fingers on the steering wheel and nodding slowly to himself, as if recalling how it was.

'It couldn't possibly be true,' Ellie said. 'I don't believe one word of it. Goddam it, I'd have *known*.'

'Why?' her father enquired. 'Why should you? She and I. We only ever saw each other at night. Deliberately. It was the only time we could, when you were all in bed. Sometimes I didn't get home from her house until four or five in the morning, only to have to get up an hour or so later. Other times I'd just come straight in from her house for breakfast.'

Ellie suddenly and sickeningly remembered those mornings, mornings she would find her father out on the back step doing up his shirt buttons, bleary eyed and still unshaven. But being a child, she had naturally assumed he'd just got out of his own bed, not someone else's.

'No,' said Ellie. 'I just don't believe it.'

'Won't, you mean. Because you don't want to.'

'You said you hated her! You called her a whore! You wouldn't have her in the house!'

'Of course I wouldn't!' her father laughed. 'If I'd had her in the house, I wouldn't have been able to keep my hands off her!'

'It's a lie! It's a lie!'

'It's the truth, Eleanor. I was Madame's great love.'

Ellie turned her face away as the tears came. Blindly she groped for the door handle and in her confusion all but fell out into the snow. The pain was unbearable, now she realized that it wasn't only her father who had deceived her, but Madame as well. Her father was out of the car now, and walking round her side took her by the arm.

'Love is blind, Eleanor,' he said. 'Love is the asses head. Madame hated the way I treated you, you can rest assured of that. But that didn't stop her from loving me. Because she loved me as a man. Not as a father. If you'd been her child, our child, well – who knows? But you weren't. And there's an end of it.'

'Why didn't you marry her?' Ellie asked, wiping her tears away with a gloved hand. 'If you wanted a wife who loved you, why didn't you marry Madame?'

Her father let go of her arm and smiled the smile he always smiled when he had triumphed. 'But I did marry her, Eleanor,' he said, 'I married her the moment you were out of my hair.'

Ellie watched him walk to the door and open it. 'Goodbye,' she called.

He turned back and frowned at her. 'You're coming in, surely?'

'No.' Ellie turned up the collar of her coat and looked down the snow covered avenue. 'I'm going back to my hotel.'

'You'll have to walk,' her father warned her. 'You'll not find a cab in this weather.'

'That's too bad.'

She had nearly reached the junction of the avenue and the road which led to the city before he fell in step beside her. 'You can't walk all the way,' he said, catching her by the elbow. 'Come on, I'll drive you.'

'I'd rather walk.' Ellie shook her arm free and turned out of the avenue. The snow was beginning to freeze and the few cars which were still about were slowing right down.

'I'll drive you,' he said again. 'Come on.' He tried to turn her round with him, but Ellie resisted, planting herself firmly into the snow and staring at him defiantly. 'Jesus God,' her father sighed. 'You really are the spit of your mother.'

A cab slewed slowly round the corner and spun in a half circle across the road. 'Cab!' Ellie called, making it to the edge of the sidewalk and holding on to a tree. 'Cab!'

The driver saw her and once he had regained control of his vehicle, stopped on the far side of the road. 'I'm headed for town, lady!' he shouted. 'Nowhere else!'

'Thank you!' Ellie called back. 'That's just where I'm headed too!'

Again her father caught her arm. 'I want to see my grandson,' he said.

'I'm sorry,' Ellie replied. 'You should have thought of that twenty years ago.'

'You're not going to let me see him?'

'No.'

'Eleanor,' he said, tightening his grip on her arm. 'What I've told you is history. Do you understand? It's history.'

'No, Pa,' Ellie replied, as evenly as she could. 'What's history is you and I.'

For most of the first day in Cairo, the party sat around under the enormous fans in the lounge of their hotel drinking gin slings. It was insufferably hot in the town itself, and Hugo felt quite extraordinarily homesick. No-one seemed in the slightest bit interested in their presence there. No-one had met them at the airport and to date no-one had even visited them where they now sat drinking.

Finally, late in the afternoon as they sat sipping tea and eating fruit cake, a thin, tall and idle looking junior officer from garrison HQ wandered into the lounge, tapping a swagger stick against his leg. Spotting the new arrivals in the corner of the room, he straightened his cap and at once changed his casual meander into a purposeful walk.

'Colonel Parker?' he asked, identifying and saluting the superior officer. 'Lieutenant Hamlyn-Jones, sir. Jolly good. Just arrived, sir?'

'No,' Colonel Parker sighed, getting wearily to his feet. 'We've been here since before midday, man.'

'Sir!' said the lieutenant. 'Jolly good. Well my orders are to see you settled in. And – ah.' He paused to clear his throat, tapping his stick nervously against his leg. 'And, ah, to make sure you've got everything. Sir.'

The newly arrived officers all stared at each other disbelievingly and then looked back at Lieutenant Hamlyn-Jones. 'We're not here on holiday, man!' Colonel Parker suddenly shouted, the reprimand bringing the young officer to immediate attention. 'We haven't come all this way to take a look at the blasted Pyramids!'

'Sir!' the lieutenant replied.

'Right!' Colonel Parker continued. 'So in that case you'd better wheel us over straightaway to HQ, hadn't you!'

'Sir,' the lieutenant replied nervously. 'My orders were – '

'Damn your orders, man!' Colonel Parker yelled, his face purpling. 'Our orders were to meet with your CO. ASAP!'

'Sir!' the lieutenant now was at full attention, as stiff as a ramrod. 'A meeting has been arranged, sir, for tomorrow morning, sir!'

'Tomorrow morning? What in hell's wrong with now, man! Don't you chaps know there's a blasted war on! Now pull your finger out, man, and take us over to HQ. PDQ!'

'Sir! With respect, sir! The CO's away, sir! And will not be available until tomorrow morning, sir!'

The Colonel took a deep breath, looked round at his colleagues, and then over-patiently back at the junior officer who was now sweating up badly. 'One good reason, man,' he said, lowering his voice to almost a whisper. 'One good reason why the CO will not be available till then.'

'Sir,' the lieutenant replied, clearing his throat and staring at the huge fan above them. 'Because he's away playing polo, sir.'

The following morning, a staff car arrived to transport Hugo and the four officers from the hotel to garrison HQ. When they arrived there was another delay, until finally the officers were invited in to meet the commanding officer. Hugo was not included. In fact no-one at HQ seemed to know why he had been included in the party. He had not been expected, and now that he was there, no-one knew what to do with him. Hugo, mindful of his brief from General Hunter, suggested he might be given the use of a driver and a car used for desert driving known as a 'flea', so that he could go into the desert on the west side of Cairo and conduct some investigations. The request was readily granted since it solved the problem of finding something for Hugo to do, and within an hour he was heading out of Cairo on the Alexandria road, with the vast open space of the desert unfurling westwards in a shimmer of heat.

Ten miles out along the long dusty road, in answer to Hugo's request, the driver pulled over and stopped to allow Hugo out.

'Take a sight more than seven maids with seven mops, eh sir? To clear this little lot,' his driver said cheerily, starting to roll himself a smoke, as Hugo stood staring at the burning sandscape.

It was midday and the heat was intense, already in the high eighties and rising, Hugo surmised, with no wind whatsoever to bring relief. He remembered his father telling him of temperatures of over a hundred and twenty degrees being recorded five or six hundred miles further west in Libya, and of sand dunes in the Algerian Sahara with a wave-length of three miles and a height of nearly a mile, and most graphically of all, exactly what it was like to die of thirst. 'How much petrol have you got, driver?' Hugo asked, climbing back into the flea.

'Three quarters of a tank, sir,' the driver replied, tapping his fuel gauge. 'And two full jerry-cans.'

'Good,' said Hugo. 'Then I think we'll go for a little drive, please.'

The driver started the little car up. 'Which way do you want to go, sir?' he asked. 'North or south?'

'Neither, thanks,' said Hugo. 'I want to go west. Due west.'

After half an hour, the driver braked and stopped. 'I don't know how well you know the desert, sir.'

'Why?' Hugo asked, without apparent concern.

The driver wiped the sweat off his brow with the back of his hand and then nodded ahead of them. 'That's a sandstorm, sir.'

Hugo smiled at the driver and undid his water bottle. 'That's why we're out here,' he said.

'To enjoy the pleasures of a sandstorm, sir?'

'I must admit,' Hugo smiled, before taking a drink. 'I must admit I was hoping we'd catch one.'

'Have you ever been in a sandstorm, sir?' Hugo could tell from his companion's tone that the man quite obviously thought him mad.

'Yes, driver, I have as a matter of fact.'

'It's not exactly a party, sir. With all due respect.'

'I know,' Hugo agreed. 'But then that one ahead, that should miss us north, by a mile. Possibly two.'

The driver lit another cigarette and stared at the dark swirling clouds which were gathering on the horizon. 'Sorry, sir,' he said, restarting the flea, 'but that little number's coming right for us.'

Hugo turned off the ignition.

'With all due respect, sir,' the driver said, restarting the vehicle, 'I've been out here a little longer than you have. And when it starts to blow and get up like that little lot, it's time to bugger off home.'

Once again Hugo switched the ignition off, but this time removing the key.

'You'd better be right, sir,' the driver sighed, with a shake of his head.

'Yes I had better be right, driver,' Hugo replied. 'I'd better be right and not just for us.'

'I don't see anyone else, sir,' said the driver.

'Not now you don't,' said Hugo. 'But you could before too long.'

They sat there watching as the cloud of sand grew bigger and darker with every minute, picked up by the fast growing wind which seemed to be blowing directly head-on at the stationary jeep.

'God Almighty!' the driver swore, ducking down and crouching under the steering wheel. 'This is not my idea of a picnic!'

But Hugo just sat where he was, transfixed by the rising storm of sand which had all but blotted out the sun. He had sat just like this with his father, except not in a motor car. They'd been in an old ruined fort and his father had calmly unwrapped them each Fuller's mint lumps as the sky had grown blacker and their guides had started screaming in panic. Hugo had to admit he'd felt panic too, as there seemed no chance that the storm would do anything other than asphyxiate them. But he knew better than to show his emotions for a second, sitting instead beside his father sucking his sweets, watching in fascination as the sandstorm swirled a mile by them, exactly as predicted.

And now, just when it seemed that he must have read it wrong, as in the growing darkness the first flying grains of sand stung Hugo's face, so too did this mighty storm change course, its epicentre passing way to the north of the jeep, perhaps even more than the two miles Hugo had guessed. It was impossible to tell, because although they were sitting it out on the fringe of the *simoon*, the air to the north of them was impenetrable, and Hugo could only estimate approximately by how much it had missed them.

'All right, sir,' the driver said, after he'd started the jeep up and turned for home. 'So how's it done, eh?'

'It's a knack,' Hugo replied. 'Rather like being able to read a googly.'

Ellie, Jamie and his nanny arrived in Los Angeles on the morning of 4 December, to be met by a car sent from Metro-Goldwyn-Mayer on the orders of Mr Patsy Milligan, who was now working as a first assistant. The party had travelled overland by train from New York, from deep snow to warm sunshine, Ellie's plan being to stay for six days in Hollywood, fly back to New York, and then sail home from there on the thirteenth to arrive back home in plenty of time for Christmas.

Ellie was driven straight to her hotel in Beverly Hills, where she bathed and changed and settled the baby in with Nanny before leaving to meet her brother for lunch at the studios.

'When your eyes stop popping out of your head, sis,' Patsy grinned, 'maybe you'll catch me up on all your news.'

Ellie apologized for star-gazing, but it seemed every time they were about to start a conversation yet another household name passed by their table, several of them even stopping auspiciously to ruffle Patsy's curly hair, or crack a joke, and occasionally, but to Ellie's intense embarrassment, to insist on being introduced to her.

James Stewart ambled by and stopped when he saw Ellie. 'Hi,' he grinned when Patsy had introduced him to Ellie. 'Listen, if I'd known the kid had such a great sister, I'd have made sure he was directing my next picture, not just assisting.'

'Look at you!' Patsy laughed, after the actor had left. 'You're the colour of a tomato!'

'Hugo and I saw him in *You Can't Take It With You* when was it? Last year. And Artemis and I saw *Seventh Heaven*,' Ellie said by way of a somewhat hopeless explanation.

'He's the nicest guy in town.'

'You seem to be doing OK, Mr Milligan. I mean how long before you're running this place?'

'I plan to take over next Thursday,' Patsy replied. 'In the meantime, tonight you and I are going to dinner.'

'You and I and Helen, I take it you mean. Or don't you include your wife on dates?'

'I did,' Patsy replied. 'Before she ran off with Cary Grant's stand-in.'

It appeared that no sooner had Patsy brought Helen out to Los Angeles than she changed. One sight of the honeypot which was Hollywood and all the former shop girl wanted to be was a show girl, and nothing Patsy said could dissuade her.

'It was my fault, I guess,' Patsy told Ellie over dinner. 'She was always hanging around the set and the canteen, watching it all happen, meeting other girls who only last month had been working behind the counter in Macy's.

You know. And then I was always working late. Well, to cut a long story short – too late – ' he joked. 'One day I arranged to take her to a movie, and when I called to pick her up, there was a note left on her rooming house door "gone off with Ricky". Ricky was a dummy she'd met a few weeks before, but he promised her a walk-on in the coronation scene of *The Prisoner of Zenda*. Oh, you know how it is. Out here. It's something in the air everyone thinks they're going to become Garbo.'

'Poor Patsy.'

'Poor nothing. Helen was a pill. Is a pill. I still see her around poor girl. She's back behind a counter, waiting for another walk-on. It's been a century since her last and Ricky went off with a show girl to help run a bar in New York. That's the banana skin of life she opted for. Trouble is, if I ever see her I still feel like kissing her, for being so stupid, so much has her bad luck been my good.'

They ate dinner and talked more generally: of how well Patsy was doing with his career, and of how he hoped it would go in the future. But Patsy's contribution to the conversation was half-hearted, as if his mind were elsewhere.

'It's the war,' he finally explained, when Ellie taxed him. 'I can't talk this off-handedly about the future when there's a war on.'

'It's not your war. It may never be.'

'I have a feeling it will be, Ellie. This is no ordinary backyard scrap, you know. Not with this guy Hitler playing the lead role. And by the by, one of the not-so-good things about this place is that Mr Hitler has a whole lot of very big fans out here.

'Which is maybe why I don't see America getting dragged in to it. People here seem to think that Britain doesn't need help, either because they're just about to negotiate a peace with Hitler, or because they've got this incredible masterplan which is going to trap and defeat the Nazis at one fell swoop. People here,' Patsy said, 'say they believe Britain doesn't want help because they don't want to give it. Britain's not exactly popular here. People in America are more worried about Stalin.'

'That was what Father said, that he'd be glad if America *did* go into the war.'

'Sure he would,' Patsy agreed.

'I'd have understood it,' Ellie went on, 'if he'd said he hoped America would come into the war on Germany's side, knowing Father.'

'Pa doesn't mind *whose* side anyone is on, just as long as it's good for business.'

'That's the other thing, how come war is suddenly so good for business?'

'You mean, he didn't tell you?' Patsy pushed his plate to one side and pulled his chair round closer to his sister's. 'Let's start from the top,' Patsy said, dropping his voice slightly. 'You know about him and Madame, I take it?'

Ellie said their father had told her everything, and while it had come as a terrible shock, when she looked at the whole picture now, rather than just a part of it, it all made sense. But Patsy became suddenly cautious, giving Ellie the impression that if what she knew was the truth, she would not really be talking in such a fashion.

'One thing at a time,' he instructed. 'Madame first.'

Ellie repeated the story as she had heard it, and when she finished, Patsy nodded but said nothing. 'Did *you* know about him and Madame, Patsy?' Ellie wanted to know. 'I mean when you were small. You can't have known, surely?'

'No,' Patsy agreed. 'I never knew. None of the boys knew. No-one knew. They made sure of that.'

'They certainly did,' Ellie nodded. 'He said – he said he loved our mother, Patsy, but that our mother never loved him.'

'Yes,' Patsy agreed. 'He told me that as well.'

'But Madame. I mean all that *time*, Patsy!' Patsy took one of Ellie's hands in his and stared down at it. Then he clicked his tongue and took a deep breath, like Ellie imagined a doctor might do when about to announce a fatal diagnosis. 'Tell me,' she begged. 'Please tell me it's all a lie, Patsy. About Madame.'

Patsy looked across at her, eye to eye, their intimacy unbroken. 'Madame was like a mother to you, and nothing can ever change that. Why should it? She was kind to you and she loved you, and nothing'll ever change that either, Ellie. It doesn't matter about her and Pa. That's something different. You and she, you're intact. I mean it.'

'He said she really loved him, Patsy.'

'I'm certain of it, Ellie,' Patsy replied. 'I'm sure she loved Pa. But I don't think for a moment he ever loved her.'

'Don't you?' Ellie paused, staring at her glass of iced water, running a finger down the condensation on the side of the glass. 'He married her, Patsy,' she said finally. 'Why should he marry her if he didn't love her? He never married her before. I mean if he loved her − '

'I know what you mean, Ellie, but let me tell you. He married her for her money.'

Ellie laughed. 'Madame didn't have any money, Patsy! Not to speak of!'

'She came into some. After you left America, Pa found out. I don't know about finding out − I guess that's when it became official. That old man you were to marry, Mr O'Hara. As you probably know, that old guy he really *had* loved Madame, way back when. You tell me. But Pa − he just made love to her. And she let him, because she really did love him. Don't ask me why. But she did. She didn't love poor old Buck O'Hara, who loved her. But then that's the way it goes. Even so, when he died, O'Hara left her a small fortune. Which was when Pa suddenly decided it was up to him to marry her.'

'I see,' Ellie said.

'Didn't you wonder about the new house and furniture,

Ellie?' Patsy smiled, putting his hand on his sister's arm. 'And the new car, and those tailor-made suits?'

'Of course I did,' Ellie replied. 'He just said business was flourishing.'

'You bet,' said Patsy. 'The business he set himself up in with Madame's money. Himself and the "broth".'

'I wouldn't have thought this was the best time for building,' Ellie ventured.

'It all depends what you're building,' Patsy said sarcastically, for a moment sounding just like his father. 'There's building and there's building. He calls it "building for the future".'

'So what is it he's doing?' Ellie asked, dreading the reply. 'If he's not building houses. What exactly is his business?'

Patsy held his breath for a moment then exhaled, leaning back in his chair and staring upwards as if he himself could still not believe it. 'Munitions.'

That evening when Artemis finally got home, tired out and aching all over, all she wanted was a large drink and a hot bath. Diana was already home, drink in hand, sunk deep in an armchair by the electric fire, a book opened but turned face down on the arm of the chair.

'What a day,' Artemis said, unstopping the decanter of whisky. 'I had to drive someone to Bath and back. To the admiralty.'

'Should one know the admiralty is in Bath?' Diana enquired.

'Only if one's a Jerry one shouldn't,' Artemis replied. 'Prosit.' She raised her glass in a mocking salute, drank, and then dropped into the chair opposite her godmother, draping her legs over one arm. ' "Your courage, your cheerfulness, your resolution, will bring us victory",' she said.

'What on earth's that?' Diana enquired.

'The latest rot from the Ministry of MisInformation,' Artemis replied.

'Oh yes,' said Diana idly, 'of course.'

'Don't you just love "*Your* courage, *your* cheerfulness, etc? Will bring *us* victory?" If that's the line they're taking, they won't just have a war on their hands. They'll have a revolution.' Artemis took another drink of whisky and then leaned backwards and put the glass down on the table behind her. 'You've forgotten the black-out curtains, Diana,' she said, struggling to get up.

'It's all right,' Diana was on her feet first. 'I'll do them.' Diana got up and pulled the black-out blinds and curtains tightly down and across the drawing room windows.

'Not that it makes much difference,' Artemis said. 'Jerry doesn't seem that bothered.'

'Don't be too sure,' Diana replied as she sat back down. 'I'm told that apparently it was only the weather that stopped Adolf dropping in on France last month.'

'Too bad,' said Artemis. 'I was rather hoping things might have got so bad over there that AH might have had to go back to painting houses.'

When the telephone rang, Artemis failed to hear it because she had fallen fast asleep. It was right beside Diana so she picked it up at once.

'Hullo?' she said quietly. 'Yes?'

While she listened to what her caller had to say, she looked over at the sleeping Artemis. Then she quietly replaced the receiver and lit a cigarette.

She sat watching Artemis while she smoked and when she was halfway through the cigarette, she stubbed it out and leaned over to shake Artemis gently awake.

'Artemis?' she said. 'Artemis wake up, darling.'

Artemis woke up and stared in surprise at Diana. 'Sorry,' she said. 'I fell asleep.'

'Rather bad news I'm afraid,' Diana told her. 'Your – your stepmother's dead.'

'Really?' Artemis enquired, after a silence. 'How? I mean what happened?'

'It seems she shot herself.'

'God.' Artemis picked up her whisky glass and swilled the drink round. 'Shot herself? Any idea why?'

'It appears, like many of her persuasion, she was afraid of being imprisoned for her Nazi sympathies.'

'I see.' Artemis stared into the bottom of her glass, then drank the remains of her drink. 'How's Papa taken it?' she asked eventually.

'He's all right. You know they haven't been together now for quite some time now, don't you?'

'I didn't know that, no.' Artemis looked surprised and reaching for her handbag, took out her compact and studied her face in its mirror.

'Your father always regretted marrying her,' Diana said. 'You probably didn't know that either.'

'No I didn't, Diana,' Artemis replied. 'But I'm not surprised. Didn't you wonder why he married her in the first place?'

'Everyone did,' Diana shrugged. 'He told me once he'd done it so you could have a mother.'

Artemis put her compact down and stared at Diana.

'Men like your father aren't very good round children,' Diana explained.

'I am very sure the very last thing Katherine wanted to be,' Artemis replied, 'was a mother to me. Or to anyone.'

Diana took out another cigarette, and then quite suddenly laughed. 'I'm sorry,' she said, although Artemis didn't look the least disturbed, 'but as a matter of fact Katherine did have plans for parenthood. It seems that the poor woman has been off her head for years and her one desire in life was to have a baby by Adolf H. himself.'

'No, that's not true, is it?'

'Darling,' Diana leaned forward and put a hand on Artemis's sleeve, 'do laugh if you want to. It's awful to bottle it up.'

'It's so funny it has to be true,' said Artemis soberly. 'But I can't laugh about Katherine I'm afraid, Diana, any more than I can laugh about Hitler.'

'No, I know what you mean. She was quite, quite ghastly, wasn't she?'

Diana poured them both another whisky, which they drank in thoughtful silence.

'If you don't mind,' said Artemis, pulling herself to her feet. 'I think I'll have a bath.'

Once she was sure Artemis was in the bath, Diana picked up the telephone and called Artemis's father.

They flew back from Cairo in a bomber. Before take-off they'd sat in the fuselage of the plane, beside the bomb bays, sweating in a temperature which in the evening was still in the mid-seventies. Now, ten minutes later as the unpressurized plane had reached its optimum cruising altitude, they sat with chattering teeth, swaddled in thick sheepskin-lined flying jackets and trousers. It made Hugo long all the more for the warmth of his fireside at Brougham and so, for the rest of the noisy, turbulent and freezing journey, he turned his mind solely to the thought of Christmas with Ellie. He could see them all gathered on Christmas Day round the big tree in the hall, laughing and exchanging presents, together once again, Ellie, and Jamie, and himself, and one more person in the corner of the picture in his mind's eye, someone whom Hugo could not quite identify at that moment. So he squeezed his eyes shut and looked again, and saw all too clearly who that last person was.

17

Ellie had just finished packing her bags in preparation for the first leg of the journey home when Nanny appeared at her bedroom door.

'It's Jamie, Mrs Tanner,' she said. 'He's having convulsions.'

Dropping everything, Ellie ran through to find James lying in his cot, with his eyes rolled upwards and almost invisible under his eyelids while his whole body twitched convulsively.

'Take his temperature while I call for a doctor.'

'We'll take his temperature,' Nanny said, finding the thermometer and shaking it down, 'then we'll pop him in a warm bath.'

Ellie was on the telephone, trying to raise reception. 'Are you sure that's wise, Nanny?'

'Oh yes, Mrs Tanner,' Nanny replied. 'Call the doctor, give baby a warm bath, and then let him rest in a warm and dark room. That's what we're taught to do at times like this.' The nurse placed the thermometer under the baby's arm and then held him tightly to her, wrapped in a blanket, to try and control the convulsions.

'His tummy was upset this morning,' she said. 'He's probably got some nasty wee American bug.'

As it turned out the doctor was of the same opinion, but even so ordered the baby to be sent to hospital immediately.

'What is it?' Ellie asked him anxiously, as they waited for an ambulance. 'Is it serious?'

'Your child has a high fever, Mrs Tanner,' the doctor replied. 'And an extremely upset stomach. We have to regard anything enteric in a baby this age as serious, I'm afraid. Are you still feeding him yourself?'

'No. I did for the first three months, but now he's on the bottle. It became painful, you see. And really I wasn't producing enough milk.'

'Perfectly understandable. It just makes baby that little bit more vulnerable to infections, that's all.'

'But why is he convulsing? Is that a sign of something else? I mean is he having a fit or what?'

The doctor explained that it was quite usual at the onset of a fever for babies to suffer convulsions. 'If it's simply a case of enteritis,' he assured Ellie, 'then taking him off milk and feeding him just glucose and a little salt in boiled water will have him back to normal in no time. I just think with a temperature as high as this, we'll be much better off keeping an eye on things in hospital.'

Ellie and Nanny stayed with Jamie all day, but things got no better. By evening the baby's temperature had risen from a hundred and one degrees to a hundred and three. As well as suffering from constant diarrhoea he was vomiting up even his glucose and water. By midnight he had begun to convulse once more, except this time even more violently.

The doctor tried to advise Ellie to go home. 'You're only a ten-minute cab ride from the hospital,' he said. 'I'll call you if there's any change.' But Ellie refused, she and Nanny sat, graven images, either side of the cot. Eventually as dawn approached and the night staff started to drift off home, Ellie went in search of the doctor on duty.

'I have to know what the chances are.'

'Not good, Mrs Tanner, I'm afraid.' The doctor took her by the elbow and led her down the corridor. 'It all depends on the next few hours. But if you want chances, I'm afraid your baby may have only a five per cent chance of survival.'

'You mean he has a ninety-five per cent chance of dying,' Ellie said desperately.

'As you probably appreciate babies also have only limited reserves of water and they pretty soon become very dehydrated. If they lose an abnormal amount of body fluids.'

'Five per cent,' she muttered. 'Five per cent.'

'If we're looking at it honestly,' the doctor replied. 'Yes round about five per cent.'

Someone brought them coffee some time later, but Ellie left it, and Nanny seemed not even to notice the intrusion. They didn't talk to each other, or even really look at each other. They just waited.

Later in the morning, as Ellie stood leaning with her back against the corridor wall, her eyes half shut, a nurse came and quietly told her that Doctor Vincent had returned and wished to see her.

'Yes?' Ellie asked as soon as she entered the doctor's office. 'Well?'

'There's no improvement, I'm afraid, Mrs Tanner.'

'Is there any deterioration?'

'No. The baby's condition at the moment is at least stable.'

'Then there's hope. More than five per cent?'

Doctor Vincent looked up at her. Ellie's face was a blank. 'While there's life, Mrs Tanner. You know what they say. We're injecting fluids into him, to make up for the losses. And provided we can keep ahead in that field—' He tried to make his smile as encouraging as possible. 'And now I really think you should go back to your hotel and rest, don't you?'

'Don't be insane,' Ellie turned away.

Patsy arrived two hours later. Ellie had called him constantly from the hospital, but he was out of town on a shoot and no-one seemed to be able to say when he'd be back.

'I've only just got your message. What happened?' Patsy listened intently as Ellie tried to explain. 'You couldn't be in better hands,' he told her walking her down the corridor. 'Doctor Vincent's a number one guy.

Does a lot of work for the studio. I mean it, Ellie, he's OK. I know Jamie *is* going to be OK. Now wait there.' He sat her on a chair and disappeared.

Three quarters of an hour later he was back. 'It's all done,' he said. 'I've fixed you a room here right next door to the baby.'

He was leading her back along the corridor now and into a big cool room, with a freshly made-up bed, and lowered blinds. All Ellie's bags were lined up against one wall, and there was a vase of flowers on the bedside table.

'You did all this?' Ellie wondered, as she sat suddenly exhausted on the side of the bed.

'M-G-M did,' said Patsy with a wink. 'You're talking to a guy with friends in high places. Now at least take your shoes off and lie down. Because if anybody needs you, you'll be right here.'

'What about Nanny?' Ellie asked, slipping off her shoes.

'She's back at the hotel,' Patsy replied.

'I don't believe it,' Ellie said. 'However did you manage that?'

'How do you think?' Patsy grinned, putting his fists up. 'I gave her the old one-two.'

Someone woke her and when they did, Ellie sat up with a start, wondering for a moment where she was. She remembered when she saw Patsy.

'It's all right, Mrs Tanner,' he said. 'It's OK. Your baby's fine. He had to put up a bit of a fight they tell me. But he did it. He's gone the distance.'

'I can't get over!' Hugo shouted down the phone. 'The most leave they'll grant me is forty-eight hours!'

'They can't do that to you!' Ellie shouted back. 'You're a civilian!'

'Not really!' Hugo replied. 'Only technically.'

It had taken the best part of two days to locate Hugo. Ellie had cabled both Brougham and his club to no avail.

In the end she'd cabled Artemis at Diana Lanchester's in Bayswater requesting Artemis to ring the emergency number Hugo had given her in order to get Hugo, if he was in England, to ring her at the hospital. When he first made contact and learned the news, Hugo'd expressed his determination to get over to America come what may, but now on his second transatlantic call he'd been forced to admit defeat.

From the start of their conversations Ellie had told him it was unnecessary, Jamie was completely out of danger, and that she'd only had to get in touch to tell him they were going to have to change their travel plans, since they wouldn't be able to sail on the intended date.

'Patsy thinks he's found some alternatives!' Ellie yelled down the crackling line. 'There's something sailing from San Diego through the Panama Canal to Jamaica on the seventeenth and then on to Portugal arriving on the twenty-second! Or there's a ship from New Orleans sailing on the eighteenth to the Bermudas and then direct to Portsmouth docking Christmas Eve! Either way we'll be home by Christmas Day!'

'You'd better be!' Hugo shouted back. 'Or I'll give up believing in Father Christmas!'

Two days later, on the morning of the 13th December, as Ellie sat in her hospital room bottle-feeding her son with glucose and water, the baby started to convulse once more, and an hour later lay in an oxygen tent with a temperature well over a hundred and three.

This time Ellie telephoned Artemis direct. 'He's out of danger again!' she said, pitching her voice over the hissing and crackles on the line, 'but Doctor Vincent thinks this can't just be any ordinary enteritis!'

'I don't know anything about this sort of thing!' Artemis shouted back. 'I mean what does he mean by that? Does he mean it's an extraordinary whatever? Or that it's something else entirely?'

Ellie did her best to explain but the transatlantic connection was at its worst and Artemis could only hear every other word. What she did gather was that Ellie had been advised not even to think about leaving Los Angeles until the hospital had discovered exactly what was wrong with the baby.

Artemis left a message for Hugo at the emergency number and two hours later he arrived on the doorstep of the Bayswater flat.

'Ellie said you're not to go,' Artemis informed him as she poured him a whisky.

'I couldn't even if I wanted to, Tom,' Hugo said glumly. 'I'm off abroad again.'

'The Middle East?' Artemis sat herself down by the fire.

'Can I see how you write the number seven please, your ladyship?' Hugo said in his best official voice.

'What's that supposed to mean?'

'Didn't you know?' Hugo smiled as he sat down opposite Artemis. 'That's how you're meant to be able to recognize the German spies amongst us. By the way they cross their sevens.'

'Well wherever it is you're going,' Artemis said, 'will you be back for Christmas?'

'That all depends,' Hugo replied, 'when I go and if I go to wherever it is they may be sending me. I'll give you a clue, Mata Hari,' he said. 'It's somewhere in the Baltic beginning with N.'

'I didn't think Norway was famous for sand,' Artemis frowned.

'For sand read snow,' Hugo said. 'Norway has snow the way Egypt has sand. And snow also has a habit of blowing in storms.'

While Hugo spent four freezing days in northern Norway, trying to chart the climactic idiosyncracies of the country for the benefit of the Allied Command, Doctor Vincent of the Vernon Clinic in Los Angeles was running a series of exhaustive tests on his son, in order to try to diagnose the exact cause of the infant's intestinal upsets. Jamie had recovered quickly enough from the last attack, and seemed back to strength, but Doctor Vincent preferred to err on the side of caution and advised against any thought of travel.

'Particularly a long sea journey, Mrs Tanner,' she said. 'Imagine two days out and the baby gets an attack like the first one.' He shook his head. 'I think we do two things. First, we have to wait and see if he suffers another attack, particularly once he's back in his normal routine. Second, I think we have to try and isolate the cause. Because I don't believe this is just an ordinary gastro-enteritis. I think either we have an allergy here, or a digestive weakness.'

Later Ellie cabled Hugo with the news that they wouldn't be back for Christmas.

Hugo received the cable midday on Christmas Eve, three hours after he'd arrived back by air from Oslo. He called the clinic, but by the time he'd been connected Ellie had left with her brother to spend Christmas at his house. The nurse to whom he spoke said his son was quite better, and there was no cause for concern, but that he would be returning to the clinic after the holiday for further tests. Hugo then telephoned Artemis on her Bayswater number but there was no reply, so having called Porter to let him know he was on his way, he picked his unpacked luggage back up, packed it into his Alvis, and drove straight down to Brougham.

It was strange to enter the gates of the park and come upon an unlit house. One of the great joys of coming home to Brougham at night had been rounding that final corner of the drive to be greeted by the lights from the house. But now the place lay in total darkness, by government orders, its fine long windows shuttered, the lanterns on the gateposts and by the doorways unlit. Hugo, on sidelights only, as he'd been all the way down from London, turned the car in through the ornamental gates and sounded the horn. Within moments figures emerged from the deep shadows of the house, from under the basement arches and out from the servants' quarters, first Porter calling out to identify his master, then Cook and Dibbs the handyman, and finally Jenkins all the way from the stableyard round the back.

Hugo dumped all his cases on the gravel and leaning back into the car suddenly switched on the headlights, blinding the party who had come to greet him and making them scuttle like moles back into the dark of the house.

'You mustn't do that, sir!' Porter called. 'We've had the special constable up here twice already!'

'Young Sally Topliffe from the village,' Cook told Hugo as they all stumbled into the house carrying various items of luggage, 'she's a very absent minded lass. And she put her bedroom light on before pulling her black-out curtains. Well before you could say knife Sergeant Ruggins was through the door and up her stairs, two at a time, and into her bedroom to turn off her light without as much as a thank you.'

'They fined 'er too,' Dibbs added. 'That Mrs Conville on the bench. Fined 'er five bob. Young Sally said it made 'er feel like a spy so it did. That's what she said.'

'It wasn't much fun driving down from town, I must say,' Hugo remarked, following the beam of Porter's torch. 'Someone's cattle had got on the road outside Calne. Some chap coming the other way had run right into them.'

Cook had prepared a tray of sandwiches and a flask of hot soup for her employer, which was ready and waiting in the 'sulking' room, as was a welcoming fire. The night was bitterly cold and Hugo welcomed the warmth. Porter fussed round making sure the curtains and blinds were tightly pulled, while Hugo fetched a bottle of whisky from the cupboard and ordered Porter to pour them all a festive tot.

As they were drinking and gossiping, the telephone rang. Porter nodded to the party to drink up and they did, leaving Hugo alone to take the call.

'Yes?' said Hugo.

'I thought it might be you,' Artemis's voice said in his ear. 'I heard a car go by.'

'When did you get down?'

'A couple of hours ago,' Artemis replied. 'I'd have been down earlier but thanks to the black-out it took me over an hour to find where I'd parked the stupid car.'

'Come to lunch tomorrow.'

'I can't,' Artemis replied after a moment.

'What – have you got people?'

'No.'

'Then come to lunch.'

'Have you got people?'

'Good lord no!' Hugo laughed.

'Then I can't very well come to lunch,' Artemis sighed in reply. 'Can I?'

'Don't be silly.'

'You're the one who's being "silly".'

'It's Christmas Day! You can't just sit over there all by yourself in your house, while I sit over here all by myself in my house! That really is silly.'

'What would Ellie say?' Artemis asked after a silence.

'She'd say you were being silly.'

'I wonder.'

'Of course she would, Tom!'

There was another silence, during which Hugo heard Artemis breathe in and out once, very slowly. 'I'll come for drinks,' she said. 'After Matins.'

'And you'll stay for lunch,' Hugo insisted, 'after that.'

As Hugo was replacing the telephone receiver and draining his whisky glass preparatory to going to bed, Ellie was seeing her brother Patsy off on his way to the studio's Christmas Eve party. He'd tried his best to persuade Ellie to go along with him, but even though her baby's health was apparently back to normal and Doctor Vincent had exhorted her to go and enjoy her Christmas, Ellie was not in the mood for revelry.

'They'll all be there,' Patsy said as one last throw, before climbing into his car. 'Nelson Eddy and Jeanette MacDonald, Robert Taylor, Clark Gable, Spencer Tracy, Judy Garland and Paulette Goddard —'

'We've already had the roll call of stars,' Ellie laughed, shutting him in the car. 'Twice.'

Patsy poked his head back out through the window. 'Practically the entire cast of *Gone With The Wind*!' he said.

'I'll wait to see it in the cinema,' Ellie replied, pinching his cheek. 'Go on. Hurry up or you'll miss all the fun.'

Ellie had moved out of the hotel and into Patsy's house along with Nanny. It was a nice house, sizeable and bright, on a tree-lined drive in the best part of an otherwise ugly and sprawling town. But the climate was wonderful, with every day long, warm and sunny, even at this time of year, and though Ellie longed with all her heart to be home with Hugo, she knew that Jamie stood a far better chance of recovering completely in the sunshine of LA than he would back home in England, which from all reports was in the grip of the coldest winter within living memory.

More importantly, the medical care was of the highest standard, and as far as paediatric medicine went, well in advance of anything England could offer. Doctor Vincent had gone home to celebrate Christmas with his family, but had assured Ellie that if he was needed he could be back at the clinic at the very most within half an hour.

On Christmas Morning Ellie broke her vow and went to Mass for the first time since her childhood to pray for James Michael. She lit fifty candles in front of the statue of the Virgin Mary before going on to visit the baby in the clinic, where she was told his condition was still stable and that he was continuing to put back on all the weight he'd lost during the previous attacks. The nurse in charge was delighted with the baby's continued progress, and after an hour Ellie kissed Jamie goodbye and left the clinic to have Christmas lunch with her brother.

Artemis had been happy to stay on at Brougham after Matins once she'd been told what the plan was, namely to have lunch in the friendly warmth of the kitchens with the staff. Even she could see no real objection to that, so she and Brutus sat down one end of the scrubbed wooden table with Cook at the head and Jenks on her right, while Hugo sat down the other end with Porter at the head and Mrs Byrne the housekeeper on his right. The rest of the party was made up of Mabel the only remaining parlour maid, Dibbs and his wife, the head gardener Bryant and his wife, and Toby Green, a young estate worker who'd failed his army medical due to chronic asthma.

As yet there was no food rationing, because although ration books had been issued in October, a campaign, led in the main by the *Daily Express*, had been successful and brought about a postponement of rationing in November. So they feasted well and merrily, warmed by the food and the wines and the roaring log fire. For those two hours there was no war, nor much talk of it, although it couldn't be left entirely out of the conversation.

'Did you know?' Hugo asked at one point, as the snow started to fall again, 'they're even censoring the weather?'

Everyone laughed but Hugo held up his hand, insisting it was true. 'I promise you,' he said. 'The Ministry of Information have officially banned the Press from passing comment on the weather.'

'Makes you laugh, don't it?' Cook said. 'We can see the poor bloomin' birds freezing to the trees, but we can't read all about it.'

'According to my newspaper,' Porter announced gravely, 'the Ministry of Information is being run by Fred Karno's Army.'

'I 'eard it was the Crazy Gang myself,' Cook replied.

'Stinker Murdoch, on the radio the other day,' Toby Green chipped in, ' 'e said a woman 'ad called into the Ministry of Information to ask the way to Clapham. And they said they didn't know. And that even if they did, they couldn't tell 'er!' Everyone roared with laughter at what was fast becoming a national joke.

'The Ministry of Malformation,' Porter declared.

'The Ministry of Muddle more like,' Mrs Byrne sniffed.

'Don't worry,' Porter said, replacing his glass on the table. 'We shall win this war in spite of the government.'

After lunch everyone sat round the kitchen wireless and listened to the King's Christmas broadcast: ' "I said to the man who stood at the Gate of the Year," ' the King read to the nation, ' "give me a light that I may tread safely into the unknown." And he replied, "Go out into the darkness and put your hand into the hand of God. That shall be to you better than light and safer than a known way." '

Later, as the two of them sat on the floor in front of the fire in the small sitting room, Hugo raised his glass of port. 'To Ellie,' he said. 'To Ellie. And Jamie.'

'Here here,' Artemis replied.

Later, when the fire began to die, Hugo went to fetch some more logs rather than ring for Porter, who according to Hugo would most probably be flat out under the table.

When he was gone, the telephone rang. Artemis, who was day-dreaming, picked up the receiver and answered the call. 'Hullo?'

'Hi,' came a crackly voice after a delay. 'Who's that?'

'Ellie?'

'Who's that?' the voice enquired. 'I can hardly hear you!'

'It's me!' Artemis shouted. 'Artemis!'

There was another delay, but a considerably longer one than just the time it took for a voice to cross the ocean. 'Really?' Ellie replied at last. 'Well hi, Artemis! Happy Christmas!'

'Thanks!' Artemis called. 'Same to you!'

Hugo struggled back in with the full log basket and Artemis held the phone up to him from the floor. 'It's

Ellie!' From his look Artemis knew immediately that Hugo was regretting she'd picked up the telephone. 'Come on, dog,' she said, pulling herself to her feet.

'Walks.'

Brutus raised his great brown head from the floor and then reluctantly left the warmth of the fire to follow his mistress out. Artemis took the torch from by the door and carefully made her way through the dark and empty dust-sheeted rooms while her dog ran before her, quite happy in the winter darkness. Finally she found a side door which she opened to let Brutus out. It was pitch dark, and the cold took her breath away, prompting her to pull her jacket round her tightly as Brutus, remembering what fun snow was, began to gambol, a puppy once more across the whitened lawns, barking with sheer joy as he leaped in and out of the huge drifts.

Closing the door against the biting wind Artemis waited for him gazing out through a window at a landscape lit only by the gleam of the snow, and thought how strange it was, to be standing where she was, alone in her old family home, alone with the man who owned it, her best friend's husband. If events in Ireland had been different she could now be returning from snow-covered gardens that again belonged to her, through her house, their house, through these their rooms, back to their fireside once more to sit down beside her husband.

'It's cold,' Artemis said, coming back in half-frozen, and pushing the cushioned draught excluder along the bottom of the door, having first listened outside to make sure the telephone call was at an end. 'What I mean is if anything it's actually colder.'

Hugo was standing with his arms out resting on the stone chimneypiece, gazing down into the rekindled fire. He said nothing, instead just pushed a log back into place on the fire with his foot.

'Everything all right?' Artemis asked overbrightly, coming to the fireside to get warm.

'We lost the line. We didn't finish what we had to say.' Hugo pushed at the log again with his foot, although it was quite safely in place.

'How's Jamie?' Artemis asked, rubbing her still numb hands together, in the gap under one of Hugo's outstretched arms.

'He's fine,' Hugo stood up to make way for Artemis to warm herself, and as he moved their faces came close. 'Sorry,' he said after a second, getting out of her way.

Artemis let the fire warm her through, until her teeth no longer chattered. 'Did you tell her about lunch?' she asked, as lightly as possible. 'You know. That we had lunch in the kitchen?'

'No, yes. I said we had people.'

'You didn't?' Artemis replied sharply, which made Hugo look up. 'I hope you didn't say "we".'

'I don't know what I said, Tom. I said there were others here for lunch. Not that it matters.'

'Why? Why didn't you tell her the truth?'

'I thought it sounded better, that's why!' Hugo glared up at her, with a look Artemis had never seen before on his face.

'I think I'd better go home,' she said quickly. 'Don't you?'

'No!' Hugo grabbed her arm and held her back. 'Don't go. Please.'

'I seem to have upset you,' Artemis explained. 'So I think it's best.'

'I've upset me,' Hugo replied. 'So don't go. There's no point.'

She wished he would take his hand off her arm. 'What's the point in me staying?' she asked.

'I don't know why, but just now I couldn't bear it if you went, Tom,' Hugo said. 'That's the point. And you know it.'

'Of course. Which is why I think it's better if I go.' Carefully she removed his hand from her arm. Hugo looked surprised, as if he'd forgotten it was there.

'Sorry,' he said, 'was I hurting you?'

'Of course not. Why should you think that?'

Hugo shrugged his shoulders. 'I just got the impression I was hurting you.'

'You weren't.' Artemis turned to go.

'Stay for a drink at least,' Hugo said, walking over to the drinks tray. 'It's not very late, so why don't I pour us a drink?'

'All right,' Artemis replied after a pause. 'Yes. OK.'

'Better still,' Hugo said, 'why don't I pour us both a drink?' Hugo laughed, overdoing the laughter, and Artemis smiled, overdoing the smile. She sat back down by the fire and stroked her dog's head rhythmically, staring rigidly at the burning logs, while Hugo poured out sherry instead of whisky and had to start all over again.

' "OK",' said Hugo, handing Artemis her drink. 'Well.' He raised his glass, but could think of nothing to say. Artemis raised her glass back, only to find that she too was speechless.

Over Christmas lunch, Patsy regaled Ellie with stories about the previous night's party, which according to Patsy had been a humdinger. But Ellie only half-heard, for her mind and her heart were miles away, ten thousand miles away, back at her home in Brougham. While Patsy told her tales of the stars, Ellie's imagination was taken up with wondering who'd been at Hugo's lunch party, and what fun it must have been, as everything always was with Hugo. It would have been an elegant lunch, of course, lit as Hugo would insist it should be, by candlelight, even though it was daytime. And where would Artemis have been sitting? And wearing what? Probably one of those two-piece tweed outfits she always looked so good in, Ellie reckoned, a mixed check with a neat little sweater underneath, and a skirt with one of those big kick pleats. And she would have sat – would she have sat herself next to Hugo? Or down the far end, in her seat? Had she taken her place at the table, opposite to Hugo? To smile occasionally up at him through the flicker of bright candlelight. Or had Hugo sat her next to him, so that he could talk to her, and she could listen, the way Artemis always listened to him, her head slightly cocked to one side, while pretending to bite the nail of a finger on one of her hands? And had she made Hugo laugh? Like she always made him laugh? With her poker-faced teases, and her oddly random remarks?

And who would be there now? Who would have stayed behind, drinking port and brandies and ginger and playing all those crazy games Hugo loved to organize? Sardines, and Pass the Parcel with forfeits, and Dumb Crambo? And how long would the party continue? And who would be the last to go? And when?

'You haven't heard one darned thing I've said to you, Ellie,' Patsy said.

'Of course I have,' Ellie replied hotly. 'I heard everything.'

'You didn't hear *anything*,' Patsy laughed.

'Oh really?' Ellie asked. 'And how do you know?'

'Because,' Patsy grinned, 'that's the fourth time I've told you that you haven't heard one darned thing I've said.'

They spent all evening in the snug warmth of the 'sulking' room, piling the logs on the fire, drinking whisky, listening to Hugo's favourite records, and playing the most frivolous paper games either of them could contrive. By the time the clock on the desk chimed midnight, they both stopped to stare at it in silent amazement.

'I thought it was only about ten,' Artemis said, looking for her stick.

'So did I,' Hugo said. 'Half past at the latest.' Artemis laughed. 'What's so funny?' Hugo demanded.

'Half past ten at the latest,' Artemis sighed, getting to her feet.

'I had to say something,' Hugo said, helping her up.

'And I must go home,' Artemis said, doing her best to ignore the hand that was in hers, and which had helped haul her up from the floor but now seemed reluctant to let her go. Hugo released her, after what seemed to Artemis an age, to set the guard in front of the fire and turn off the lamps.

'Know something, Tom?' Hugo said, opening the door and letting in a blast of icy air.

'God,' said Artemis, buttoning the tweed check jacket of her suit over her oatmeal jumper.

'Something we haven't thought of,' Hugo continued, leading the way slowly by torchlight. 'We haven't thought exactly how you're going to get home.'

'Meaning?'

'Meaning – ' Hugo stooped by one of the windows in the drawing room and pulled open a shutter. 'Meaning,' he said, flashing the torch through the glass at the snow covered landscape, 'have you brought your snow shoes?'

They opened the front door to get a better look at the blizzard. The wind had dropped a little, but it was still viciously cold, and if anything snowing even more heavily. The steps on the great staircase had quite vanished from view, as had the driveways, as had the parkland, and indeed as had Artemis's car, which lay buried somewhere beneath a huge drift of snow that had blown up against the front of the basements during the evening.

'You're the sand and snow expert,' Artemis said, shivering immoderately.

Hugo shut the door. 'The expert says you're going to have to stay the night.' He turned round and shone the torch at the stairs. 'Come on,' he ordered. 'Up the little wooden staircase to Bedfordshire.'

'I should have gone home when I said,' Artemis said, following him across the hall.

'That's my fault,' Hugo said, 'you can blame it on me.'

'Blame what?' Artemis enquired from behind him on the staircase.

'For detaining you. I wanted company.'

'So did I. I didn't have to stay.'

'Yes, but we didn't think – *I* didn't think – ' Hugo stopped and looked back at Artemis, who appeared to be looking back at him as if she had never seen him before. Then he continued on upstairs. 'Take this torch,' he said, when they reached the landing. 'I've got another one in my bedroom.'

'Where am I sleeping?'

'Where you always sleep. Where you always used to sleep.' Hugo flashed the torch along the landing to a bedroom door. 'In your room.' Then he handed her the torch.

'Thanks,' Artemis said. 'Good night then.'

'Good night, Tom.'

They both went to their separate rooms, without even a formal kissing of cheeks. Hugo undressed quickly and got into the large four-poster bed, where he lay staring at the ceiling above him, the room lit by the faint white gleam of the fallen snow. It was bitterly cold, but Hugo burned, for all he could think of was Artemis, of her mouth, and the shape of her breasts under her sweater, of her pale pink complexion, and the tousle of her blonde hair. 'God,' he whispered to himself, biting the knuckles of one clenched fist.'Christ I must be mad.'

Artemis thought she too was mad, but no longer worried about it, as she lay waiting in bed, knowing that he would come, facing the door she knew he would open. She put a finger to her mouth and ran her teeth along the top of a nail, backwards and forwards, backwards and forwards, no longer trying to make sense of the madness which gripped her, happy just to sense the excitement, the intense excitement she imagined all women must feel as they lay waiting for a man to come and make love to them.

She bit at the fingernail harder, pressing her lips round the top of her finger, as dry mouthed and with the sound of her heart pounding in her ears she heard his footfall in the corridor, and rolled involuntarily away from the door, across to the far side of her bed.

'Tom?' she heard him whisper against the door. 'Tom?'

'What do you want?' she asked.

'It's me, Tom,' Hugo whispered. 'Can I come in?'

Artemis didn't reply.

'Tom?' Hugo asked once more. And then turned the door handle. And then again, and finally once more. 'The door's locked, Tom,' he said.

Artemis put a hand to her mouth, biting the ends of her fingers as hard as she could.

'Tom?' Hugo said. 'Please open the door.'

'I can't,' Artemis called back. 'Sorry.'

'Why not, Tom?' Hugo asked. 'Why can't you open the door?'

Artemis said nothing.

'Tom?' Hugo repeated. 'Why can't you open the door?'

'I can't open the door, Hugo,' she said, 'because I've thrown the key out into the snow.'

Hugo let her out of her bedroom the next morning with a spare key. 'Did you sleep well?' he asked.

'Brilliantly,' she replied. 'Did you?'

'Not a wink.' Hugo smiled and walked over to a window.

'Seen the snow?' he asked.

'Yes,' Artemis said, joining him and looking out on the whitened landscape. 'How am I going to get back to London?'

'You're not going to be able to get out of the front drive,' Hugo said. 'Let alone London. Let alone back to your house.'

'No?' Artemis was standing by the fire, warming her hands.

'Not today anyway,' Hugo said. 'Which means you're shut in here, I'm afraid.'

'Yes,' Artemis agreed. 'I suppose it does. But then that's not going to pose any problems, wouldn't you say?'

Hugo said nothing. He just smiled at her and Artemis smiled back, one of her all too rare smiles, but which when granted allowed the recipient to be able briefly to imagine the look of angels.

At the end of the first week of the new year of 1940, Jamie suffered another sudden and unaccountable attack of enteritis. It was every bit as serious as the previous attacks and left the baby weaker and even more dehydrated than before, taking everyone by surprise. Jamie'd seemed to be making such a good recovery that Ellie had even gone ahead and started making plans for their return to England, plans which given the circumstances she had to cancel immediately.

Hugo was back in London when he received the news. Frantic with worry he called Artemis and asked if they could meet as soon as possible. Artemis, who'd just returned from work, said she would come round at once.

'I can't get over to America, Tom,' Hugo explained, as he poured Artemis a drink. 'I have to fly out again to Norway on Friday and then there's a rumour I might have to go to France.'

'I don't know what it is you do exactly,' Artemis said. 'But I'd have thought if you're a civilian – '

'I'm not a civilian, I have to do what I'm told, and I can't say what it is I do,' Hugo replied rather shortly.

'Sorry.'

Hugo came and sat down opposite her. 'Supposing the worst happens, Tom?'

Artemis shook her blonde head and said nothing. She couldn't bring herself to look at Hugo. She thought she'd locked everything out when she'd thrown the key out in the snow that Christmas night, but seeing

Hugo now she realized the key might have been thrown out but it wasn't buried. 'I could go over. I mean my work's only voluntary, and there's not exactly a lot happening.'

'Why?' Hugo asked, the hope in his eyes betraying his real feelings. 'I don't see why you should.'

'Don't be such an idiot. Of course you do. Besides, if anything did happen, and Ellie was by herself,' she paused to pick up her whisky glass, staring into it before continuing. 'And just suppose the war really did begin in earnest, and we were all really stuck here. And Ellie was stuck over there.'

Hugo took his glasses off and rubbed a hand over his eyes. 'I didn't ask you here to make you volunteer this, you know.'

'Don't be such an idiot,' Artemis told him again.

'I just wanted to talk to you about it.'

'Of course.'

'It never even occurred to me, Tom. As an idea.'

'It was my idea. Now I have to get back to work.' Artemis finished her drink and got up.

'Are you quite sure, Tom?' Hugo asked her.

'Of course,' Artemis replied. 'You know I'd do anything for Ellie.'

'Yes,' said Hugo, seeing in his mind's eye the key buried deep in the snow.

Artemis turned to go but Hugo stopped her. 'I'm going to be late,' she said.

'Thanks, Tom.'

'Don't be an idiot,' she replied as always.

After a considerable amount of string pulling Diana managed to procure a seat for Artemis on a transatlantic flight with a party of British diplomats bound for Washington. Hugo left for Norway on the same day and while they were both in the air, Ellie was summoned to the clinic where a worried Doctor Vincent told her that Jamie's condition appeared once more to be worsening.

456

'I think we may have to operate, Mrs Tanner,' Doctor Vincent said. The thought of such a small person undergoing surgery was terrifying. 'It would just be exploratory,' Doctor Vincent continued, 'but there could be some internal cause which we've failed to diagnose, and which is at present concealed.'

'What's the alternative, Doctor Vincent?'

He got up and came round to sit on the front of the desk. 'I guess we could try to smoke it out. Gamble on it being a viral infection, hope that it's some microorganism which is trying to put down roots but which Jamie will reject once his body's rebuilt its defences. I reckon it has to be that, or something physically wrong. Because I don't read this as being an allergic reaction. Like to milk. Because during these last two attacks and then after, Jamie can't even contain his water and glucose.'

'Which is more likely? Or to put it another way, which is the greater risk? Smoking it out, as you put it? Or – or operating?'

Doctor Vincent shook his head, nonplussed. 'Fifty-fifty, Mrs Tanner. Evens.'

It wasn't as if Ellie hadn't sought second opinions. On Doctor Vincent's advice, she had agreed for four other paediatricians to examine her child, none of whom could shed any more light on the disease. Two of them rather tamely suggested that it might be teething problems, something Doctor Vincent dismissed out of hand.

'To my mind, gentlemen,' he'd told them, 'babies may be teething or ill, or teething *and* ill. The two things are co-incidental, not interrelated.'

'Let's go for smoking it out, shall we?' Ellie said, after much deliberation. 'I just have this feeling, a mother's feeling maybe, but anyway whatever it is. I just don't think surgery is the answer.'

Patsy was out of town filming when Artemis arrived in Los Angeles, so Ellie took the Chrysler rag-top and drove to the station to meet her friend. It was a cloudless morning, warm and clear, and the bougainvillaea was in full bloom outside the picturesque railway terminus, itself a building which Ellie thought looked as though it were part of a Hollywood film set. The train arrived in perfect time, and Ellie stood on tiptoe as the passengers disembarked around her, searching for the slender figure of her friend.

She saw her finally, climbing carefully down the steps from a first class carriage, helped by a uniformed steward and started to run towards her.

'Artemis!' she called, and on reaching her, threw her arms around her. 'Oh heavens, this is so wonderful!' Ellie let her go, only to take hold of her by both hands and look at her. 'You look wonderful.'

'I don't feel it,' Artemis grumbled. 'I feel I've been travelling for a year. God, America is big.'

They talked all the way back in the car, Artemis recounting in her droll way her various adventures, but all Ellie wanted to know about was Hugo.

'Is Hugo really all right?' was the one question she kept asking. 'He hasn't been too worried, has he?'

'Oh no. He goes out dancing every night.'

'What's he doing in Norway?'

'I don't know. Skiing, probably.'

'I wouldn't be at all surprised. I hope you've brought some lighter clothes.'

'Is it always this warm out here?' Artemis was already itching to get out of the wool suit she was wearing. 'Yesterday, wherever we were passing through yesterday, there was snow.'

'The climate here is wonderful. And you're quite sure Hugo is all right?'

'He'd rather be over here than in Norway,' Artemis told her, taking her hat off and letting the wind ruffle her blonde hair. 'Now, tell me about my godson.'

By the time they reached Patsy's house, and Artemis understood the gravity of the situation, the two women had fallen silent.

Ellie drove the car up the concrete driveway that led to the garage and jumped out as soon as she turned the engine off. 'Telephone,' she said and hurried inside the house.

They were at Jamie's bedside in ten minutes.

'I think the worst is over,' the doctor reassured her. 'Jamie has been stable now for what.' He looked to his nurse.

'Well over an hour, doctor.'

'He was doing just dandy,' Doctor Vincent continued. 'Nurse here had him standing and bouncing, and first thing today he had a big game with those toes of his. Isn't that right, nurse?'

'He sure did,' the nurse smiled. 'He was grabbing away at them, and laughing like nobody. And then the next minute – '

Artemis stood staring at her godson, who was lying on his front with his head to one side. He was deathly pale, and his breathing was quick and shallow.

'His temperature is down a point,' Doctor Vincent added thoughtfully. 'Which is good. He was up over a hundred and two again. What bothers me is the acuteness of the attacks.'

'What's that?' Artemis pointed to a red blotch on the baby's leg, which was visible now his gown had rolled up.

'It would appear to be eczema,' the doctor said.

'That's rather what I thought,' Artemis said pensively.

'I don't know what I'll do,' Ellie said at one point. 'If anything happens to him.' They were walking round the hospital gardens.

'Nothing's going to happen to him,' Artemis said. 'Because I think I might have the answer.' Ellie stopped and stared round at her. 'It's that patch of eczema. Diana, you know, my godmother, she was on holiday once. She told me all about it. And this friend of hers had a baby, about Jamie's age, and she wasn't feeding it either. But not like you. She just didn't feed it at all herself, because

459

people didn't. At least, you know – anyway. She had a wet nurse for a long time, then the wet nurse dried up or something and she put the baby on a bottle. And it nearly died. Just like Jamie.' She felt Ellie's grip on her hand tighten, and she smiled. 'It's all right, because if I'm right, Jamie's going to be fine. Because what's wrong with him, you see, is he probably just can't take cow's milk.'

'No,' said Ellie, after some thought. 'That's not possible. Jamie was on cow's milk long before he fell ill. And he was just fine.'

'Exactly,' Artemis replied. 'And then he fell ill, and after he was ill with his tummy, what happened? He couldn't drink his milk any more. Or rather he couldn't – what does that doctor call it?'

'Contain it.'

'He couldn't *contain* it. Exactly. Because apparently, do you see, it's having whatever –'

'Gastro-enteritis.'

'It's the gastro-enteritis exactly. That's set up the what is it? The allergy.'

Ellie stared at her again. 'Are you quite sure?' she said.

'Absolutely positive,' Artemis replied. 'I'd stake Brougham on it. If it was mine to stake.'

Doctor Vincent listened attentively to Artemis's theory, and then nodded. 'How did I miss it?' he said. 'I even remember the paper. I read a paper on it, last year I think it was. The point of it being a baby can be perfectly happy on cow's milk until it suffers an attack of gastro-enteritis, which so many babies do when they're not being breast fed. And it's only after an attack that the baby loses tolerance. The theory is that it's possibly due to a subsequent deficiency in the enzyme lactase, which breaks down the sugar lactose in the gut.'

'So even when Jamie was just on sugar and water –' Ellie guessed.

Doctor Vincent nodded in agreement. 'Sure. And there's plenty of sugar lactose in cow's milk, you bet.'

'And Jamie started to develop eczema.'

'I thought that was just a related reaction to the illness. Or even to how he was being treated. But it was just straightforward eczema. Which is a hard and fast symptom of an intolerance to cow's milk.'

'OK,' said Ellie, 'so far. But what now?'

'You'd better ask the expert,' Doctor Vincent said, looking at Artemis.

'Yes,' Artemis said. 'I forgot that bit. You're going to need a sheep.'

Within twenty four hours the laboratory staff at the clinic had prepared a sheep's milk formulae, and as soon as Jamie was back to normal, he was introduced to the new regime, which he took to apparently quite happily.

'Let's take it little step by little step,' Doctor Vincent advised. 'Each day at a time. I'd say this first week is the all important one.'

While they waited to see, Ellie showed Artemis around Hollywood, and the north Californian coastline. Artemis found herself surprisingly glad of the break, and as every day brought better news, the two women began to enjoy themselves more.

'I just wish Hugo was here to enjoy it as well,' Ellie said wistfully one day as they walked along the beach. 'Don't you?'

'Not really,' said Artemis. 'For you, yes, of course. But I'm enjoying just being here.'

After they'd walked some more, Ellie stopped and stared out at the ocean. 'My God,' she said. 'What *would* have happened, Artemis? If you hadn't come?'

When they got back to the house that evening, Ellie called the clinic and was told that Jamie's improvement was still one hundred per cent. Nonetheless, she naturally wished to visit him, but Artemis asked whether Ellie would mind if she stayed behind because the walk along the beach had left her feeling quite tired.

'I'm not surprised,' Ellie said. 'I've rushed you off your feet ever since you hit town. You stretch out here and have a sleep. I won't be long.'

Artemis lay down on the sofa and started to flick through a copy of *Saturday Evening Post*, but five minutes later she was fast asleep.

She didn't hear him come in. She was dreaming, of long green fields and soft winds, which riffled through her hair as the horse carried her along. Everytime they jumped it was like flying, and suddenly she was really flying, still on the horse, and there was a city far below her, where everyone was looking up and pointing.

He came into the house, opening the door and looking round, but still she dreamed of being high over this city, and she knew where she was now, it was Los Angeles, because she could see the clinic far below her, and there was Ellie looking up and waving, and there was the sea, much nearer than it should be, a blue big waved sea running right up to the house she was in now. A house which was on the edge of the ocean, its windows opening silently and shutting silently as the curtains streamed out and the surf broke slowly over Artemis as she stood at the window and then she saw him, standing over her, looking down on her, brown eyes, dark thick curly hair, brown eyes with thick lashes that smiled, a man wearing a short sleeved sports shirt, well muscled, his arms brown and his hands on his hips as he stood there looking down at her.

'Who are you?' she said.

'It's OK,' he replied. 'There's no need to be frightened.' He was smiling, but Artemis was frowning, sitting up now and putting a hand to the top of her chest.

'Why should I be frightened?' she asked, nevertheless hoping that he couldn't hear her heart, which was pounding in her chest.

'You look frightened,' he insisted.

'More like half-asleep,' she said.

The man put a soft-sided travelling bag down on the floor and then turned back to regard Artemis, who had swung her legs off the sofa and was now sitting up properly. 'You didn't look frightened when you were asleep,' he told her, with a broad grin.

'How long were you standing there?'

'Long enough.'

Artemis took a deep breath, to try and pull herself together. But there was something about the man's face that held her spellbound, something about the shape of his eyes, the candid expression, the humour of his mouth, something that was dreadfully familiar. 'Don't you think you should tell me who you are?' she heard herself asking.

'Sure. Although I don't need to ask who you are. You're Ellie's friend Artemis.'

And all at once Artemis knew who he was.

'I'm Patsy,' he said, an announcement which was greeted with silence. 'Ellie's brother?' he ventured.

'Yes, of course,' Artemis agreed.

'Where's Ellie? At the clinic?' Artemis nodded. 'Any improvement?' He waited for a reply, but Artemis was still looking up at him, as if she hadn't heard. 'I mean with Jamie,' he continued. 'Is there any improvement? Has he had any more attacks?'

'No,' Artemis replied, shaking her head. 'I mean no — no more attacks. Not, no.'

'Right,' Patsy nodded.

'If you see what I mean,' Artemis added.

Although she was now looking away from him, past him, down at the floor, she could feel him looking at her and she knew he was staring at how white she was, because she could feel there was absolutely no blood in her cheeks. She wanted to slap them, or pinch them, to give them mock roses, but all she could do was just sit there, and hope that he would go away. But he wasn't going to go anywhere.

'Look, I'm really sorry. If I frightened you — '

'If I could just have a drink of water.'

'A drink of water,' he repeated. 'Sure. Coming right up.' From the kitchen he fetched her a glass of iced water, the base of the glass wrapped in a small paper napkin. Artemis thanked him, and took it from him two-handed, but even so she still managed to spill some.

'Be honest,' he said. 'I did. I startled you.'

'To be honest,' Artemis replied, 'you did more than that.'

She waited until he'd taken his bags and gone to unpack, before she reached for her stick and took herself off to the privacy of her own room, where she closed the door and sat on the bed. Nothing had happened to her like this since the first time she'd seen Hugo, and even the memory of that experience seemed suddenly to have vanished.

She kicked off her shoes and lay full length on the bed, staring up at the ceiling. It wasn't just how Patsy was and how Patsy looked that had so overcome her. It was because she felt she had known him all her life. Of course it was because he was Ellie's brother, and since Ellie was her best friend, then it only stood to reason she would feel at ease with her brother. Even so.

She was still lying on her bed, staring at the ceiling when later there was a knock on the door and Ellie came in, full of her old zest and high spirits.

'Hi,' she said. 'I have such good news, really. And it's all because of you.' She sat on the edge of the bed and took one of Artemis's hands. 'Doctor Vincent thinks Jamie's turned the corner.'

Artemis sat up, smiling in delight, all thought of her own feelings forgotten.

'Of course it's still a little early,' Ellie continued, 'but the signs are so good! Jamie's sitting up and taking notice of things again, and I mean he just *looks* so different! Doctor Vincent is convinced! He is! He says if it hadn't been for you – ' Ellie stopped, and suddenly looked at her friend. 'He's right, Artemis. If it hadn't been for you.' She let go of Artemis's hand. 'Patsy's taking us out to dinner,' she said. 'OK?'

'Of course it's OK,' Patsy said, appearing at the open bedroom door. He picked Artemis's stick up off the floor where she had dropped it and handed it to her. 'Wagons roll,' he said, smiling right at her.

The evening they spent reminded Artemis so much of the evenings spent in Ireland, when Ellie, Hugo and she would fool and joke and tease. But in those days it had been Artemis who had gone first to her bed, leaving Hugo and Ellie to whisper in front of the dying embers of the fire, while this night Ellie had gone upstairs first, leaving Artemis and Patsy alone to talk and listen to the radio.

'Do you like this sort of music?' he asked.

'I like this song,' Artemis replied.

' "Stardust". Hoagy Carmichael.'

'And I like the band.'

'You should.' Patsy said. 'It's Tommy Dorsey. And what about this singer?'

Artemis had listened to the young voice, a voice full of confidence and nerve, a voice which played dangerous games with the words of the song, stretching them, delaying them, almost seeming to invent them. 'I don't know,' Artemis had said. 'It's odd. It feels as though he's – well. As if he's singing to you. Just to you.'

'You bet,' Patsy agreed. 'It's this new guy. Frank Sinatra.'

For a time they sat and listened to the band and the singer, who as far as Artemis was concerned, seemed much better able to express everything for her. Which was just as well, for compared to someone as easy, assured and charming as Patsy, she found she'd little to say.

In a place like this, in Hollywood, he must know so many girls, beautiful girls, perfect girls. 'Such rotten luck, my sweet,' her stepmother used to say. 'Men are so odd about deformities. A girl I once knew had a club foot. Well, when I say a club foot, it was nothing like your poor leg. It was only very slightly deformed. And she did marry. But once her husband caught sight of it, it was separate bedrooms from then on, and that was it.'

Artemis stared into the darkness and wished she could be American, like Patsy, in love with life, brimming with confidence, warm and funny. Instead of 'such an odd girl', with a poor leg, and not a very great deal to which she could look forward, as her stepmother had so often reminded her.

Staring into the darkening night, Patsy also found himself reviewing his chances, and deciding he was more likely to beat Babe Ruth's record of sixty home runs in one season than he was to get a girl as beautiful, as talented, as intelligent and as refined as Lady Artemis Deverill to take a second look at him. Girls such as she came from great families and had pedigrees as long as menus. They might sometimes idly amuse themselves with young men like him, but only ever as a passing fancy. Lady Artemis Deverill was as aristocratic as he was commonplace. She was sophisticated and he was unrefined. She was cut-glass and he was plastic. She was pure gold, he was nickel. For all the chances he had of interesting her further, he might as well go try and catch a moonbeam. Patsy gave a deep groan, and turned to lie on his side.

The next day Patsy returned from the studios with the news that he'd been invited to attend the academy awards dinner the following week.

'You see I worked on *Goodbye Mr Chips*,' he explained more for Artemis's benefit than Ellie's. 'And both Robert Donat and Greer Garson have been nominated. And Miss Garson has very kindly asked me if I'd like to join her party.'

'What's she like?' Ellie asked curiously.

'Red-haired and Irish,' Patsy grinned, before looking back at Artemis. 'And yet very gentle and aristocratic looking,' he added shyly. 'Like Artemis here.'

'I saw the film in London,' Artemis told him.

'And what did you think?'

Artemis thought. 'The acting was awfully good.'

'But the film was sentimental?'

'Yes,' Artemis said carefully. 'I suppose so.'

Patsy nodded and smiled, but said no more because he agreed. Artemis smiled and said no more, because she thought she'd said too much.

Finally Patsy cleared his throat and stared at the ground. 'I'm allowed to take a guest,' he said. 'I don't suppose you'd like to come.'

'Is that a question?' Ellie asked. 'And if so, to whom is it addressed?'

Patsy looked straight up at his sister. 'Why – ' he stammered, 'why to – to Artemis, of course.'

Ellie raised her eyebrows exaggeratedly and pulled a sisterly face at Patsy's confusion. 'Well I never did,' she said. 'What a surprise.'

'He didn't have to do this, you know,' Artemis said from inside the dress into which she was attempting to wriggle.

'Who didn't have to do what and why?' Ellie asked, helping to pull the beautiful dress down over Artemis's hips. It was the one good gown Artemis had brought with her from London, a dinner dress by Strassner, in clinging black crepe with a gold embroidered 'sweetheart' neck, which looked sexy by being demure, and showed off Artemis's figure to perfection.

'Wow,' Ellie said approvingly.

Artemis sat down at the dressing table and checked her hair. 'Your brother,' she said.

'What about my brother?'

'Nothing. He's just rather nice, that's all.'

'Isn't that enough?' Ellie teased. 'So taking it that he's the "he" in "he didn't have to do this", what didn't he have to do?'

'Could you pass me up my handbag, please?' Artemis asked, eyeing Ellie in the mirror.

Ellie passed Artemis her purse from the bed. 'You mean he didn't have to take you to the awards.'

'I seem to have lost my lipstick,' Artemis said, having emptied the not inconsiderable contents of her purse on to the dressing table.

'Sure he didn't have to take you to the awards,' Ellie agreed, picking the missing lipstick up off the floor. 'Like you didn't have to accept.'

'It would have been rather rude not to, don't you think?'

'Maybe Patsy thought it would have been rather rude not to ask you,' Ellie said poker-faced.

'Yes,' Artemis agreed, carefully applying the lightest of rouges to her mouth. 'Probably.' She rolled her lips together and then stared at herself in the mirror. 'What do you think?' she said, enquiring about her makeup. 'Is that too much?'

'What I say,' Ellie stated firmly, 'is look out Lana Turner.'

That year the annual banquet of the Academy of Motion Picture Arts was held in the Cocoanut Grove of the Ambassador Hotel. The fans stood five or six deep along the streets, and many people had to walk five blocks from where they had finally been able to park their cars. There were so many arc lights illuminating the scene that night had become day, and the only stars that were visible were the ones who got out from their rented limousines to wave at their thousands of fans. Bob Hope was the master of ceremonies, and after the members of the academy and their guests had stood in silence in remembrance of the recent death of Douglas Fairbanks, MGM's *Gone With The Wind* made an all but clean sweep of the Oscars, including best actress, which went, to no-one's undue surprise and least of all the modest Miss Garson's, to Vivien Leigh.

'If I were to mention all those who've shown me such wonderful generosity through *Gone With The Wind*,' the raven-haired star said in her speech of acceptance, 'I should have to entertain you with an oration as long as *Gone With The Wind* itself.'

The only real major surprise was Clark Gable losing out to Robert Donat for the best actor statuette, but since *Goodbye Mr Chips* was also an MGM production, the company had a more or less clean sweep of all the major awards.

The joy was unalloyed at the party afterwards. Patsy and Artemis squeezed through the throng of stars who were household names and Patsy discreetly whispered to Artemis who most of them were.

At one point they found themselves standing near a group of English actors away from the main body of the party, and in a very different mood to most of their fellow guests. The reason for this soon became apparent. They were talking about the war.

A tall handsome young man with a moustache was holding forth. Artemis recognized him as Fritz von Tarlenheim from the film of *The Prisoner of Zenda*, which she and Ellie had seen in Ireland.

'I wish I could go back and enlist now,' he was saying. 'But they won't release me until I've finished *Raffles*.'

'Me too,' another actor agreed. 'I can't wait to get out of here. You know what Ralphie said before he left, don't you? "There's a very fine trade in white feathers going on out here," he said.' Everyone laughed, but at the actor's impersonation of Ralph Richardson, rather than at the reported quip.

'Well, as one of tonight's victors put it,' von Tarlenheim continued ruefully, 'as Scarlett O'Hara herself said, off-screen, the Americans are quite inconceivably patriotic.'

'Excuse me, sir,' Patsy interrupted. 'I know a lot of you British think that we're not behind you in this war. And while it shames me to say that there are a fair number who do think it's your business and no-one else's, there's one hell of a lot more of us who can't wait to get in the scrap, and help you guys beat the daylights out of Hitler.'

Von Tarlenheim smiled at him. 'That's what I like

about the Yanks,' he said. 'They're not afraid to come out with it. Why don't you sit down and join us?'

Patsy and Artemis sat down and were introduced around the table. All the actors in the party were single-minded in their determination to get back as quickly as they possibly could to rejoin their squadron or to re-enlist.

'Although I hear Dicky Greene's none too keen,' someone said.

'Don't worry,' von Tarlenheim replied. 'We'll soon get to work on him. We don't want any more of those cheap jibes from Westminster about English actors gallantly facing the footlights in America, thank you.' Then he turned to Artemis. 'You're frightfully pretty,' he said. 'Would you like to dance?'

'Sorry, sir,' Patsy said with a smile as he stood up. 'But this dance is already taken.'

As they walked away towards the dance floor, Artemis took Patsy's arm for support. 'Thank you,' she said.

'What for?' Patsy asked her.

'For being such a gentleman.'

Now that they were out of sight of the party at the table, Artemis let go of Patsy's arm and used her stick to help her across the room.

'I thought we were going to dance?' Patsy said.

'You don't have to,' Artemis said. 'There's no obligation. Really.'

'Supposing I want to?' Patsy asked. 'Really?'

'It's a little awkward,' she said.

'You mean you want to dance with someone else?'

'Meaning it's a little awkward.'

'Oh.' Patsy nodded, and then gently took her stick, hanging it over his arm. 'I don't think so. Not if you let me hold you tight.'

He led her on to the dance floor, his arm around her waist, and then as soon as they were among the other dancers he took her other hand and held her up just enough, just as Hugo had held her, sufficiently high so that she could still dance, and was not just a helpless rag-doll in his arms. A beautiful black girl with bright red lips and a midnight blue sequined dress came on in front of the band and started to sing:

Do you love me – as I love you?
Are you my life to be – my dream come true?
Or will this dream of mine fade out of sight,
Like the moon growing dim,
On the rim of the hill,
In the chill,
Still of the night?

They stood outside on a vast flagged and stone balustraded terrace. Patsy leaned on it, on both his elbows, and looked out across the garden. Artemis stood beside him, her back to the view, watching through the windows the dancers gliding round the floor.

'How long are you over for?' Patsy asked, half-knowing the answer.

'Oh,' said Artemis with a shrug. 'You know. Not long.'

'How long is not long?' Patsy turned to her with a smile.

'Um –' Artemis studied the dancers some more, without really seeing them. 'I'm going back on Monday actually.'

'Monday?'

She could hear the sudden gasp in his voice, and hoped that he might be feeling just a little of what she was feeling. 'Yes,' she went on. 'Monday. Although from the way you said it, you obviously think Monday's an awful day to travel.'

'That wasn't why I said "Monday?",' Patsy replied, repeating his inflexion exactly. He turned back to look out across the floodlit gardens. He knew why he'd said the day that way. Because he didn't want her to go that soon. In fact, he realized, he didn't want her to go at all. 'Artemis,' he began, once again turning to talk to her, and as he did, she turned away from him coincidentally, so it seemed, so that she might study the floodlit grounds.

'I do hope you're not going to tell me that Monday's a bad day,' she said, 'because that was the only flight I could get to New York.'

'Why do you have to go back? Ellie said the work you do –'

'The point is, you see,' Artemis interrupted, 'about what I do being voluntary. The point is it isn't really. In a war, if one volunteers for something, you can't just chuck it up if you feel like it. Otherwise soldiers who volunteered, once they started getting shot at, and if they didn't like it, they could chuck it in, too. Couldn't they? And then where would you be? I'm a little cold. Do you think we might go inside?'

'You could get killed. If you go home, if you go back to England, you could get killed!'

Artemis hardly dared to look at him, in case she was mistaken, and that the emotion in his voice wasn't passion, but something else. 'I know I might get killed,' Artemis agreed. 'But that's why I'd rather go home. And get killed in England. Better that than to be accused of funking it out here.'

'But you're a girl,' Patsy said. 'It's different for girls.'

'Not really,' Artemis replied. 'The war's changing all that.' She looked at him, with that particular wide-eyed look of hers, an expression she had long ago adopted to conceal her real feelings, designed specifically to look like a challenge. It was a most successful look, although Artemis hadn't any idea of its real effect. Which was to shut Patsy up. To him, as a newcomer to Artemis's odd ways, the look suggested to him that any further conversation would be an intrusion on her privacy, and that he'd be well advised at this point to mind his own business.

'Can I ask you something?' she said.

'Sure,' he nodded. 'Anything.'

'Just this,' she said. 'If things were the other way round, and we were in England. And it was America who was fighting Hitler, what would you do?' Would you stay in England? Or would you go home?'

'What do you think?' Patsy asked.

'Exactly,' Artemis said. 'Now if you wouldn't mind, it is nearly four in the morning, and I'm actually a bit tired.'

The next day, as Patsy was driving to drop his sister off at the clinic on his way to work, Ellie got to talking about Artemis and told her brother all about Artemis, all the things she knew full well Artemis would never tell anyone about herself, the things it had taken Ellie so long to discover. When he had heard these things, things that made sense of this strange, shy and sensitive creature, Patsy pulled the car up in the park of the clinic and poured his heart out to Ellie. Ellie listened without surprise.

'So why not tell her?' Ellie asked. 'It's no good telling me.'

'Never in a million years!' Patsy exclaimed. 'Never in a thousand million years! I'd never dare tell her I was falling in love with her!'

'Why ever not?'

'Have you seen that look she gives you?' Patsy replied. 'I tell you, if England has an army full of people who can give that look, Hitler hasn't a bat's hope in hell!'

Ellie shook her head. 'The only way to win her, Patsy,' she advised, getting out of the car, 'is to come out of your corner and go straight for the knock-out. Artemis doesn't spar. Artemis is perfectly prepared to stand there and slug it out, but she doesn't spar. Next time, when the bell goes, go for the chin. She's just psyching you with that look of hers. Believe me. I know.' Ellie shook her head and smiling, ruffled her brother's dark hair. He bent away from her with a good natured grin. 'I'm serious, Patsy,' Ellie said as she left. 'And don't worry. Where you're concerned, she's got a glass chin.'

Ellie waved, kissed her hand to her brother, and disappeared into the clinic.

It was a different Patsy who the following day invited and took Artemis to the studios. He was much more relaxed, less anxious and didn't make one more reference to Artemis's decision to return to England. He was kind and sweet and attentive, but above all funny, making Artemis laugh with his stories about filming and the outrageous behaviour of certain stars, as well as keeping her constantly amused with a wonderful flow of native Irish wit.

Artemis was more relaxed too, determined not to worry any longer about what he might think of her, but to enjoy herself and live for the moment, however short and sweet it may be. After all, she was in Hollywood, the home of the makers of fairy-tales, the place where lived the dreamers of dreams, while back home, across the cold Atlantic, the world, the real world, was at war. And when she returned to it, this time of enchantment would be just a memory, something which her heart and mind could search for and feel reassured by when the bombs started raining down from above, as she knew that they must soon do.

And then, two days later and quite suddenly everything changed, in the time it takes to light a cigarette, or pour a cup of coffee.

Patsy had invited Artemis back to the studio to watch filming on a picture called *The Shop Around The Corner*, starring James Stewart, of whom even Artemis had heard, and Margaret Sullavan. Patsy had placed Artemis in a canvas-backed chair to one side of the set, and although what was happening on the floor was enthralling and fascinating Artemis found her eyes kept straying after one person, and that person was Patsy as he went diligently about his work as assistant to the director. It seemed he was popular with everyone on the film, technicians and actors alike, most of whom whenever there was a break spent time joking with the amiable young man and, as everyone else always did, ruffling his thick brown curly hair.

Patsy, having had to build his body from nothing as it were, kept himself in first class physical shape. Of medium height, he was exceptionally well proportioned, with long legs, a strong chest, and a narrow waist, and when at work his well muscled arms were shown off to their best, thanks to his habit of pushing the sleeves of his short-sleeved sports shirts up even higher.

But it wasn't his athletic figure that made Patsy Milligan so noticeable. Hollywood was full of beautiful bodies, male and female. It was his smile. Artemis noticed all morning as she sat and watched the activity around her, that whenever there was a minor crisis or misunderstanding, Patsy was the task force that was sent in. And all it took was a joke from him and a few words, and then a smile, a smile that started in his Irish eyes, before dancing down to his lips and stealing everyone's hearts away.

'Are you OK?' Patsy had appeared at her side from somewhere out of the blue, as she had been sitting there day-dreaming. She smiled and then told him she was fine.

'OK,' he said. 'We've broken, so let's go and have some lunch.'

They started to walk across the studio, discussing the morning's shoot. Patsy stopped to show her the camera close to, only to discover the cameraman was still at his post.

'Hey, Pat,' he said. 'Just the fellah I need. Got a moment?'

'Sure, Mr Daniels,' Patsy replied. 'But first I'd like you to meet a friend of mine. Mr Daniels, this is Artemis Deverill.'

The cameraman climbed down off his seat and shook her hand. 'Hi,' he said. 'You an actress?'

'No,' Artemis said, and then during the silence that followed as the cameraman stared at her, she added. 'No. No I'm not.'

'You should be. You have the most fantastic eyes.'

'Mr Daniels is our top cameraman, honey,' Patsy continued. 'He photographed Miss Garbo in *Anna Christie*, *Grand Hotel*, *Queen Christina*, *Camille*, *Ninotchka*.'

'Pat,' William Daniels took him by a forearm. 'Would you mind just standing in? It won't take a moment? And I'd really appreciate it if Miss Deverill wouldn't mind as well.'

Patsy led her to the mark on the studio floor where the cameraman wanted them to stand.

'I think I've found a better angle!' he called from behind the huge movie camera. 'So if you two wouldn't mind just edging a little closer to each other!'

'Which scene is this, Mr Daniels?' Patsy called.

William Daniels, with his eye to the view finder, called back, 'First scene after lunch, Pat! Where Jimmy and Margaret get to kiss!'

Artemis knew she was blushing and felt it to her horror. She turned her head slightly away from Patsy and tossed back her hair.

'Miss Deverill?' William Daniels called. 'I'm sorry — I'm sure this is one heck of an imposition — but if you could just look at Pat, do you think?'

Artemis took as silent a deep breath as she found possible, and then clenching her hands so that the nails dug into the palms, turned back to face Patsy.

'A little closer, if you wouldn't mind, kids! I'm very tight on you!' Patsy moved his face closer to Artemis. 'Closer?' Daniels called. They were even closer. Artemis had to shut her eyes. 'Good!' the cameraman called.

And then Patsy kissed her, long, slow and gentle. And continued to kiss her, until when he finally let her go, and the world came slowly back into their vision, they saw that the cameraman had gone.

'That's a pity,' Patsy said, frowning.

'What is?' Artemis just about managed to ask.

'Mr Daniels going,' Patsy said. 'I hoped he might need a retake.' And then he grinned. 'Except on second thoughts, I don't think we need Mr Daniels for that,' he said, before kissing her again.

When they finally wandered off to lunch, Artemis holding on to Patsy's arm, his hand clasped over hers, she quite forgot her walking stick, leaving it hanging where she had left it on the handle of the camera trolley.

The plan was for them all to go up to Santa Barbara for the weekend, to stay at a friend of Patsy's empty beach house, but on the Friday morning Ellie had to cry off.

'Doctor Vincent is so pleased with Jamie's progress,' she explained, 'he wants to send him home earlier than planned. He's anxious to see if Jamie can keep his improvement up with a change of environment.'

Artemis had been greatly looking forward to spending her last weekend in America by the sea in company of Ellie and most of all of Patsy. But she realized the recovery of her godchild was more important than a brief vacation by the sea and so she concealed her disappointment.

'There's nothing to stop you two going,' Ellie said, as Artemis started to pack her things preparatory to flying to New York rather than motoring up the coastline. 'I've got Nanny, and Doctor Vincent is going to be on call all weekend. It's not as if there's anything you can do. It's just I can't very well take Jamie with me to the coast and I do so want to have him home.'

Artemis went on packing for want of something to do while she silently tried to find the reason she knew must exist as to why she should not spend the weekend with Patsy. 'It won't be the same,' she said finally. 'Not without you.'

'No,' said Ellie, giving her a smile. 'I don't suppose it will.' And then she went off in search of her brother.

'Say something!' Patsy called. 'You've hardly said a thing since we left town!'

'Sorry!' Artemis called back over the noise of the wind.

They were driving with the roof of the rag-top down, along the almost deserted highway to Santa Barbara, and having small talked their way out of the city limits, once they had hit the open road Artemis had fallen into a thoughtful silence. For the first twenty or thirty miles Patsy had covered the lack of conversation by happily singing a selection of the latest popular songs in a fine tenor voice, but as Artemis's silence had grown deeper, he had begun to cast anxious looks in her direction. Finally he slowed the speed of the car down so they could talk more easily.

'You're thinking you shouldn't have come, aren't you?' he asked. 'You still think it's a bad idea.'

'I don't think it's a bad idea, it's not that,' Artemis replied, retying the knot in her headscarf. 'I don't think it's a bad idea at all. I think it's a lovely idea.'

'So what then?' Patsy said. 'Why the brooding silence?'

'I suppose,' Artemis answered, looking round at him, 'because it's a lovely idea.' She smiled at him and his heart sang once more, and a minute later so did he.

Is it for all time, or simply a lark?
Is it Granada I see, or only Asbury Park?
Is it a fancy, not worth thinking of?
Or is it
At long last Love?

The sun was fast sinking in an erubescent glow beyond the Pacific as Patsy turned the car off the road and started to head down a track leading directly to the beach house which could be seen nestling at the bottom of the cliffs. There were no other houses anywhere in sight, and no other people, just the ocean, the rocks, and the sand.

As soon as they'd unpacked the car and explored the comfortable wooden house, Patsy built a fire on the sands from a pile of dry driftwood under the verandah and cooked them hamburger steaks which they ate sitting on the rocks. The tide was high, but on the ebb, falling back down the beach with a hiss and a rattle of shingle.

'Isn't this just a wonderful spot?' Patsy asked her. 'Tommy and me, we come up here as often as we can, which unfortunately isn't very often.'

'Tommy and you?'

'Tommy, this pal of mine. Sure. Tommy and me.'

'Tommy and you and – ?'

Patsy smiled at her. 'Tommy and his girl Mo, and me,' he said. 'And Greta Garbo, Rita Hayworth, Madeleine Carroll, Dorothy Lamour. It depends who's not filming.'

Artemis eased herself down from the rock, and taking her stick, began to walk off. Patsy hopped down after her. 'Hey!' he called. 'Where are you going?'

'Just to look at the sea,' Artemis replied.

He let her go ahead of him, slim and elegant, her blonde hair blown by the breeze, as she made her way to the edge of the sea, where she stood, leaning on her stick and staring at the receding tide. And then he went and stood at her shoulder.

'I haven't brought anyone here who mattered to me,' Patsy said.

'Of course you have,' Artemis replied.

'Not anyone who matters to me. Not until now.'

He took her hand, and felt her suddenly clasp it, which was better than any answer she could give. They both stood for a while, silent at the water's edge. It was a very calm night, and although the tide was running out, the ocean seemed almost still. Patsy put his arm around Artemis's slender waist and she leaned against him.

'Are you a good swimmer?' she suddenly asked him, turning round as if it was very important for her to know and at once.

'Not bad,' he said. 'Yes, I can swim.'

Artemis stared at him, holding his eyes with her's. Then she pointed without looking along the beach. 'I'll race you,' she said quietly. 'To that next lot of rocks.'

'The tide's on the turn,' he said. 'There may not be much of a sea running, but – '

'I'm a strong swimmer,' she interrupted, kicking off her shoes. 'It's all right.'

Patsy hesitated, and then turned to go back to the house. 'We'd better fetch our costumes,' he said.

'Why?' Artemis asked, about to pull her sweater over her head. 'There's no-one around.' And then she continued to undress, surprisingly quickly and gracefully, without having to lean awkwardly on her stick as Patsy had imagined she might. In fact she had already discarded her stick, as she had done for years when it was time for her to get undressed, and in no time at all she stood before him in just her underthings, waiting for him, balancing herself evenly by dint of standing tiptoe on the foot of her shorter leg.

'Well?' Artemis asked, with deliberate impatience, challenging him to break the gaze between them and for him to look a little more specifically at her.

'You're perfect,' he said. 'Absolutely beautiful.'

'Not quite,' she replied. 'Not absolutely.'

'Yes you are,' he disagreed. 'You are absolutely perfect.'

She looked at him, the bright blue eyes still wide, but the challenge had gone from them. Then she reached up, and putting her arms around his neck, kissed him very gently on the mouth.

'Come on,' she said.

Patsy stripped quickly down to his shorts and followed her into the inky blue sea. She started to swim as soon as he was alongside her, powerfully and easily, taking Patsy completely by surprise, so much so that he found himself three or four lengths adrift of the slender blonde mermaid who was vanishing into the darkness ahead.

He swam after her as hard as he could, overarm as she was swimming, kicking on through the warm Pacific waters, but unable quite to peg her back, so that when they reached the appointed mark Artemis was still half a length up.

She flipped over on to her back and floated, looking up at the moon above them. 'You know what they say, don't you?' she said, when she had caught her breath. 'In a two horse race, always back the outsider of the two.'

Patsy stood beside her, the water up to his chest. 'You sure can swim,' he said. 'You're full of surprises.'

'What about you?'

'I'll let you be the judge of that.'

He lifted her out of the water and carried her back along the beach. Halfway back to the house, she started shivering.

'Are you cold?' he asked.

'No,' she replied. 'Not at all.'

He wrapped her in a thick white towel when they got back to the house and rubbed her dry, before carrying her into the bedroom still well wrapped in the towel.

'You look so serious,' he whispered.

'Sorry,' she replied, her arms around his neck. 'But then this is quite a serious business, I imagine.'

'You imagine?' Patsy asked.

'Yes,' Artemis replied, and then as he laid her gently down on to the bed, asked, 'do you mind?'

'No,' Patsy whispered, bending down to kiss her. 'The very opposite.'

The love he made to her was nothing like Artemis had ever imagined it or even dared hope it might be. She told him so, and when she did, he took her to him once again, while outside beyond the windows of the house the now distant sea pounded faintly on the sands, with a soft rhythmic thunder and a long dying sigh.

Ellie and Patsy both went to the airport, but Ellie made sure she was the first to say goodbye. 'I'll be back in England,' Ellie promised, 'as soon as Hugo blows the whistle.'

'Any particular message?' Artemis asked. 'When and if I see him?'

'*When* you see him,' Ellie replied. 'Tell him I love him.'

'Sure,' said Artemis in her best American. 'I meant anything new.'

Ellie smiled, before kissing her friend goodbye. 'I'm going to miss you.'

'Yes,' Artemis said. 'Me too. I mean – I don't mean me, too. I mean – oh you know what I mean.' And this time when they embraced, Artemis hugged for the first time ever about as hard as Ellie hugged her.

Patsy walked her to the gate. 'You won't reconsider, I suppose?' he asked.

'Staying here, you mean.' Artemis, afraid she was going to lose her carefully constructed composure, narrowed her eyes and pretended to search the distant horizon for something.

'You know what I mean,' Patsy said.

'Let's get the war out of the way first,' Artemis replied, still unable to spot the mythical object for which she still scanned the skyline.

'It might just make it a whole lot easier to get through, that's all.' Patsy gently turned her to him. 'If I knew we were going to get married.'

'I don't agree,' Artemis replied, fixing him with her wide eyes. 'I think it would make it practically impossible.'

'I see.' Patsy let go of her hands, deliberately. 'You're just going to kind of pretend this was just one of those things, right?'

'Of course not. Don't be an idiot.'

'Look, I'll stop behaving like an idiot if you say you'll marry me.'

Artemis took one of his hands in both of hers. 'The moment it's over, I promise,' she said. 'The moment they sound that last stupid all clear, and we can all walk along – you know – without staring up at the skies. Or sit by the sea without worrying about what might be coming over the horizon, I promise.'

'That's great,' Patsy grinned. 'And typically British. You just haven't said what you'll promise.'

'Ask me then,' she replied, 'and you'll find out.'

The official at the gate finally had to tap Patsy on the shoulder. 'Hey, mac,' he said. 'I don't wish to spoil the party, but that was the final call.'

Artemis smiled at Patsy, and then moved away. He caught her and kissed her. 'I love you,' he said. 'Don't ever forget that.'

'I won't,' Artemis promised, and then looked round suddenly very shyly at the gate official.

'Go ahead, lady,' he said. 'I won't listen.'

'I love you too,' she whispered in Patsy's ear, and then was gone.

Once airborne, the plane banked and began to wheel slowly round to head for its New York bound flightpath. As the wing tipped, Artemis could see the airport far below, and the distant glimmer of the ocean, and then the plane climbed higher and into the clouds.

When the visibility cleared, Los Angeles was just a speck, and then it was gone, as was Ellie and her handsome, laughing, loving brother.

18

Following Dunkirk and the fall of France, an unease hung over Britain. Her main ally, who traditionally had always been her oldest enemy, had collapsed so quickly and with such bitter recriminations against the British, blaming them unconditionally for the two crushing defeats France had suffered, that the inhabitants of the British Isles were in a state of delayed shock. The evacuation of Dunkirk had indeed been little short of miraculous, and the newspapers had done their best to make the retreat seem like a victory, but few people believed them, preferring instead to give their attention to Churchill, their new prime minister, who had somewhat grimly reminded them that wars were won in battle, not by evacuations.

'We're on our own, I'm afraid,' Hugo said to Artemis over dinner at his London house the night the French cabinet finally rejected Churchill's proposal for a Franco-British union. 'The Germans are in Paris and the French Army is scattering southwards in ribbons.'

'Next stop Dover, I suppose,' Artemis replied, with a toss of her blonde hair.

'Absolutely,' said another female guest. 'Time for us girls to stop cutting our nails and get out the woad.'

'I don't think so,' a slender pale-faced American opposite Artemis said. 'I was in Paris just before the jackboots came in, and the word was that Mr Hitler thinks the war is as good as over. At least that's the impression he has given his generals.'

'Because he thinks the British government's going to agree to a compromise peace,' Hugo said.

The pale-faced American nodded as he carefully replaced his wine glass. 'Mmmm,' he said. 'Yes. Hitler is rumoured not to want to go all the way with you delightful people. He feels you have so much in common. So many visitors from these shores, people shall we say in high places? They've given him the impression that there's really absolutely nothing for you two to fight about.'

'That might have been so,' Hugo allowed, 'if Chamberlain was still in charge, which he's not.'

'Thank God,' the man on Artemis's right put in. 'He'll find Winnie a very different kettle of fish.'

'I'm sure Mr Churchill is a very fine man,' the American continued. 'And a most patriotic one. But there are still a great number of very influential people in this country of yours who it appears are most anxious to be friends with the Führer. And they won't let old "Winnie the Windbag", as they so roguishly call him, stand in their way.'

'Cranks,' the man on Artemis's right said. 'Should be taken out and shot.'

'My,' the American laughed, 'I don't think you'd be saying that if it was *their* pictures on your postage stamps.'

When all the other guests had gone, and before she herself left to go home, Artemis asked Hugo what he thought the state of play was.

'Grim,' he said, 'and about to get a great deal grimmer.' The only faint hope he held out was that the Germans were not yet prepared for the invasion which everyone knew must come. 'Hitler's also in two minds,' he added. 'He's quite anxious to have a crack at Russia, and if he does, Germany most certainly won't be able to support a war on two major fronts.'

'And where are you off to next?' she asked, as Hugo fetched her coat.

'The Middle East apparently,' he replied. 'Seems like we need shoring up out there. Now the Italians have joined the bun fight.'

'Aren't there rather a lot of them out there?' Artemis

enquired. 'Aren't we a bit outnumbered? At least that's what Diana was saying last night.'

'If you call ten of them to one of us outnumbered,' Hugo grinned, 'yes, then I'd say we were outnumbered.'

'When do you leave?' Artemis looked up at him.

'On Monday,' he said. 'But don't tell Mussolini.'

'Hugo?'

'Yes, Tom?'

'You know I was – er in America?'

'I did notice, Tom.'

'Well, I met Patsy. Ellie's brother. You know.'

'Yes –'

'And I, that is – we.'

'Very handsome fellow, by all accounts, Ellie's brother Patsy,' said Hugo slowly. 'Very handsome.'

'Yes, he is.'

'I expect one thing led to another, didn't it?'

'Yes, Hugo, it did really. Do you mind?'

'No. Do you?'

Artemis shook her head. 'Rather the reverse,' she said, turning away.

'Good, then that's settled then,' said Hugo, suddenly. 'I must go and play at soldiers now.' He stopped at the door. 'This will make us something or another, sister- and brothers-in-law to each other or something. Rather fun.'

Artemis went to get up, but before she could get to her feet Hugo was gone, and as she heard his footstep retreating it seemed as if he too was fading away with the sound.

By the first week in July, Hugo had arrived at Fort Capuzzo, an important desert frontier stronghold which the British had captured in a lightning raid on 14 June. The small column of troops there were in good heart, for despite being bombed and machine gunned from the air, the British had suffered only five dozen casualties so far compared with the Italians who had suffered over one thousand. After advising on the prevailing conditions, which were of paramount importance to a force whose strategy was to keep mobile in order to make the Italians concentrate their positions and thus provide more or less sitting targets, Hugo was called back east to Mersa Matruh where the main body of the British force under General Sir Archibald Wavell were establishing and consolidating their main position. During the next month Hugo studied the weather, and advised when asked as to the suitability of the conditions. Happily, what Hugo liked to call his inspired guesses enjoyed a high success rate, and General Hunter, who had preceded him out to the desert, congratulated him unofficially on his contribution. By September the British forces, according to the published casualty list, had lost only one hundred and fifty men since mid-June, compared to the enemy's three thousand five hundred. And then came the news that the Italians, having massed six divisions, were beginning a big push forward.

At precisely the same moment, the Germans bombed London for the first time and the Blitz began. Artemis had managed to get down to Brougham for the weekend, so missing the devastating raids on Saturday and Sunday nights. But she heard all about them on the wireless and on Monday morning prepared to drive back to London.

'You can't go back there now, your ladyship,' Jenkins said, as she once again gave him charge of Brutus.

'Of course I can, Jenks,' Artemis replied, kneeling down and nuzzling her beloved dog's brown head, which was now quite heavily flecked with grey. 'I can and I must.' The dog put his paw up and rested it on her shoulder, looking at her with his oddly flecked boss eyes. 'He seems thinner this weekend, Jenks,' Artemis said. 'Has he been eating up?'

'He eats same as ever, your ladyship,' Jenks told her. 'He just pines, that's what. He misses you.'

Artemis gave Brutus a last hug, and then with a wave

to Jenks got in her car and disappeared down the drive. Jenks held the big dog's collar, who after a moment stopped trying to run after the car, and instead sat down, head to the sky, and bayed a deep long howl.

Finally arrived in Westminster, Artemis found herself in a very different city. The first wave of bombs hadn't struck deep into the West End of London, falling mainly on the City and beyond. But as soon as she drove her first official passenger on a tour of inspection down the Embankment and on past London Bridge she became aware of the terrible damage inflicted on a city in the space of two long nights. There was rubble and glass everywhere, and by the sides of the roads gas mains belched uncontrolled flames up into the still dust-laden air. People were half-heartedly searching through the debris, seeming uncertain of what it was they were searching for, while firemen, who from the look of them had been up both nights without sleep, stood around as if in a trance.

Later Artemis learned it had been estimated that on the Saturday night alone over four hundred people had been killed and over one and a half thousand seriously injured.

'They've advised everyone to sleep underground tonight,' Diana told her when Artemis had finally struggled home. 'I'm for my bed myself. What about you?'

'Absolutely,' Artemis agreed. 'If I'm going to get blown up, I'd much rather be comfortable.'

Ellie wondered where Hugo was exactly and how he was. 'The worst thing about all this,' she explained to Nanny, 'is not just being separated. It's not knowing. It's not knowing whether he's at home or abroad, alive or dead.'

Nanny nodded, only half-attending. 'I really should go home, you know,' she said after a silence. 'To look after my parents.'

'Yes of course you should,' Ellie agreed, although they'd discussed the problem endlessly.

'The trouble is,' Nanny continued, looking at the tousle haired baby romping in his play pen, 'I find it so hard to leave Jamie.'

The Italians had only advanced fifty miles, less than halfway to Mersa Matruh where Hugo waited with the main body of the British contingent, and were now encamped in an ill thought out line of fortified camps.

'They're too damn far apart from one another, do you see,' General Hunter explained to Hugo, 'much too widely separated to support each other.'

'Perhaps it's only a temporary resting place – where is it?' Hugo enquired.

'Sidi Barrani,' the General replied. 'And I disagree. Scouts tell me there's no sign of their moving.'

'All to the good,' General Wavell said. 'Reinforcements arrive tomorrow.'

Which they did, in the shape of three armoured regiments, which had been rushed out on Churchill's express orders.

'The plan apparently,' Hunter explained to Hugo as he briefed him a week later, 'is to surprise 'em. Hit 'em a short sharp blow and knock the wind from their sails, and then push on down to the Sudan and have a go at the second Italian army down there.'

Hugo studied the wall map detailing the enemy positions and their own and asked how the attack was to be effected. General Hunter indicated the initiative would come from the east, hitting the line of camps frontally.

'With respect, sir,' Hugo said after studying the lie of the country, 'that will be where they're expecting us to come from.'

'My point entirely, Tanner,' a staff officer agreed, tapping the table with his swagger stick. 'They'll see us coming a mile off, and not only that, they're not going to have laid out the welcome mat on that approach, are they? They'll have laid a damn good minefield.'

'Brigadier Dorman-Smith,' General Hunter explained, 'favours the indirect approach. From the rear.'

Hugo nodded. 'From what I've seen that has to be the way, sir. The weather is in your favour if you head round behind and sweep up from here – ' Hugo tapped the board west of Tummar and Nibeiwa. 'Because at this time of year,' he continued, 'the prevailing winds blow from here.' He tapped the direction and traced the path of the winds down the map. 'South-easterlies,' he said. 'Which will give you a good cover of sand. In fact, they make such easy reading at the moment, we should be able to time to within five or ten minutes the very best moment to strike.'

'Good,' Dorman-Smith said. 'Now let's try it out on God.'

General Wavell was all in favour, as was General O'Connor who, it emerged, was going to be running the show, although it was General Hunter who privately suggested that Hugo should be invited to go along in person rather than be expected to advise on the feasibility of the weather from such a distance as Mersa Matruh was from Sidi Barrani.

'He's a civilian,' General O'Connor pointed out. 'We can't order him about, you know.'

'I know, I know,' Hunter replied tetchily. 'But we could ask him.'

Hugo agreed readily, having decided to volunteer his presence should he not be officially invited. General Hunter advised him what to expect if as a civilian under such circumstances he should fall into enemy hands, but Hugo just smiled and said there was no chance of that, because the British were going to win by an innings.

'We'll get you a lift with the Hussars,' Hunter said. 'We'll fix you up with an armoured car.'

Hugo attended the final briefing on the morning of 7 December, and gathered that although numerically they could expect to be outnumbered nearly three to one, thirty thousand men against eighty thousand, General

Dick O'Connor's forces had two hundred and seventy five tanks against the Italians' one hundred and twenty.

'And don't forget,' the general reminded his officers, 'fifty of our tanks are "Matildas". And they can take anything anti-tank the enemy care to throw at us.'

Under cover of dark that evening, the tanks and armoured cars and accompanying forces began their seventy mile approach through the desert. The following night, after consulting the weather conditions, Hugo forecast a light sandstorm which arrived as promised and covered the force's move through a wide and seemingly unguarded gap in the Italians' line of fortified camps. Early the following morning, out of a screen of sand the infantry of the 4th Indian Division, led by the 7th Royal Tanks, fell on the garrison of the Nibeiwa camp from the rear, and catching them completely by surprise, took four thousand prisoners for the loss of only seven tankmen.

In the afternoon the 'Matildas' knocked over the camps at Tummar West and Tummar East, while the 7th Armoured swept westward and took the coast road, cutting off the enemy's line of retreat.

At the briefing that evening, the initial feeling was to move on as soon as possible and strike at the heart of the Sidi Barrani position, but General O'Connor advised caution because he was sure the Italians there would have been alerted, and the British were bound to meet much stiffer resistance. Furthermore he had been advised by Hugo of the chance of severe sandstorms early in the day. Hugo was asked when he considered the storms would have blown out.

'If at all,' an opponent to the plan argued. 'And even if it does get up a bit, it's all to the good. Give us the cover we need.'

'Not this time, sir,' Hugo corrected the officer. 'This time we're heading north-west, so we'd get the lot straight in the face.'

It was finally agreed to postpone what O'Connor hoped would be the final push in the light of Hugo's argument, although not everyone agreed, and he was given some distinctly dirty looks by certain officers.

'They don't like being told their job by a civilian,' General Hunter said as he wished Hugo good night. 'So I hope you're going to make 'em eat crow.'

'Just look at the sky,' Hugo said, as they stood outside the tent. 'The horizon is disappearing already.'

Even so, despite his apparent confidence, Hugo spent most of the night outside, watching the sky, trying to read the sands, waiting for any change in the omens. But nothing changed. The night turned dark and moody as Hugo thought it would, and by early morning, the wind was howling and already whipping up the sands. Half an hour later it was screaming and shrieking, carrying acres and acres of sand on the air to half bury the waiting tanks, armoured cars, and the attendant armoury.

'Well done, Tanner,' General O'Connor said when the storms had passed and the task force prepared to move out. 'Wouldn't have done to get stuck in that little lot within range.'

Hugo found his lift and within minutes the column of tanks and armoured vehicles ground out from their position and swung towards their target. Hugo's vehicle was well to the rear, as ordered, but even so he was still able to get a first-hand view of the engagement. And as so correctly predicted by the commanding officer, resistance was considerably stiffer, with the result that the initial assault was checked, and it necessitated two flanking moves by tanks from the 7th Armoured before Sidi Barrani was overcome late in the afternoon.

All evening the thunder of battle rang in Hugo's head. The earlier engagements had been somehow tame, as the Italians had offered such little opposition, but the engagement at Barrani was a different show altogether, and even though victory seemed assured due to the great skill and courage of the tankmen, the reality of the battle and the sight of bloody death left Hugo silenced and shattered.

He slept very little that night, his mind filled with

images of stricken and blazing tanks, of men on fire, of decapitated and dismembered corpses, with the result that by dawn he had been up and dressed for two hours, watching the skies, and waiting for the desert to declare its hand.

The sands were still, and it was a breathless day, searingly hot and crystal bright. The Italians were on the run now and there was nothing to do but push on, which the force did, meeting no resistance. A reserve brigade from the 7th Armoured Division swept westwards, beyond Buq-Buq, to cut off a huge column of panic-stricken Italians, capturing a further fourteen thousand and netting another eighty-eight of their guns.

It was a glorious day, a victory drive with the enemy running like hunted quarry in front of the approaching vehicles. Soldiers threw down their rifles and started waving to their conquerors as if to old friends, many of them smiling happily as they surrendered themselves and their weapons. Some fell to their knees to pray as the British swept by, while others sat shell-shocked on the ground, uncertain whether to laugh or cry. Out of the smoke and dust of battle, column after column of captured Italians appeared, hands raised or flat on their heads, under the watchful rifles of the Infantry, young dark-skinned thick-haired men who, now that all chance of meeting death in battle had gone, smiled and joked and exchanged smokes with their captors.

Hugo hardly had time to appreciate the vagaries of war before the armoured car he was in swung away from the main column and started to head across the desert towards an encampment just visible in the middle distance. Hugo, who was now standing up in the turret for a better view of the proceedings, asked the officer who reappeared beside him what was the purpose of the diversion. The young Hussar explained that they had just been given orders to check the abandoned enemy encampment for snipers.

'Best get your head down, sir,' the officer advised as

they neared what seemed to be a quite deserted outpost. 'Better safe than sorry.'

The two of them disappeared down into the well armoured depths of the car as the driver peered through his letter box window in order to line up their best approach.

'Just in case of mines, sir,' he said, 'there's a set of wheel-tracks a hundred yards or so right, so let's follow those, sir, shall we?'

'Well done, Bates,' the officer agreed. 'Sounds like sense.'

'They have to be fresh today,' Hugo added, 'after the storm this morning.'

'Correct,' the officer said. 'And they're hardly going to have had the time to bung any mines down in their hurry to leave, yes?'

'No, sir!' the driver called back, as he swung the car right and picked up the ruts made by some fleeing enemy vehicle. A second later he was dead, sprawled across his wheel, killed by a sniper's bullet which had hit him in his right eye and blown away half his head. Hugo stared horrorstruck at the carnage, while the officer, once he had grasped what had happened, shouted to Hugo for help as the vehicle began to weave out of control. Hugo grabbed the dead man, pulling him sideways off his seat and half on to his lap while the officer seized the steering wheel in an effort to swing the careering car back on to the rutted tracks.

He was too late. As the Hussar pulled the wheel round hard to the right from beneath came the almighty thud of an exploding landmine, and a split second later the armoured car was catapulted high into the air, turning half a somersault to land on its side and on fire some twenty yards away in the sand.

19

The boat was late. So late that a rumour began to circulate among the waiting crowd that it had been torpedoed. When there was no official confirmation or denial after a wait of six hours, what had started out as a faint possibility had become an unquestionable fact. The liner had been sunk.

Artemis remained seated in the waiting room at the head of the quay, refusing to panic like most of the others around her, although deep inside her she knew there was every chance the ship may well have been attacked, even though it was only an innocent passenger liner. To the Germans, any ship seemed to be fair game, as earlier in the year one of their U-boats had attacked and sunk the liner *Andorra Star*, inflicting five hundred casualties and causing a panic at the lifeboat stations.

Finally, ten hours late and still unannounced, the ship for which everyone was waiting appeared at the entrance to the harbour, and was cheered by the waiting crowd all the way to its berth. As the first passengers disembarked, Artemis heard that they had indeed been attacked by a submarine that morning off the west coast of Ireland, and the captain had engaged in a brilliant evasive action which had undoubtedly saved the liner and the lives of those on board.

The crush was tremendous, and at first Artemis failed to find Ellie, who was finding it impossible to get down the gangway and off the ship. Finally, one of the officers who'd looked after Ellie on what had turned out to be an arduous journey, found her one of the very few porters to carry her luggage and escorted her through the crowds and down on to the quay, where she at last saw Artemis.

Ellie's step quickened, and then she broke into a run, pushing her way through all the people until they faced each other at last. They found they had nothing to say.

'You managed to drive down?' Ellie asked, as the porter followed.

'Not only that,' Artemis said, 'I managed to drive down in an official car. You're official business.'

Ellie hesitated, and then took Artemis's arm, who hurried her as fast as she could through Customs and Immigration and on to where she had parked the official car.

As soon as they were in the car, Ellie turned to Artemis. 'Now,' she said, as a matter-of-fact as she could be, 'tell me how it happened. How, when and where. I want to know everything. I must know everything.'

They'd spoken briefly on the telephone, but the line was worse than ever, and Artemis was afraid that they might be cut off. In breaking the news she had given Ellie chapter and not verse.

'I'm not quite sure where to begin.'

'When are they bringing him home?' Ellie asked. 'Maybe we could start with that.'

'As soon as possible.' Artemis carefully buttoned up her gloves. 'We've chased everyone up this end, Diana and I, and they've promised just as soon as they can get the transport from Cairo. How's Jamie?'

'He's just fine,' Ellie replied. 'I so nearly brought him and Nanny back. But then I remembered.' She stopped and gave Artemis a look. 'I thought of what Hugo said. He said if anything happened to him, to Hugo –'

'Absolutely, I remember.'

'I mean what we said, what was agreed. I shouldn't even be here, actually.'

'Yes I know.' Artemis put the key in the ignition and glanced at Ellie. 'I think we ought to start heading back.'

'I must just know one thing.'

'Of course.'

'Is it really true?' Ellie asked. 'Is it true that his mind is a blank? That he doesn't even know his own name?'

'So they say,' said Artemis suddenly impatient. 'But who knows? They could have got him mixed up with somebody else. Apparently things are in quite a muddle out there, what with one thing and another.' She glanced at Ellie, who believed what Artemis had just said even less than Artemis did. 'Look,' she added, 'I mean at least he's alive, Eleanor.' She pressed the button on the dashboard and started the car.

'Yes,' Ellie said, looking out of the window. 'Yes at least he's alive, thank God.'

Hugo was returned by sea to England over three months later, in April, just after Rommel swept the British out of Cyrenaica, and back into Egypt, in one brief campaign negating all the hard-won and magnificent victories of the year before.

'It kind of makes it worse,' Ellie said to Artemis. 'It makes it all seem so pointless.'

'Diana says it's all Churchill's fault,' Artemis replied. 'Sending the troops to Greece instead of mopping up North Africa. She says everyone out there was convinced they could have taken Tripoli. But they needed the transport Churchill had reserved for Greece.'

They were on their way down by a slow and desperately over-crowded train to Salisbury, where Hugo was in hospital. Ellie had insisted that Artemis accompanied her, hoping that if perhaps he saw not just her, but both of them, the image might be more emotive, something might jog his memory. Artemis was dreading it, since she now knew Hugo couldn't even remember the events of the previous hour, let alone those of previous months or years. But she saw no point in disillusioning her friend, who like so many others at such a time lived only in hope.

'How many more stops?' Ellie asked as the packed and smoke-filled train ground to yet another unannounced and unsigned halt.

'I'm not sure,' Artemis said, trying to peer under the arm of a huge soldier who was standing between her and the window. 'Five or six. I think this must be Hook.'

'No, miss,' the soldier corrected her. 'This is Winchfield.'

'I don't think it can possibly be,' a woman from behind them said. 'If it's anywhere surely it's West Heath?'

'Is it like this everywhere?' Ellie asked Artemis. 'They've painted out all the signs on every station?'

'Oh yes,' Artemis replied. 'It's a total nightmare after dark. You can end up anywhere, and people usually do.'

After an unrealistically long delay at the unnamed station, where dozens more weary travellers pushed themselves into the already jam-packed carriages, the train moved off again, even more slowly. A child was passed over the heads of those packed in the corridor until it reached its destination, the lavatory just beside where Ellie and Artemis were standing. Ellie knocked on the door and one of a party of soldiers inside opened it.

'Another caller, I'm afraid,' Ellie said.

The soldier took the little girl in and turfed one of his companions off the closed wc which he was using as a seat. They all then discreetly turned their backs and shut the door.

'Thank God I'm a camel,' Artemis sighed. 'It doesn't bear thinking about.'

The child was passed back out to them again, and Ellie helped fix her clothes tidily before lifting her up and passing her back overhead. At the next station, the guard came round and shouted into every carriage that the train was overloaded and would not proceed until everyone who had got on at the last station got off and waited for the next train. No-one moved and the train stayed put. Finally two dozen or so people drifted out on to the platform and the train moved out, only for those who had stepped off to step back smartly on again. At last the train arrived in Salisbury, two and a half hours later than it should have done.

In the station car park there was a pony and trap waiting for them. 'I suppose you arranged this,' Ellie said to Artemis.

'Yes,' Artemis replied. 'Or rather my great-aunt did. She lives just outside Salisbury.'

The dog-cart took them to the hospital where Hugo lay.

'I'll wait here,' Artemis said, settling into a chair in the reception area. 'When you want me, if you want me, just give me a call.'

'Come with me,' Ellie said, suddenly turning back. She took Artemis by the hand before she could sit down. 'Please. I need you with me now.'

'Don't be silly, of course you don't.' Artemis looked at her shocked.

'I do,' Ellie pleaded. 'Please. Please come with me.'

A doctor appeared at that moment and asked for Mrs Tanner. Ellie fell silent. Artemis signalled to the doctor. 'This is Mrs Tanner, doctor,' she said.

'If you'd like to come this way, Mrs Tanner.'

Ellie refused to move, holding on to Artemis. 'Artemis,' she said. 'Please.'

Behind her back, Artemis shook her head furiously at the doctor, who understood at once. 'I'm sorry, Mrs Tanner,' he said. 'Your husband is allowed only one visitor at a time.'

Ellie ignored him, and turned to whisper to Artemis. 'Please. Just think – if he saw us *both* –'

'I'll be here if you want me,' Artemis replied, easing Ellie forward. 'Go on.'

After a moment's hesitation, Ellie followed the doctor down the corridor. Artemis sat down in a chair and picked up an old magazine through which she flicked uncomprehendingly for the next half-hour.

When she saw him, Ellie's heart missed a beat. Hugo was sitting up in bed doing a jigsaw puzzle, and apart from some strapping on his shoulder, just visible under his pyjama jacket, he looked gentle and handsome and donnish, like he always looked. Ellie's heart started to race as she hurried to his bedside.

'Hugo,' she said, as she reached him. 'Hugo?' Hugo didn't look up. He just continued whistling to himself and doing his puzzle. 'Hugo?' Ellie asked again, her heart now beating abnormally, but for quite another reason. 'Hugo it's me. Ellie.'

The doctor moved near to Hugo and tapped him on the arm. 'You've got a visitor, old chap,' he said, bending down to him.

Hugo looked up and saw Ellie. 'Hullo,' he said.

'Hullo, Hugo,' Ellie said gently, coming to sit on the side of his bed. She took one of his hands, failing to see the doctor signify for her not to, with a shake of his head.

'It's me, Hugo. Ellie.'

Hugo stared at her, his face unsmiling, and his forehead puckered. Then he slowly withdrew his hand, as if deeply suspicious of her touch. 'Hullo,' he said, and then returned his attention to his jigsaw.

'Hugo, it's me. Ellie.' A note of desperation was creeping into her voice, as she racked her brain for something different to say, something which wouldn't sound stupid, as stupid as the phrases which were going round in her head. 'Hugo sweetheart,' she whispered. 'Don't you know me?'

'Who are you?' Hugo asked, looking at the small piece of blue sky in his hand. 'Why are you calling me sweetheart?'

'I'm Ellie, your wife, Hugo. It's me. Eleanor.'

Hugo smiled round at the doctor. 'Who are you?' he asked him. 'Are you Hugo?'

Ellie looked up at the doctor for help, but all he could do was return her look with sympathy.

'Sweetheart.' Ellie put her hand under Hugo's chin and tried to turn his face to her so that he could see her closely. Suddenly a hand reached up and clasped her wrist, with savage strength.

'Look,' he said. 'I don't know who you are or what you want, but I'm trying to do a jigsaw!' He kept hold of her wrist for a moment, while he stared at her. Then he let go and returned once more to his puzzle. Ellie turned her head away quickly then rising walked away from his bed. The doctor followed.

'I can't tell you what to do, Mrs Tanner,' he said, taking her by the elbow out of Hugo's earshot. 'And I can't tell you what to say. I don't really want to tell you anything categorical. Such as how severe your husband's condition is, or what hope there may be or there may not be for him. That is, you understand, for him getting any memory back. Physically he is in very good shape. I don't want to make what I could call an informed guess about your husband's condition, because it would be wrong to do so, because I believe every case must be judged on its own especial merits. But I have to say something to you, otherwise I'll only send you away full of false hopes. And what I say to you must be coloured by my previous experiences in this field, of which I have had plenty, I do assure you.' He paused.

'Which is?'

'It's very unlikely, I'm afraid, that there will be any significant recovery of memory.'

'Ever?' asked Ellie, and she took out a small lace handkerchief and wiped her lips with it.

'It's unlikely. I don't wish to get too technical, because I don't think it will help.'

'Because you don't think I'll understand.'

'That's not what I think at all, Mrs Tanner.' The doctor took his glasses off and slipped them into the top pocket of his housecoat before proceeding. 'If it was just a simple blow, a case of concussive damage, then I could probably offer you a more optimistic and certainly a more accurate prognosis. But if, as I fear, it is something more subtle, such as an unrecognized subdural haemorrhage, then the problems are more severe.'

'What is an unrecognized – ?'

'Subdural haemorrhage,' the doctor repeated.

'Thank you,' Ellie said. 'And why should it have gone unrecognized?'

'A subdural haemorrhage results from a blow to the head, or as in your husband's case a severe concussion caused by being inside a vehicle such as he was in when it is quite literally blown up. It's bleeding, in or around the brain, and it can happen quite surreptitiously, over weeks, even months. The patient becomes sleepy, gets bad headaches, becomes confused, loses his memory, he may even become paralysed. Now please, don't worry more than you have to.' He stopped and looked her in the eye. 'This isn't going to happen to your husband,' he said. 'The point is, with the exception of any paralysis, I think it already has.'

The doctor then went on to explain that back-tracking as best he could under the conditions of war and distance, he believed that when Hugo was admitted to the hospital in Cairo, he was conscious, and that he fell into a coma there because no-one had diagnosed or even considered the possibility of a subdural haemorrhage.

'With the result,' he concluded, 'there could be lasting damage to the cerebral cortex, more particularly to the part of the brain which controls various conscious processes, such as perception, thought, decision making and more particularly, memory.'

Ellie looked at the doctor then turned away to study the view out of a window. The April day had turned from sunshine to heavy rain, as if in keeping with the news. 'You knew all this before you let me see him,' she said. 'Wouldn't it have been better to have explained first and then let me see him?'

'I don't think so, no,' the doctor replied. 'When I saw you, when I saw how . . . how beautiful you were,' the doctor hesitated, anxious to sound neither foolish nor flirtatious. 'It has not been unknown,' he said, 'for very positive images to produce a quite unexpected return to normality.'

Ellie turned back to him, and saw that he was blushing. 'Thank you,' she said. 'Then in that case I think we ought to reintroduce my husband to the person who came with me.'

When the two of them returned to the ward, taking Artemis with them, Hugo had almost finished his jigsaw.

'Hullo, old chap,' said the doctor.

'Ssshhhh,' said Hugo, putting a finger to his lips without looking up. 'Damn it, there's a bit missing.' He started to look around the bed and under the blankets for the missing piece of the puzzle.

Artemis stared at him. 'Hullo, Hugo,' she said finally.

Hugo took no notice. Instead he suddenly held up the missing but now found piece of jigsaw triumphantly. 'Got it!' he said. And then he noticed Artemis.

'Hullo, Hugo,' she said again.

Hugo stared at her, and then smiled. 'Hello, Tom,' he said, and then bent over his puzzle happily, to put the last piece in place.

The excitement was intense, electrifying, as the three of them waited in silence, hardly daring to ask Hugo another question lest they had all imagined the moment. For his part Hugo behaved as if nothing whatsoever abnormal had happened. He just pressed all the pieces in the puzzle flat with his hand, then turned the tray round for all to admire. The completed puzzle was a picture of Blenheim Palace.

'Nice, isn't it?' he asked them. 'Though I wouldn't thank you to clean all those windows.'

The doctor nodded again to Artemis, to prompt her to continue. 'Yes, it's lovely, Hugo,' she said. 'But not nearly as nice as Brougham.'

Hugo took no notice. He just pushed the puzzle flat again with his hand.

'Hugo?' Artemis asked. 'Hugo?' She sat down a little awkwardly on the bed, on the opposite side to Ellie.

He stared at her, as if he'd never seen her before. 'Yes?'

'I just wondered if I could have another look at your puzzle,' Artemis replied.

Hugo stared at each of them slowly and in turn, deeply suspicious once again.

'Let Tom see your puzzle, Hugo,' Ellie said, doing her best to smile.

'Which of you is Tom?' he asked.

'I am,' Artemis replied.

Hugo stared at her, and then burst into laughter. 'Don't be silly,' he laughed. 'Tom's a boy's name.'

In order to be near Hugo, Ellie moved into a hotel in Salisbury. It was full of what she later heard described as 'rich refugees', a caste of people who had even been attacked by *The Times* as a body of people who had fled from nothing, and who were just sitting around eating and drinking and making no effort to involve themselves in the war beyond the news they read in their newspapers. Ellie felt uncomfortable in their company, but she knew it was vital for her to be at hand lest there was any change in Hugo's condition, or even more hopefully in case her presence might finally and quite literally bring him to his senses.

She visited him every day, and it took her no time at all to realize that to Hugo every day was exactly the same as the last, and as the one which had still yet to dawn. She would greet him and he would fail to respond to his name, she would introduce herself and remind him who she was and who he was, and on every visit he solved precisely the same jigsaw puzzle, while Ellie would go over in fine detail the life they had spent together before his injury.

Hugo would pay no attention. Occasionally he would look up from his puzzle and ask Ellie to pass him a drink, or to help him with his jigsaw, or simply to ask yet again who she was. He never once recalled her name, not even during the course of a visit, and when shown photographs of himself in the company of Ellie, on their wedding day, at Brougham, in London, or with Jamie, and snapshot after snapshot of himself as a child, he simply stared at them briefly and without any interest whatsoever, before smiling politely at Ellie and thanking her for showing them to him. He would then invariably turn his full attention back to his puzzle.

'This is you, Hugo,' Ellie would say to him, day after day as they went through the routine with the photographs. 'This is you when we first met –'

'I don't think so,' he said to her once, when Ellie had stopped at the photograph taken of them when they had become engaged. 'No I don't think you meant that. That isn't right.'

Seeing this was a different sort of response from usual, Ellie immediately pursued it further. 'Why don't you think so, Hugo?' she asked. 'Why isn't it right?'

Hugo stared at the portrait for seemingly ages, his finger tracing round both faces in the photograph. 'That's you,' she said, as he traced his own image. 'And that's me,' as Hugo ran his finger over the photograph of her.

'No,' Hugo replied, shaking his head slowly. 'That isn't you. It isn't possible.'

She asked him to look at her, and he did so, more with a petulant frown than any real curiosity. And as he looked, Ellie then held the photograph up beside her face. 'That is me, Hugo. And that is you.' Hugo silently disagreed, shaking his head slowly. 'Why don't you think it's me, Hugo?' Ellie asked.

'Oh why do you think!' he said, suddenly impatient. 'Your hair's the wrong colour!'

That was as far as Ellie got that day, because when she tried to press him further, Hugo tipped his half-finished puzzle on to the floor and disappeared in a burrow under his bedclothes.

Ellie could not even get him to recognize himself. When she realized the photographs meant nothing, she tried sitting with a mirror held up to him, followed by a framed portrait of him. But all Hugo did was stare in silence at both of the images and then at Ellie.

'That's you,' she said. 'That is you in the mirror, and that's you in the photograph.' Once again Hugo just shook his head in contradiction. 'Why don't you think it's you, Hugo?' Ellie persisted. 'This is a mirror, so the mirror's not going to tell you any lies, is it?'

'I don't know,' Hugo said slowly. 'But that isn't me. I don't look like that.'

'No?' Ellie asked, carefully. 'So what do you look like, Hugo?'

'I know what I look like!' he shouted. 'And I certainly don't look like that!'

Doctor Allen's explanation of Hugo's refusal to look his real self in the face was that since he no longer mentally knew who he was, and since he had no recollection of anybody or anything, his brain had also lost the ability to make a decision as to what he might or could look like. 'This probably all sounds like something out of Lewis Carroll to the layman, Mrs Tanner,' he explained. 'But when it comes to dealing with injuries to the brain, be they injuries caused by direct concussion, explosive concussion, or in some cases simply by trauma, we're dealing with uncharted territory. Who knows? There could also be a reason for your husband not wanting to remember. Imagine the shock of what happened to him in that armoured car at a moment when he most certainly thought they were out of danger. Perhaps it was an event which his brain, particularly since now it's malfunctioning, perhaps his brain wished to blot it out altogether. And by erasing that terrible moment when he stared death in the face, along with that his brain could also have removed the memory of all past and present history.'

'And there is nothing you can do.' It was a question Ellie had found herself asking so persistently, it had now become a statement of fact rather than an interrogative one.

'Just hope,' Doctor Allen would answer. 'And pray. Miracles do happen.'

'I'm sorry, doctor,' was Ellie's response to this. 'I think if we believe in miracles, or the need for them, then that's a criticism of our own ability.'

'So what do you think we need, Mrs Tanner?'

'I think we need to apply ourselves even more to the problem, Doctor Allen, and to keep applying ourselves, even if it appears that all hope has actually gone.'

The doctor promised that for his part he would keep on doing everything he could to effect a cure for her husband, but Ellie, who had been wise since childhood, had grown wiser by the moment, and she knew that with a war which was worsening daily, the amount of time any one doctor had to devote to one patient must by necessity and rightly so be limited. She determined to take charge of Hugo's welfare.

For once fortune chose to smile on her. While she was in Salisbury, she learned Brougham was to be requisitioned as a military hospital. She immediately returned to the house to make all necessary arrangements with those of the staff who still remained. Hugo's blue print for times of crisis had already been implicated, and all the art treasures and fine furniture had been stored away in the vaults as planned. Knowing that no-one understood the house as well as she did, Ellie volunteered to stay on as the hospital's administrator, an offer which the hard-pressed authorities were only too happy to accept. Within a week, helped by her loyal skeleton staff, the house had been converted into a hospital, with the main drawing room, the dining room and the music room adapted into wards, the upstairs bedrooms into secondary wards, part of the stable block into a gymnasium, and the library into a recreation room. The only rooms which Ellie left unaltered were Hugo's and her suite of bedroom and dressing rooms.

By the end of the second week, there was a full complement of Red Cross nurses, under the supervision of two nursing sisters and a matron, the idea being to run Brougham as a convalescent home for soldiers, sailors and airmen. Porter, while more than keen to do his bit, was however, very pessimistic as to what the end result would be.

'They've done terrible things to Heathdown, ma'am,' he informed Ellie. 'From what I've heard.'

'Heathdown's not a hospital, Porter,' Ellie had been forced to remind him. 'Heathdown's been requisitioned by the Army.'

'I know, ma'am,' he had replied. 'But the things they've done. They've chopped up the bannisters of the great staircase for firewood, and shot all the eyes out of the portraits. And last week, I'm told, they near as anything burned the whole place down.'

'I'll see they behave, Porter,' Ellie had assured him. 'Don't you worry.' She left him, as always, in a hurry.

By the time arrangements had been made to bring Hugo home, the hospital had a full complement of patients, which included, amongst others, soldiers still recovering from wounds received over a year ago at Dunkirk, and pilots who had been injured the previous summer and autumn in the Battle of Britain. Ellie made sure that those well enough were given a free run of the place, and in direct contradiction to Porter's gloomy prognostication, it seemed to bring out the best in them. They quickly came to love the beautiful house and park, and when they were strong enough, set about doing all they possibly could to help. Some of the tougher men used to laugh about the change in their behaviour, telling Ellie that if anyone was caught swearing, they received a right dressing down from their comrades.

'Don't ask me why, miss,' one sailor said to her one day, 'but you feel you can't blaspheme 'ere. And don't ask me why. Me mates are the same. Sounds daft, but they all say they don't want to.'

'I think it's because you fellows don't want to let yourselves down in front of the nurses,' Ellie replied.

'They're such a great bunch of girls, and I reckon you're thinking of them. And of how they feel. And I think that's very nice.'

'Maybe you're right, miss,' the sailor said. 'But meself, I think it's this 'ere place. Straight up, it's as if you've come out of hell and landed in bloomin' 'eaven, believe me.'

One of the fleet of Red Cross ambulances which were used to ferry blood supplies and patients to Brougham brought Hugo up from Salisbury along with the week's supply of dressings, drugs and medications.

'Hullo, Hugo,' Ellie said as the driver unlocked the rear doors. 'Here we are.'

'Hullo,' Hugo replied, as if to a total stranger. 'Where are we?'

'Home, Hugo,' Ellie said. 'Brougham.'

'Broom,' Hugo pondered. 'Why is home a broom?'

Ellie offered him her hand, to help him out of the ambulance, but he ignored her, preferring instead to climb out unaided. He stood in front of his home, dressed in his hospital issue dressing gown, striped pyjamas, and worn brown slippers, staring with a deep frown at his new surroundings.

'What happened to your dressing gown?' Ellie asked. 'And the pyjamas I brought you?'

'They weren't mine,' Hugo said vaguely. 'They were someone else's. What is this place, another hospital?'

'This is your home, Hugo.'

'This is another hospital,' Hugo replied. 'Hospitals, hospitals, hospitals. I've been in so many hospitals.'

'Can you remember all the hospitals you've been in?' Ellie asked, as she started to lead him up the stone staircase.

'I don't know,' he said. 'Can you?'

Accompanied by one of the nursing sisters, Ellie took him straight upstairs to their room. There was a notice on the door which read 'Please do not enter,' but even so, the door was unlocked. As planned, the sister stayed just outside while Ellie led her husband in and stood with him in the centre of their bedroom. Hugo looked round the room slowly and carefully, but without moving. While he looked Ellie watched him for any sign of recognition. After he had finished his long and silent appraisal, Hugo suddenly yawned and took his spectacles off, to rub his eyes.

'I'm tired,' he said. 'I really am tired.'

'Why not have a sleep then?' Ellie said, going to the bed and turning it down.

'Not in that bed,' Hugo replied, stepping back and away from it. 'I don't like that bed.'

'This is your bed, Hugo,' Ellie told him, coming back to his side and gently taking his arm. 'Come and sit on it. Come on.'

Hugo pulled his arm away, roughly, and stared at Ellie. 'No,' he said. 'I do not like that bed!' He spoke very slowly but emphatically, like a child refusing to eat up its food. 'I don't like that bed,' he repeated, 'and I'm not going to get in it.'

Ellie walked over to the dressing table and picked up some more family photographs, pictures of Hugo holding Jamie when he was first born. Hugo and Ellie and Jamie at the christening.

Jamie. She missed him even more now that Hugo was here, which was odd. It was as if having Hugo here, but not there, made Jamie's existence even more precious, and infinitely further away. She telephoned, she wrote, and Nanny was stalwart, but even so she often found herself crying suddenly, alone, in the night. There seemed to be no-one left, only Artemis.

Hugo barely glanced at Jamie's photograph, before he knocked it flying out of Ellie's hand and across the room. 'Stop showing me all these blasted snapshots!' he shouted. 'I hate all these stupid, blasted snapshots!' Before Ellie could stop him he was out of the door, but happily straight into the arms of one of the staff outside.

'There we are,' said the nurse crisply. 'Just in time to get settled in.'

Artemis managed to travel down to Brougham for the weekend, but all the time she was there, Hugo was, if anything, worse.

She returned to London that evening, standing all the way to Paddington in a darkened train. When she got back to the flat in Bayswater, Diana was out, and was still out when Artemis finally went to bed an hour later. At three o'clock the air raid siren suddenly sounded, and rather than take shelter, Artemis simply covered her head with two pillows and waited for the inevitable pounding to begin.

Five minutes later a bomb fell directly on the building opposite, blasting out all the windows of the flat and showering her bed with splinters of glass and timber. There was a brief uncanny silence after the explosion and crash of the collapsing building, and then the sound of people shouting, and then of people screaming, and then of general mayhem. Artemis scrambled carefully out from under the thick covers of her bed, to find the bed itself half tipped back against the wall and the floor of the room deep in debris. She picked her way through the darkness and finding her slippers and overcoat, and finally her walking stick, went down the main stairs and out of the building into the street to see what she could do to help.

The bomb had knocked a giant hole in the row of buildings opposite, as if the terraced houses were teeth, one of which had been punched out by a street fighter. The air was full of choking dust and smoke, and every so often a piece of masonry or timber from the buildings either side would finally fall loose and crash on to the debris below. Bombs were still dropping with dull thuds all around as the enemy planes droned in the skies above them, occasionally caught in a searchlight, or briefly in the flashing explosions of the ack-ack fire. Other doors opened down the street as those who had not sought shelter looked out to see who had been hit. Tin-hatted wardens appeared from nowhere to assess the damage, while people in their dressing gowns or coats pulled hastily on over their nightwear stood staring at the mound of dust and rubble which a moment ago had been the home of a neighbour.

'Anyone know if they was in?' a warden called to the small crowd of onlookers. 'We don't want to start diggin' if they was all down the shelter!'

A woman in hair curlers, with a mackintosh over her long nightdress called back from her doorway, two houses down. 'They never went down the shelter, chum!' she shouted. 'They couldn't stick it! They went under their stairs!'

There were no stairs. The bomb had scored such a direct hit it had simply demolished the house entirely. As the crowd began to realize there was only a faint hope of anyone surviving such a bombing, they began to drift away, leaving what digging out there was to be done to the rescue men.

' 'Ere, love,' a woman said at Artemis's side, 'you're shakin' like a bloomin' leaf. You'd best come in for a cuppa.'

Artemis spent the night on the woman's sofa. When she left to return to the flat in order to get dressed for work, the rescue party was already digging for survivors on the bomb site. As Artemis passed by, one of the men stopped digging and reached down into the rubble. From it he plucked a small pink fluffy slipper, shaped like a little rabbit. He stared at it, pushing his hat back on his head, and wiping his brow with the back of his hand at the same time, before placing the little shoe carefully on the ground and continuing to dig down to where he hoped, albeit faintly, its owner might be lying somewhere still alive.

After she had dressed, and swept up as much of the debris as she could, Artemis made herself a strong cup of tea and sat at the kitchen table. She was still shaking badly and had to hold her cup to her mouth with both hands. The telephone rang in the hall, and she went to answer it. It was Diana. Artemis told her what had happened.

'Dear God,' Diana said. 'Are you sure you're all right?'

'Fine,' Artemis replied, holding the telephone two-handed. 'A bit jelly-like.'

'I should think so too,' Diana agreed. There was a short silence. 'Look,' she said. 'I'm sorry I wasn't home last night, but you see the point is – ' She lapsed into silence again.

'Yes?' Artemis prompted.

'Perhaps we could have lunch,' Diana suggested.

'I have to drive someone up to Malvern,' Artemis said. 'Someone from the MOI. Sorry.'

'Damn.' Artemis could hear Diana lighting a cigarette up at the other end of the line. 'Well look, the point is, darling, because you're going to find out sooner or later. I was with your father last night. And the point is we're going to get married.'

The reality of the night's events didn't really sink in until Artemis arrived for work at Westminster and promptly passed out. She was sent home at once in a taxi with the instructions to see her doctor and not to report again for work until she was one hundred per cent fit. Her doctor, who was a family friend, examined her and pronounced her to be suffering from delayed shock and profound exhaustion.

'I don't think you know how hard you've been pushing yourself, my dear,' he said.

'There's a war on, Alistair,' Artemis replied. 'You've seen the faces of the people out there. Everyone's exhausted. But we've all just got to keep going. You look a bit tired yourself.'

'Maybe, but I'm used to it. As a matter of fact I prefer being this needed. I can't pretend. I prefer it a sight more than just looking after society poodles.'

Artemis smiled. 'Is that what you think I am?' she asked, feigning indignation.

'You know perfectly well I don't. I wish all my patients were like you. But you must realize it, you are a bit run down.'

'Come on, Alistair. I mean we are in the middle of a war.'

'I know, dear girl,' the doctor replied. 'I have noticed. I'm getting so good at getting up now, I can be dressed and in my car before the siren's finished wailing.'

'I didn't mean that,' Artemis said. 'Sorry. It's just that there's a lot that needs doing.'

'It's a bit more difficult for you, young lady, than it is for some others.' The doctor leaned back in his chair and smiled at her. 'Think about a change. Just for a short while. There are other things you can do to help, you know. You don't have to stay in London.'

Artemis promised to think about it, and she did. And the more she thought about it, the more she realized that she was needed elsewhere, at Brougham. Not that she was afraid to stay in London, although the bombing had left her a bit shaken. Normally such a thing would only strengthen her resolve. Even so, she found herself deciding to leave London, but when she did she knew that it was nothing to do with her doctor's advice, nor to do with the near miss. It was all to do with her godmother's sudden decision to marry Artemis's father.

As far as Ellie was concerned Hugo's recovery was all that she could think of. She found him one morning out of his ward, wandering round the great hall, which was too large and cold to be used as part of the hospital. She waited, unseen, while Hugo ambled round, staring at the niches where the statues had stood, looking up above him at the three round skylights.

Finally she could bear it no longer. 'Does it ring any bells?' she found herself asking, foolishly.

Hugo whipped round and stared at her, taking a moment before he answered. 'Does what?' he asked, raising his eyebrows. 'This isn't a church you know.'

'I meant,' Ellie began, finding herself beginning to falter under his gaze. 'I thought – what I meant was I wondered if you recognized anything in here.'

'Such as?'

'You don't recognize this room? The great hall?'

'Any reason why I should?'

'Of course,' Ellie persisted, finding her tongue again. 'This is your home.'

'This is a hospital,' he corrected her.

'It's also your home,' Ellie replied. 'But even so, I think we'd better take you back to the ward.'

She took his arm, but he shook her off. 'I don't like you,' he said. 'I don't like this place, and I don't like you.' He started to walk past her.

Ellie called to him. 'Hugo?'

'My name is not Hugo!' he shouted. 'When will you get it into your blasted heads, my name is not Hugo!'

'OK,' Ellie said, as calmly as she could. 'But you must have a name.'

'Of course I have a name! Everyone has a name!' He was still furious, his eyes narrowed and dark behind his glasses.

'So if it's not Hugo,' Ellie asked, 'what is your name?'

'Tom!' he yelled. 'That is my name! I am somebody called Tom!'

The train was packed and the journey was interminable, but at least it gave Artemis time to think.

'Nothing will change,' Diana had assured her over dinner the night before. 'Everything will be just as it was, only better.'

Everything will be just as it was, only better. Everything will be just as it was only better. She repeated the words to herself over and over in time with the rhythm of the wheels on the line below her feet, but still they made no sense. How could things by not changing get better? If things changed and got better, then quite obviously they weren't going to remain the same. Everything will be just as it was only better, went the train.

Artemis did her best to try and avoid the thought of Diana and her father together, but she could not keep the idea out of her head altogether as she sat crushed up in one corner of the dark and smoke-filled carriage. Diana had done her best to explain what her reasons were for wanting to marry her father, but when they were talking about him it was as if they were discussing two entirely different people. To Diana John Deverill was a shy and much misunderstood man, while to his daughter he was a cold and remote and unloving father. Diana supposed then that she had probably always loved Artemis's father, a thought which appalled Artemis, so much so that she at once had got up from the table, and excusing herself, gone straight to bed. The idea of her godmother having always loved her father was tantamount to infidelity. All the time she had been growing up she had counted on Diana as her true friend and her ally, and now it appeared that all that time Diana had had a foot firmly in both camps. It was the final act of familial betrayal. Everything-will-be-just-as-it-was-only-better.

At least there was Patsy. If she hadn't had Patsy, Artemis thought, as the train swayed and lurched through the darkness, there was no saying how she would have felt. He'd written to her once a week, sometimes twice since her return to England, cheering her with his news from Hollywood, and touching her deeply with his professions of love. She'd written back to him just as regularly, but could not match his honesty when it came to expressing her feelings, discovering that as a writer she was just as reticent as she was as a person. Happily it didn't seem to bother Patsy at all, and in his replies he joked about her inhibition, giving it Californian names. Patsy and his letters were carrying Artemis through the war.

Sometimes, in the wait between letters, she would remember the night by the ocean and wonder whether she had been right to turn her back on the happiness that had been so patently on offer to return to the strife of war-torn England, particularly to find that Diana and her father had taken up with each other. Artemis had run away from the chance of happiness with Patsy because she felt guilty, she felt it was undeserved, that the time was not right. Now she could see little sense in making such a sacrifice just because there was a war on, because her fellow countrymen were dying every day. In fact because there was a war on and men and women were dying every day in their hundreds there seemed all the more reason in the world to get married and take the chance of being happy, if only for a matter of a few weeks, or days or even hours.

Everything will be just as it was only better.

She had the latest letter from Patsy in her purse, unopened, as yet unread, as in her rush to leave London she hadn't found the time to read it. She thought about it, wondering what was in it, what Patsy had been up to, and what was the latest American news. When she got back to the Dower House, she would pour herself a glass of whisky, sit by the fire Rosie would have laid, and read the letter at her leisure.

Artemis finally arrived at Malmesbury well after midnight and yet she found Jenks waiting for her at the station.

'Good lord. How long have you been waiting, Jenks?' Artemis asked as they walked towards the old Humber.

'No time at all, your ladyship,' Jenks replied. 'I've a nose for trains.'

There was another surprise. In the front seat, well wrapped up in rugs, sat Ellie.

'I can't say how good it is to see you,' she told Artemis.

'Patsy's joined the Air Force,' Artemis said, as factually as she could. 'He joined up six weeks ago.'

Artemis had taken Patsy's letter to bed to read, where she had read it, and she had re-read it and then read it again, as if she simply could not believe it. Then in the morning, she had gone straight up to the house to tell Ellie, whom she assumed wouldn't have known either, and had run her to ground in the 'sulking' room, which Ellie had kept for her official office being the room formerly occupied by the estate manager.

'He was bound to enlist,' Ellie poured them some coffee. 'Wouldn't you say?'

'But why didn't he mention it?' Artemis wondered, to Ellie still sounding wondrously calm. 'I mean in an earlier letter? He didn't even hint at it. Not once.'

'Listen, it's not even certain that America's going to come in. They say if they lift the oil embargo – '

Artemis shrugged. 'They say – at least it's what I've heard from the back seat of the car I drive about the place – that they're not going to lift it. Not unless the Japs get out of Indo-China. And China. And apparently they're not likely to do that. Which means war in the Pacific.'

'I'm afraid it will. If that's the case.'

'Exactly.'

Ellie drained the last dregs of her coffee and put her cup down. 'You knew Patsy wasn't one to sit at home.'

Artemis said nothing, but sank into a chair by the fire and sat staring up at the ceiling.

'Any idea where he'll be?' Ellie asked. 'Does he say anything in his letter about where he's being posted.'

'No.' Artemis replied. 'No idea at all. Which is just as well.'

'Why?'

'Because nothing would stop me joining him.'

Ellie looked at her, understood at once, and felt even more alone.

As Christmas approached, Artemis did her best to involve Ellie so deeply in the preparations that she would have less time to brood on the change which had come over

Hugo. The old Hugo, the real Hugo had rarely if ever sworn. If he had, it would be only the mildest of oaths, and one never sworn in a hot temper. Nor did he lose his temper. Ellie was the temperamental one, the one with what they all called the 'Irish', a flaring but short-lived temper for which she would get unmercifully teased by Artemis and Hugo. But now he suffered terrible rages during which he would throw whatever was to hand at whoever it was he thought had offended him, before burrowing deep down at the bottom of his bed where he would stay for hours. It was a nightmare come true, and to Ellie he now seemed like a total stranger. Small wonder then, Artemis thought, that she wore such a fixed smile all the time, and seemed day by day to be just going through the motions.

So Christmas presented Artemis with the ideal chance to distract her. She managed to make Ellie as determined as she was to make sure the men would have a Christmas to remember, so that if they all survived the war they'd be able to recall Christmas 1941 as the year they were at Brougham.

Early on Ellie set about organizing Cook on errands of begging, borrowing and scrounging food and drink for the coming feast while Artemis and she sat up every night in the 'sulking' room making decorations for the tree and the wards. They also, on an inspired whim of Artemis's, made small papier mâché models of all their patients, all in their various service uniforms. Artemis passed on to Ellie the knowledge of modelling and painting she had learned at the hand of Miss Dennis, her governess, who had taught her in a room two floors above the room in which they sat. Ellie and she would sit by the fire modelling and painting and talking until midnight every night, until Artemis was glad to see that the worry lines on Ellie's face were growing slightly less.

But there was no reprieve it seemed as far as Hugo was concerned. He had now become totally apathetic, which in some ways was even worse than his tempers and tantrums, and would just lie in bed staring at the ceiling, not even bothering with his puzzles, and ignoring all invitations for a game of draughts or Halma. Seeing him like this, moody and sulky, Artemis often got an uncontrollable desire to go and slap him, and tell him to get up and out of his bed. After all, he had the full use of his limbs, unlike so many of his less fortunate compatriots.

'Don't you feel like that?' she asked Ellie one evening, as they sat winding bandages. 'I do. I want to go and slap him, because it's as if he's pretending.'

To her surprise, Ellie suddenly laughed. 'That's one of the things I love most about you, you know!' she exclaimed. 'You're so darned honest! Sure I do! There are so many times I want to slap him! Not on the hand, or even the face! You know where? I'd like to put him over my knee and slap his backside!'

They both collapsed with laughter. They knew it wasn't that funny, but they also knew they needed to laugh.

As if he'd sensed it, Hugo suddenly turned over a new leaf, on the morning of Christmas Eve, actually getting up from his bed unprompted, for the first time in weeks, to go and wash and shave. Later, after he had helped with everyone else to put up the decorations on the Christmas tree, which Ellie had placed deliberately in its usual position in the hall in the hope of jogging his memory, he then asked one of the nurses if she would fetch his clothes. Running upstairs, but only after she was well out of Hugo's sight, Ellie hurried to their bedroom to fetch something for Hugo to wear, which she gave to the nurse.

Ten long minutes later Hugo reappeared, immaculately dressed in shirt and tie, fair-isle sweater and grey slacks. Ellie kept out of sight, hidden with Artemis, as the nurse helped dress her husband. Hugo seemed like his old delightful self, not cursing the nurse when she did up his shirt and trousers, or pushing her aside when she pulled on his socks. He sat there smiling happily, as if he'd more important things on his mind.

'Come on,' Ellie whispered to Artemis, taking her hand. 'Let's give it a try.'

'No,' Artemis replied, withdrawing her hand. 'You go. If he's going to recognize anyone, it has to be you.'

Ellie stared at her, but Artemis just stared back, nodding her head for Ellie to go to Hugo. After taking a deep breath, Ellie went.

'Hullo,' Hugo said, giving Ellie a warm smile. 'Just the person I was looking for. Come on.' He took her by the elbow. 'Take me round this rotten old hospital you run, nurse.'

Ellie took him round the house, about which Hugo asked questions as if he had never seen any of it before. This at least was encouraging since Ellie considered it had to show a return to a certain level of consciousness which had previously been absent. He also wanted to know what he was doing in hospital? Ellie told him he'd suffered a head injury, that it had affected his memory, but that hopefully he was now well on the way to recovery.

'Where did I hurt it? Did I fall over?'

'You hurt it abroad,' Ellie said. 'In the desert. You were in an explosion.'

Hugo turned and stared at her, then started to laugh. 'I've never been abroad,' he said. 'So that's not true. And I'm too young to have been in a war.'

Before Ellie could discuss the point further, although she could see the ground falling away in front of her, Hugo's attention was suddenly arrested by what he saw in front of him, and he stopped dead in his tracks.

They had been returning from the saloon the back way, quite deliberately, so that Hugo would have to pass through the hall where he had been painting his murals before he left to join up. This was where he had come to a halt. Without moving or saying anything he stared at the wall, covered in his unfinished paintings. Then he went to the foot of the stairwell and started to climb the stairs to get a better look. For ages he stood there, in complete silence, staring with mute astonishment at the figures before him, and the depiction of life at Brougham. Then he slowly sank down, on to a stone step, and started to weep.

'What is it, Hugo darling?' Ellie asked quietly, putting a hand on one shoulder.

Hugo moved his shoulder away sharply, away from her touch. He stared up at her, through his tears. 'Tom,' he said. 'It's Tom. I must find Tom.'

'What do you want me to do?' Artemis asked, when Ellie found her.

'I don't know,' Ellie said, twisting a handkerchief in her hands. 'I don't actually know.' She looked round the doorway and saw Hugo still sitting where she had left him, rocking backwards and forwards on the step. Then she looked back at Artemis and grabbed her by the arms. 'I don't know!' she whispered urgently. 'Just go to him. Go on! Go to him!'

Artemis hesitated. She looked up at the wall paintings and then back to Hugo, who was looking straight ahead of him, somewhere back in the past. She went through the huge colonnaded doorway and walked across to where he sat. He never looked round as she approached, not once.

'Hullo?' she said as she reached the staircase. 'Hugo?'

She held on to the iron balusters, not far from where he sat. He looked round at her, and when he saw her, a smile spread right across his face. 'At last,' he said. 'Artemis. Thank God.'

Artemis was convinced there was only one person who was mad, and that was Hugo. She swore she had seen the light of madness in his eyes the night before when Ellie, against Artemis's better judgement, had gone, as Ellie called it, for broke.

'Look at me, Hugo, please,' Ellie had said, very calmly and quietly when all other reasoning had failed. 'Look at me, Hugo,' she had said, 'and then look at Artemis.'

'No.' Artemis had countered, knowing what was coming. 'Don't be such a damned fool, Eleanor.'

'We're going to have to find out sooner or later, Artemis,' Ellie had returned. 'So come on look at us, Hugo. Look at me, and look at Artemis, and tell us who you love.'

Hugo had absolutely no hesitation in telling them. 'Artemis,' he'd said, smiling, eyes shining. 'Artemis. She's my wife.' And then he had taken up her hand and kissed it.

Ellie sent for a specialist. Someone Artemis had heard was brilliant. Mr Peake locked himself away with Hugo for most of the day. When they emerged, Hugo looked relaxed and happy, while the consultant looked at his wit's end. He summoned Ellie back into her own office where he had conducted the examination and once again sat her down opposite him.

'It would be easier if I could find him to be mad,' he said finally. 'It would make it all so much easier all round if we could just say it's a very sad case, but the poor chap's off his head. But it's not as easy as that. You see, apart from this one central confusion, your husband seems about as sane as the next man.'

'I see,' said Ellie, 'I'm a central confusion am I?'

'I have to explain this in medical terms, Mrs Tanner. I have to view this totally objectively.' Ellie stared at the floor, embarrassed for both of them. 'Obviously your husband's memory process is not properly repaired, of that there's no doubt. That's what I meant by a central confusion.'

'But why has his mind done this to him? Has it done it because that's what he wished all along? That he wishes subconsciously he'd spent his life with – ' she stopped and looked back down at the floor, then raised her head again, shaking out her hair. 'You know what I mean, Mr Peake. Some people get a blow on the head and lose their senses. Perhaps other people get a blow on their head and come to theirs.'

'I don't think so,' Peake replied. 'No I don't think that's really the case at all.' But from the look in his eyes, and from the way he stared over-deliberately into Ellie's eyes, Ellie knew he must be lying.

She was only half concentrating when she opened the door of her house and found Hugo on the step, smiling at her. She had been reading a cablegram which had just arrived from Patsy, confirming his well-being and promising more news in a following letter. If she had been concentrating to the full, she might have better read the look in his eyes, the look she had seen the night before, when she had tried to prevent him from entering her house until she'd found out what he wanted. As it was, she didn't, and before she knew what was happening Hugo was in the house and had taken her into his arms.

'Hugo – ' she said. 'What the hell do you think you're doing!'

'I followed you, Tom!' he whispered. 'Down from the hospital.'

Artemis struggled to get free from his arms.

'You're not on your own, are you?'

'Of course I'm on my own, Tom,' he said. 'We don't want anyone else here, do we, when we're making love. Love's a secret.'

She pushed against him, but he had her held fast. Yet it wasn't the Hugo she knew who was holding her, she could see that from his eyes. She was being held by a stranger, and all at once she felt a little of the fear and desperation that poor Ellie must constantly be feeling.

'Why don't we go into the drawing room?' she suggested. 'Let's go in there and talk.'

'All right,' he agreed. 'In a minute. First, I want a kiss.'

'No,' said Artemis.

'Yes,' Hugo insisted. 'Christ knows I've waited long enough for another one.' He lifted her off her feet and kissed her.

Artemis struggled, pushing at his chest with all her might, trying to move her mouth away from Hugo's mouth which he was forcing against her own. But he was too strong, and even when she did manage to turn her face half-away from him, he simply turned her face back to him with a smile and continued kissing her.

Moments later, while she struggled to catch her breath, he lifted her off the ground completely, and with one hand under her knees and one round her slender waist, carried her into the drawing room.

Artemis realized there was no sense in shouting or screaming for help because there was no-one to hear her. Rosie was out, of course, gone away down to the village for some provisions, and there wasn't anyone else within earshot. And she had shut Brutus away in the kitchen to finish off his food. Besides, from the strange detached way Hugo was looking at her, Artemis had an odd feeling that if she did try to shout or struggle, she might upset the precarious balance of his mind and put herself in even graver danger than she already was. So she decided to try and humour him, and perhaps to talk him down.

As he carried her over to the sofa, where he put her carefully down, Artemis thought fleetingly of the irony. For so long all she had done was resist Hugo, and bury the love she had for him: in Ireland when they first met and then in London and in Brougham when they had been left alone with each other. On every occasion she had refused him, although she would have given anything, at times she thought perhaps even her life itself, to have him make love to her just once. Now she was desperately trying to find a way to stop him doing so, to prevent him doing the very thing she had so often hoped and prayed he might do, sweep her up in his strong arms, and make love to her.

'So what do you want to talk about, Tom?' he asked, as he sat down on the sofa close beside her, putting a hand on her arm lest she move away.

'Oh I don't know,' she said vaguely. 'We've got so many things to discuss.' With her free hand Artemis brushed her hair once again from her eyes, while she cast a careful eye around to see if there was anything she could use as a weapon to protect herself, or if it came to it, with which to hit Hugo. They were sitting by the fireplace, but all the heavy fire irons were arranged on the far side and well out of reach.

'I don't really think I want to talk, Tom,' Hugo sighed. 'I think I just want to make love.'

'No, Hugo,' Artemis began. 'No! Wait!' But it was too late. Hugo had turned her to him and once again was kissing her. 'No, Hugo!' Artemis cried, getting free momentarily. 'Please!'

Hugo just smiled, and kissed her into silence. He pushed her back on to the sofa, half lying, half sitting against the cushions, smiling at her all the time, as he undressed himself. Then leaning over her, he began to undress her, slowly, taking his time, still smiling, unbuttoning her wool shirt and then bending down to kiss her as he ran a hand inside her open shirt to touch and hold one of her breasts. He looked at her again, right in her eyes, but the smile was gone and his own eyes were open wider, as if he was surprised by what he saw as he eased off her shirt and slipped the straps of her camisole down from her pale white shoulders, running a hand through the back of her soft long blonde hair, and then leaning over to her again, but lower now, to kiss both her perfect breasts. And as he did Artemis hardly moving, hardly daring to breathe, reached out as slowly as she could to pick up the decanter from the drinks table, which she then raised very slowly. Wrapping Hugo's head to her breasts with her other arm and moving her arm at the last moment to leave herself a clear target, she brought the heavy decanter down on the back of his head and Hugo fell away, slipping silently and slowly to the floor, where the blood from the wound on the back of his fair head trickled on to the floorboards.

Artemis reached for the telephone, never taking her eyes off the unmoving body, as she felt for the dial and rang Brougham. 'It's me,' she said when Ellie was at last fetched to the telephone. 'Look, I think I've killed Hugo.'

'I don't quite understand how he got here,' Artemis said to Ellie, after explaining what had happened. 'Normally you keep such an eye on him.'

'He gave his nurse the slip,' Ellie explained. 'He complained of a headache and took himself back to bed. Then he stuffed some pillows under his blankets – '

'That old trick.'

'Yes. That old trick,' Ellie agreed. 'But it worked. What about you? Are you all right?'

'Yes,' Artemis said. 'I'm all right. It just gave me a bit of a fright, that's all.'

Ellie looked at her as they sat together in the drawing room, waiting for the hospital's resident doctor to finish his examination of Hugo, who had been carried half-conscious upstairs to the spare room.

'Is something the matter?' Artemis asked, noticing Ellie's odd look.

'No of course not,' Ellie replied. 'I was just wondering.' She paused and looked down at her fingernails, before continuing. 'It's just that I don't quite understand why you let him in?'

Artemis explained that she had already explained. 'I just wasn't thinking,' she said.

'I know,' said Ellie. 'But it still seems rather strange. I mean you must have wondered what on earth he was doing down here. By himself.' Ellie lapsed into silence for a second. 'Unless – ' she went on with a little shrug of her shoulders.

'Unless what?'

'Nothing. It doesn't matter.'

'I let him in, Eleanor,' Artemis said quite crisply, 'because I didn't have much choice.'

'Of course,' Ellie agreed.

Artemis would have liked to pursue the point, but there was a knock on the door and Doctor Leigh, one of the hospital doctors came in.

'Right,' he said breezily. 'I'd say things could have been a lot worse. I should imagine you didn't have much room to take a good swing at him – ' he stopped and smiled at Artemis, who felt as if she was a cricketer who had taken a chancy swing at the fast bowler. 'Anyway,' the doctor continued, 'I'd say the wound's only superficial and we're not going to end up with our skull fractured.'

'Is he conscious yet?' Ellie asked.

'Not fully,' the doctor replied. 'But we're showing signs of rejoining the party.'

Doctor Leigh stood aside at the door, and the two women went upstairs. Hugo was lying on the bed white-faced and propped up against the pillows, his head well bandaged but his eyes still closed. Ellie and Artemis stood at the end of the bed, waiting for his full return to consciousness, which according to the nurse could be expected any minute since the patient had already opened his eyes twice.

Then he opened them for the third time, and this time kept them open, focusing first on the ceiling, and then on the two women who stood facing him. He opened his eyes as wide as he could, before blinking several times. Out of his sight, behind the footboard of the bed, Ellie twisted a handkerchief she was holding in her hands. 'Hullo, Hugo,' she said. 'Are you OK?'

'Yes,' he said slowly, and after a moment. 'Yes I'm fine. What happened?' He put a hand up to his head and felt the bandage. He also felt the pain, because he grimaced and closed his eyes. 'God,' he whispered. 'Ouch.'

'I'm afraid you got a nasty bang on the head,' Ellie said.

'You don't say,' Hugo replied, with a boyish grin. 'I'd hoped it was just a hangover. So who hit me?' There was a silence, during which Ellie and Artemis looked to the doctor. 'How did it happen?' Hugo insisted. 'Did I fall over? Or out of bed? Or what?'

Doctor Leigh shrugged and nodded at Artemis, as if to tell her to go ahead if she so wished. Ellie frowned, and was about to say something herself, but left it too late.

'I hit you, Hugo,' Artemis said. 'It was me.'

'You did?' he said. 'Why?'

'It doesn't matter,' Ellie said quickly.

'Of course it does,' Hugo laughed, and then grimaced again, putting a hand to his head. 'I want to know why she hit me.'

'Because,' Artemis said quite deliberately, 'you tried to rape me.'

Hugo stared at her wide-eyed, and then frowned, his hand still to his head. 'Don't be ridiculous,' he said. 'You can't rape your own wife.'

20

'Eleanor,' Artemis said defensively. 'Look, it really isn't my damn' fault that he thinks I'm you.'

'He doesn't think you're me, that I reckon maybe I could live with. But he doesn't think you're me, damn it. Hugo thinks you're you!'

'Whatever,' Artemis replied. 'It's not my fault.'

'I wonder.'

Artemis looked up quickly, aware of the edge in Ellie's tone. 'Sorry?'

'Are you sure?'

'Sure of what, Eleanor?'

'Sure it's not your fault, Artemis.'

Ellie looked at her steadily, and Artemis noticed just how pale and drawn Ellie looked. Her skin had lost its normally wonderful sheen, her beautiful eyes were dull and darkly shadowed, she had lost weight, and even her hair seemed lifeless and mousy, instead of lustrous and thick.

Rather than argue with Ellie when she was in such an obviously dispirited state, Artemis decided to try and return to her own point. 'The fact is, Eleanor,' she said, 'we both know we can't go on like this. I know I can't. I can't spend this part of my life hanging around a man whom I don't love and who whatever he says now, actually doesn't love me.'

'He thinks he does,' Ellie replied.

'I know, but that's neither here nor there. When he gets his memory back completely – '

'If he gets his memory back completely.'

'It doesn't matter, Eleanor,' Artemis insisted. 'I have a life of my own. A life that is nothing to do with Hugo.'

'Not now it isn't,' Ellie agreed. 'Now you have Patsy.'

'Absolutely. Now you'll have to excuse me. I have things to do.' Artemis pulled herself up from where she was sitting and made a move to go.

'Artemis – why were you here last Christmas?' Ellie asked, at last getting to the point. 'And why did Hugo pretend there was a party?'

'Hugo asked me to stay to lunch,' Artemis replied after a moment. 'I don't know why he told you there was a party. We had lunch with the staff. In the kitchen.'

'Like one big happy family.'

'It would have been absurd to sit up here all by ourselves.'

'But you were all by yourselves when you stayed the night,' Ellie said. Artemis turned round and stared at Ellie, wondering how she could possibly have known. Ellie stared back at her, unsmiling. 'Cook told me,' she said.

'Then Cook's a silly ass,' Artemis replied. 'It was all perfectly innocent.'

'So innocent you couldn't even mention it?' Reaching over to the table beside her, Ellie picked up a leather covered book and tossed it at Artemis who, surprised, just caught it. 'What about those?' she asked. 'Are they all perfectly innocent?'

Artemis opened the book. It was one of Hugo's sketchbooks, but one Artemis had never seen. It was full of studies of her, just her, asleep, half-dressed, half-naked, curled up in bed, stretched out on the ground, sketches of her walking, eating, drinking, sitting, or of just her head, smiling, in repose, serious, and once again, asleep. They were exquisite drawings, full of emotional power, and obsession. 'I don't care what you think, Eleanor,' Artemis said, closing the book and handing it back. 'As I said, it was completely innocent. And as for these, I don't know when Hugo did these. Hugo was never alone with me, not – not like this.' She paused, opened the book once more, and then shut it. 'He must have drawn those from his imagination.'

'Hugo doesn't draw from his imagination,' Ellie said quietly. 'Not when he's sketching. I know that, and so, damn it, do you.' She swore very quietly, which frightened Artemis all the more. It was all very well being accused of something you had done, she thought, because one could prepare a defence. But the very worst was to be accused of something in which you had played no part.

'He must have done these in Ireland,' she said. 'When he was doing your portrait.'

'Why would he do these in Ireland?' Ellie asked. 'When he was doing *my* portrait?'

The two women stared at each other, neither giving best. 'You don't have to believe me, Eleanor,' Artemis was the first to break the silence. 'But I'm telling you the truth. It was all perfectly innocent.'

'What about London?'

'What *about* London?'

'You saw each other in London.'

'You know we saw each other in London, Eleanor. Don't be such an idiot!'

'I was an idiot, wasn't I?'

Again they regarded each other, and again Artemis spoke first. 'Nothing happened. I promise you. Nothing.'

'Not for want of wishful thinking. That's perfectly obvious from those drawings.'

Artemis threw the sketchbook down on a chair. 'I can't help how Hugo felt, or what he felt.'

'You could have done,' Ellie said. 'You could have done, goddam you.'

Ellie was the one who left the 'sulking' room first, walking out past Artemis, leaving her to sit down on the arm of a chair and wonder what on earth to do next.

'I don't think Lady Artemis should be encouraged to go to London now,' Mr Peake said after giving the matter his usual full deliberation. 'Not when so much progress has been made. If I can draw a somewhat apt analogy?'

Ellie nodded at him to proceed but continued to walk around her office.

'When we began, when your husband was first injured, he was like one of his jigsaw puzzles, all to pieces. Then, when he arrived here, it was as if a child had done the puzzle, finished it, but put it together all wrong. Nothing fitted, bits were pushed in here, other bits there, the picture just didn't fit. Now, having taken the puzzle back apart, we have a picture, where nearly everything fits.'

'But it still isn't the picture on the lid of the box,' Ellie said.

'Correct,' Mr Peake smiled. 'Good. But it very nearly is. A little more study, a little more work, and who knows? But if we lose Lady Artemis now – ' He shrugged and fell to silence.

'Humpty Dumpty,' Ellie said suddenly.

'I'm sorry?' the doctor enquired of her.

'The nursery rhyme,' Ellie replied. 'I used to say it to Jamie, when I held him on my knee.' Jamie was so far away from her, like everything she loved. 'Humpty Dumpty sat on the wall,' Ellie said, looking out of the window across the frosty parkland. 'Humpty Dumpty had a great fall. All the king's horses and all the king's men – '

'I don't think it's as bad as that, Mrs Tanner,' Mr Peake's voice said quietly from behind her.

'I do,' Ellie said. 'I think it's twice as bad as that.'

It was at least agreed that until Mr Peake had finished assessing Hugo's present condition, he was to be moved to a single room upstairs and kept under constant surveillance.

Hugo took it badly. 'I'm not a raving lunatic, Elsie,' he said to Ellie suddenly one day.

'Ellie,' said Ellie, less patiently than usual. 'And I agree, Hugo, you're not a raving lunatic – I am.'

'Send my wife in,' was all Hugo would say.

Towards the end of the month, Artemis received good news. Patsy was coming to England. He had volunteered to be transferred to Britain as part of the American task force whose proposed purpose was to carry out a series of daytime bombing raids on important German industrial targets, and fighter cover was going to be required.

Artemis's joy at the thought of seeing him again was not unnaturally tempered by the thought of the dangerous missions he would be flying. He was to be stationed in East Anglia, which, with a daily worsening in the country's transport system was going to make the job of getting to Brougham on leave an arduous one.

'But at least you'll be seein' one another,' Rosie said to her when she cleared away her breakfast. 'Imagine. You could be same as Mrs Tanner and young Jamie, you could go the whole war without seein' him.'

Artemis agreed and then picked up the telephone to find out her duties at the hospital that morning. Ellie answered the telephone.

'Patsy's coming here,' Artemis told her abruptly.

'I know,' Ellie replied. 'I had a letter from him myself.'

'How's the patient? How's Hugo?'

There was a pause on the other end of the line before Ellie answered. 'He's much better, as a matter of fact. He said today he wanted to start painting again.'

'That's good,' Artemis agreed, and then chancing her arm, added, 'From life? Or from his imagination?'

From the subsequent silence Artemis thought as usual she had gone too far. Then she heard Ellie laugh, quite like herself. 'From his imagination,' Ellie said. 'What else?'

One bright sunny day at the end of the month, Artemis wrapped up well and took a walk up to the house. She had been in bed with the 'flu, but was feeling better, and all too anxious for some fresh air. Brutus as always went with her, but seemed a little out of sorts himself, no longer willing to chase the winter winds, or put up the game birds who strutted round the parklands. Artemis called to him, and threw him a stick, but although

Brutus fetched it a couple of times, Artemis noted he was panting more than usual, and was slightly dragging one of his back legs.

'Come here, old chap,' she called, and having hugged him, and kissed the top of his noble old head, which was now very grey, asked if she could have a look at his paw. Brutus panted, but lay down and rolled over on his back, thinking he was going to have his tummy rubbed. Artemis smiled at him, pulled his whiskers, and rubbed his tummy for him, and the big dog thumped his tail in response against the grass. Then she carefully took hold of his bad leg and examined the pads of his feet. As soon as she held his leg, the dog cried sharply in pain, and frowned at her from under his shaggy eyebrows.

'Sorry, Brutus, I wouldn't hurt you for anything. But you've got something in that foot of yours. We'd better get McCabe to have a look at that when he comes by.'

The dog followed Artemis as she continued her way to the house, but when she reached the main gates she looked round for him and saw that he was no longer behind her. Instead he was sitting some hundred yards away by a gate leading into one of the paddocks. She whistled to him and called, but having looked round at her, he decided to remain where he was.

'Fair enough,' Artemis called to him, 'you do what you want old chap.' And then calling to him to wait for her, she turned and made her way up into the house.

They'd approached the house from the rear, so Artemis made her way up the steps and in through the saloon and then across the back hall, where to her surprise she found Hugo up some re-erected scaffolding, at work repainting his mural. He was hard at work at such close quarters he failed to notice his visitor.

Artemis stared at the wall painting and found herself gasping. Whereas before the work had depicted Hugo and Ellie's life at Brougham, with Artemis seen only in the background on her horse, now she was everywhere, and Ellie was nowhere. Hugo had painted Ellie's face out altogether, and was busy painting Artemis's likeness in her place.

Artemis was pictured doing everything that Ellie had previously done in the mural, laying picnics, holding Jamie, playing tennis, cards, redecorating rooms, hosting dinners, standing out on the steps, climbing trees, swimming, and everywhere Ellie had been portrayed with Hugo, Artemis now was, embracing Hugo, standing with her arm through his, or both arms through one of his, or with her arm round his waist, or his arms round hers, or both of theirs round both of theirs, or with an arm draped casually round his shoulder, or with his arm draped casually round hers, or whatever. Hugo was busily perpetuating his mythic memories for posterity.

'Hey!' Artemis called up to him. 'Hugo, what the *devil* do you think you're playing at?'

Hugo stopped and looked round and down at her, staring upside down through the scaffolding. 'Tom!' he said with sudden delight, wiping his paint-covered hands on a rag before hopping down from his tower. 'Heavens, I haven't seen you in an age!'

'I've had a bit of 'flu, but I'm quite better now. Obviously you're not.'

'Sorry?' Hugo said, still wiping his paintbrush.

'Oh, stop being such an ape,' Artemis snapped, staring up at the mural. 'And just tell me what you think you're playing at? I hope to God Ellie hasn't seen this.'

'What's wrong with it? Don't you like it?' Hugo asked, with a hurt frown. 'I hope you do. I'm doing it for you.'

Artemis was suddenly, uncontrollably furious. 'Why the devil have you painted my face on everybody? Look! Look even the blasted cat looks like me!'

'Everything looks like you,' Hugo answered simply. 'I see your face in everything.'

'Oh be quiet, will you!' Artemis hissed at him. 'Just be quiet! For God's sake!'

'I don't know why you're so angry. Please tell me why you're angry.'

'Because of this, you fool.'

He frowned at her again, and then looked back up at the wall. 'But why?' he said. 'That's us. Look. That's our whole life here together.'

Artemis stared up at the senseless painting, and then back at the man beside her, the man she had once imagined she could love, a man she had even imagined briefly she did love. He was standing staring at her, a lovesick schoolboy. 'I'm going back to London,' she announced.

'What?'

'I said I'm going back to London, Hugo. And as soon as possible.'

'Back?' he laughed. 'How can you go back? You don't live there. You live here.'

'No I don't, and you damn well know it. And if you don't damn well know it, then it's high time you did. I am going back to London, and I am going back to work there, doing what I did before, before I was fool enough to come down here.'

'You mean before we married?'

'We aren't married, Hugo. You are married to Ellie. Not to me.'

'Ellie?' He stared at her blankly.

'You know full well who Ellie is, Hugo.'

'I know who you mean by Ellie, yes, Tom. But I'm not married to her. I'm married to you.'

'Prove it.'

'Prove it?' he laughed. 'Has everyone gone quite mad round here? Tom I love you! I always have done!'

'I don't care, Hugo. I simply *do not care*! I am not your wife, Ellie is. And if you don't like it, too bad. I don't love you. I told you I'm in love with Patsy, Ellie's brother. As a matter of fact I'm going to marry him when the war is over. Are you listening to me? I don't *love* you, Hugo!'

Hugo looked as though he had been punched in the face, almost visibly reeling away from Artemis as she told him how she felt, supporting himself on the upright poles of the scaffolding, holding on to them as if should he let go he would simply collapse.

Artemis watched him feeling oddly detached. 'I'm sorry,' she said, 'but that's the way things are. The way things *really* are. Not how you *imagine* them to be, Hugo, or even how you like to imagine them to be. I am going back to London, which is where I'm going to stay. And then perhaps, please God, you'll finally come to your senses.'

Hugo stood listening, his hands holding on to a pole high above him, his chin resting on a horizontal piece of scaffolding. He made no attempt to interrupt and now that Artemis had finished, neither did he attempt to say anything. Until she said goodbye, and finally turned to go.

'I think I should tell you, Tom,' he said, still resting his chin on the scaffolding. 'If you go to London, Tom, I shall kill myself.'

'That's your business, Hugo,' Artemis said, doing her best to sound matter-of-fact. 'What you do with your life is entirely your affair.'

Artemis stayed on at Brougham for the whole month of March, trying to persuade herself that it was nothing to do with the threat of suicide, but knowing the truth to be different.

And so remain she did, although to avoid further complications, she saw as little of Hugo as possible, keeping away from him in the house, and avoiding any chance of meeting him when he was in the grounds. After a couple of weeks, Ellie told her that Hugo hardly ever mentioned her name, or even asked for her. Artemis felt encouraged, hoping that although she hadn't had the courage to walk out and go back to London, nonetheless a version of her plan had worked.

And so did Ellie, until her butler dashed her hopes.

'Apparently Hugo's been asking Porter,' Ellie told Artemis on her next visit. 'First thing in the morning he finds him and asks whether or not you're still here,

538

and as soon as he finds that you are, he never mentions you again all day. I never thought of warning Porter.'

Inevitably the mural had caused a scandal. The nursing staff and also all the patients could talk of nothing else.

'That was all you needed,' Artemis said one day as they walked past the painting. 'Can you imagine.'

'It's not what I can imagine,' Ellie said with a sigh, nodding towards the nurses and their charges. 'It's what that lot can.'

'Patsy's arriving in a couple of days,' Artemis said, again switching. 'But you probably know that.'

'I hadn't forgotten,' Ellie smiled. 'The thought of it's keeping me together. To be on the safe side, I think it would be better if Patsy stayed with you, at the Dower House. I can come and visit.'

'He's going to be awfully disappointed,' was all Artemis could think of by way of a reply. 'He was so looking forward to seeing the house.'

'There'll be all the time in the world after the war,' Ellie said, suddenly sounding very weary. 'I'm sure Brougham will still be here.'

'Yes of course,' Artemis agreed, doing her best to forget there were any such things in a war as casualties.

That evening, late, the telephone rang in the Dower House. It was Patsy. He could hardly speak.

'What is it?' Artemis asked. 'Are you unwell?'

'I can't make it, honey. They've cut our leave.'

'What, you mean you have no leave at all?'

'Not as from seventeen hundred hours tomorrow. Which means I'd never make it. Not down to Wilshire and back.'

'Wiltshire,' Artemis said vaguely. 'Not Wilshire.' She thought for a moment, and then decided. 'I'll have to come up to you then. Let me see, when's the first train up to London?' She stopped to consult the amended and re-amended railway timetable which was always left by the phone.

'You can't drive up?'

'We have petrol rationing, remember?' Artemis replied. 'Anyway, we've laid all the cars up. Even the vet comes by horseback.' She ran her finger along the times of the early trains.

'You have no transport down there at all?'

'Only the ambulances. And the pony and trap. And much as I love you –'

'As long as you still love me.'

'Afraid so. Even more than ever.' She left a small pause. 'Do you mind?'

'I think I can live with it,' Patsy replied, and Artemis could almost hear his grin.

'There's a train that leaves at nine o'clock, which is the only one which goes all the way through. It gets into Paddington just before twelve, with a bit of luck, and the way the trains are at the moment, we're going to need plenty of that –'

'That'll give us over four hours. That's better than nothing.'

Artemis instructed him to go and stay at the flat, which was once again fully operational, told him where the key was, where to find anything he might need, and that she would join him there as soon as possible. 'You're the light in my life,' she said finally.

'Good,' he said. 'So will you marry me?'

'Not tomorrow,' Artemis replied. 'It would waste too much precious time.'

Hugo was in the 'sulking' room when Artemis rang. Ellie had been taking him through some more family memorabilia to try yet again to make the pieces fit the puzzle, but Hugo had got wise to these question and answer routines, and had devised ways to avoid directly answering questions he did not like.

'Hullo?' Ellie said, picking up the telephone. 'Oh, hi there, Artemis.' She dropped her voice and glanced across at Hugo, who was pretending to take no notice, before continuing. 'Hold on,' she said. 'I'll go and take this in my office.'

She got up, replacing the receiver, and went to the door. 'Will you be all right for a minute?' she asked Hugo. 'I just have to find some papers.'

'I'll be fine,' he said. 'Don't worry about me, Elsie.'

As soon as she was gone, Hugo quietly picked up the receiver and listened. Finally he heard a click as Ellie picked up the receiver in her office, and he covered the receiver with his hand.

It was quickly arranged. Ellie would drive Artemis to the station at a quarter past eight in the morning, picking her up from her house in one of the smaller ambulances. And because at some time of day someone was going to have to put some blood samples on a train to Bristol, it was a journey that could be justified if anyone asked.

Artemis was up and dressed and ready at half past seven. It was a cold dark windy March morning, and by the time the clock struck the hour, it had started to pour with rain. Quarter of an hour later, on the dot, the ambulance, with Ellie at the wheel, pulled up outside her front door and hooted. Artemis hugged her dog goodbye, reminded Rosie that the vet was calling in the afternoon, and hurried out through the wind and rain to the waiting vehicle. As Ellie leaned over to open the passenger door for her, Artemis heard her telephone ring.

'Who on earth?' she wondered, pausing for a second.

'Do you want to go and find out?' Ellie asked. 'You've time.'

'No.' Artemis decided. 'Rosie's there, and what the eye doesn't see and all that.' She sat on the passenger seat and swung her legs in.

They were just about to drive off when Rosie appeared at the front door and called to them to stop.

'What is it?' Artemis asked.

'It's Mrs Tanner!' Rosie told her, arriving breathlessly at Artemis's open window, her face and hair dripping with rain. 'You're wanted up at the house, Mrs Tanner! Urgent!'

'Where is he?' Ellie asked as she jumped out of the car.

The nurse pointed round to the side of the house. 'He's on the top of the church tower!' she said. 'He left this note on his pillow!' The nurse flapped a piece of paper at Ellie, which she grabbed before getting back into the ambulance to drive round to the side of the house.

'Are you sure there's no way anyone can get up to him?' Artemis asked as the whole of the church came into view.

'You heard Rosie,' Ellie replied, tight-lipped. 'He's locked all the doors behind him. What does the note say?' She handed it to Artemis who did her best to read it in the speeding vehicle.

'Well,' she said, 'as far as I can make out if I go to London, he throws himself off the tower.'

Ellie glanced round at Artemis. 'How in hell did he know you were going to London?' she asked.

'I haven't a clue,' Artemis replied. 'I was going to ask you the same thing.'

Hugo was standing on the parapet of the tower, holding on to one of the stone carvings which sprung up in each corner. Ellie threw open the ambulance door.

'Look,' she said without thinking. 'You drive yourself to the station, or you'll miss your train.'

'Don't be such an idiot,' Artemis replied. 'How can I?'

Ellie was out of the car and looking up at the figure high above her. 'Hugo!' she called. 'Hugo – can you hear me!'

Hugo swayed, leaning over dangerously far, with only one hand holding on to the pillar. He needed the other to cup to his mouth. 'Has Tom gone?' he shouted down slowly and clearly. 'Has Tom gone?'

Artemis pulled herself slowly out of the ambulance and walked round to the front. She looked up at Hugo, one hand sunk deep in her coat pocket, the other on her stick. 'You go!' he shouted down, slowly and clearly. 'And I go too!'

'The bastard,' Artemis said, half to herself as she sat back wearily on the bonnet of the vehicle. 'The rotten, stupid bastard.'

'Rotten, sure,' said Ellie, pulling her coat collar up against the driving rain. 'But stupid, no.'

They both stood staring up at the figure above them. After a moment he called down to them once more. 'I mean it, Tom!' he shouted. 'You go, and so do I!'

After a long silence, Ellie turned her back on the church and put her hands on Artemis's shoulders. 'Go on,' she said, almost in a whisper. 'Get in the van and go.'

'You're mad,' Artemis said. 'I can't possibly.'

'He won't jump. Believe me.'

'I don't imagine he will,' Artemis agreed. 'But just suppose he did.' The two women looked at each other and then Ellie gathered Artemis to her.

Hugo shouted down at them as they embraced. 'You're not saying goodbye, are you, Tom?' he yelled. 'Because if you are, say goodbye to me!'

The last word sounded like a scream, and letting go of each other Ellie and Artemis turned to stare at the tower. Hugo had let go and was standing on the edge of the tower, his hands stretched out either side of him.

'Sweet Jesus,' Ellie whispered. 'I think he would jump.'

Artemis cupped her hands to her mouth and yelled at the top of her voice. 'Get back, Hugo!' she shouted. 'Get down! I'm not going anywhere! I promise!'

After a moment, which seemed like an hour, Hugo grabbed hold once more of the stone pillar, and then a moment later stepped off the edge down behind the parapet, where he stayed, staring down at them.

'OK, Hugo!' Ellie shouted. 'You heard Artemis! She's not going – so you can come down now!'

'No!' Hugo yelled back. 'I'm staying up here until the last train has gone!'

Artemis and Ellie sat in the ambulance out of the rain, and Artemis looked at her watch. The train would have left ten minutes ago. Without her. And Patsy would be waiting. She asked one of the nurses to go and call the flat, but after ten minutes the nurse returned with bad news.

'We can't get through to your flat, Lady Artemis,' she said. 'The operator has just told us all the lines are down as far as Swindon.'

Ellie put her arm round Artemis's shoulder, but Artemis said nothing. She just leaned her head on her friend's shoulder and folded her arms tightly across her chest.

Artemis went straight into the kitchen to find Rosie the moment Ellie got her home, and asked if there were any telephone calls.

'How can there be?' Ellie asked from behind her. 'You heard. The lines are all down.'

'I thought they might perhaps have been mended by now,' Artemis replied, sitting suddenly down at the kitchen table. 'No I don't. I don't know what I thought.'

Ellie asked Rosie to make them some strong coffee, and sat down opposite Artemis, but said nothing. They had said all they had to say in the ambulance.

'How am I going to get hold of him?' Artemis finally asked, looking up into the bulb of the light above her to stop herself crying. 'I don't have a clue where he is.'

'He knows where you are,' Ellie said. 'And where I am. He'll get in touch here.'

'How? When we have no telephone?' She put her head on her arms which she had folded in front of her on the table.

'Sweetheart,' Ellie said. 'Patsy will understand. Heavens above, there's a war on!'

'I know,' said Artemis, suddenly staring Ellie in the face. 'That's exactly what I was thinking.' Then she got up and went upstairs to shut herself in her bedroom.

Late the next day a telegram arrived for Artemis from Patsy, in which he gave her a number and address at which she could contact him. Artemis drove herself to the village in the dog-cart, hoping perhaps to find an operable telephone somewhere, but the lines were still down, the result, it seemed, of a heavy bombing raid on a munitions factory in the Swindon area, which had put the main telephone exchange out of order. Naturally Artemis assumed she could send a wire, since she had received one herself that very morning, and then listened with a sinking heart as the postmistress told her the roundabout route it would have to take to get there.

'It is rather urgent.'

'And there is a war on, you know,' came the inevitable reply.

It was difficult to find the right words. Finally she settled for 'Delayed unavoidably due to accident at Brougham. Am unharmed. Love you with all my heart.' To her embarrassment the postmistress read it back to her, and to the whole village shop.

On her way home, the vet caught up with her, and walked alongside the dog-cart, mounted as he was on his big grey cob. 'I'm sorry I missed you yesterday. I gather there was a bit of a drama.'

'It was nothing much,' Artemis replied. 'Just one of the patients misbehaving.'

'Your dog,' the vet said, coming straight to the point as he usually did. 'How old is he now?'

Artemis told him she was not too sure because he was full grown when he first had arrived in her life. 'He must be about ten.'

'Yes, I should think he's all of that,' Mr McCabe said. 'And more.'

They walked on in silence for a while, to just the sound of the horses' hooves on the road and the occasional slap of the reins down the pony's flanks.

'I'd like another look at him.' The vet had somehow still managed to get his pipe lit even though he was on horseback. 'I think it could be his heart.'

'I thought it was his leg that was wrong,' Artemis answered in some surprise. 'He's been dragging it.'

'That can sometimes be a symptom,' Mr McCabe told her. 'Let's give him a day or so, to see how things are. I'll look in some time at the end of the week.' He raised his cap to Artemis and turned his horse away, kicking it on, as together they trotted off to visit their next patient.

Artemis kept the pony to a walk as she thought over what the vet had told her, then with a slap of the reins, urged the pony on homewards.

Ellie was receiving the news she'd been dreading.

'You know what I'm going to say to you, Mrs Tanner,' Mr Peake told her. 'And you know that if it was just my decision alone – ' He tapped his pencil on the desk and sighed.

'He'll never get better in an asylum, Mr Peake.'

'He might.'

'No chance.' Ellie shook her head. 'Not if we go along with your theory, that all it needs is something familiar to jolt his memory back to normal.'

'Agreed. But like I said, if it was my decision – ' The consultant left the sentence unfinished, as they both knew the matter was now out of his hands. Beds were needed for wounded military personnel, regardless of the fact that the man the authorities wished moved to a mental institution was the legal owner of the requisitioned house.

'I know,' Ellie interrupted. 'You've been so kind. And so helpful.'

Peake tapped his pencil on his desk half a dozen or so times, before getting to his feet, and coming to stand by Ellie, who was at a window, gazing out across the park. 'If only it hadn't looked like attempted suicide,' he said. 'I managed to brush the attack on Lady Artemis under the carpet, but unfortunately everyone seems to know about the incident on the tower. It just couldn't go unreported.'

Out on the lake, Ellie could see two people boating. She was wearing a long pale yellow summer dress, and Hugo was all in white, white aertex shirt, his old cricket bags, and his old school cricketing cap which he loved to wear in the summer. It was a memory from that long hot August, the month before the war had broken out. Cook had packed them a picnic lunch, which Ellie and Hugo had eaten at their leisure on the banks of the island, with their feet dangling in the cool waters, their beautiful house and home reflected in them.

'If you do have to move him,' Ellie began.

'It won't be for a week or so,' Peake replied. 'If we do have to move him, I want to make sure we send him to the best place.'

'Is there such a thing?'

'There are a few quite well-run small nursing homes.'

'I see.' Ellie held on to hope, pushing the image of her beloved Hugo shut away in a mental home out of her mind. 'And in the meantime?'

'In the meantime we just keep a close eye on him. I don't think we need to lock him up,' the doctor replied. 'Only at night.'

As soon as the telephone lines were back up, Artemis put a call through to the number she assumed to be the air base, and asked for the officers' mess.

'This is the mess, ma'am,' an American voice informed her. 'How can I be of help?'

'I'd like to speak to Lieutenant Milligan, please,' Artemis said. 'If that's possible.'

'It sure will be, ma'am, if the lieutenant is here,' the voice replied. 'Please just hold the line for one moment.'

Artemis waited, for more than one moment. It seemed an age before she heard the voice again on the other end of the line. 'I'm afraid you're out of luck, ma'am,' the duty officer told her. 'Lieutenant Milligan is airborne right now, but I'll certainly make sure he gets any message. Who shall I say called?'

Having left her name and a brief message, Artemis replaced the receiver, and sat down by the fire with the last of her precious whisky to await what she hoped and prayed was Patsy's safe return. It was still daylight, and even if his squadron had only just taken off, Artemis guessed that at the very latest he should be back around about midnight.

In fact the small force of twelve B17 Flying Fortresses protected by six Thunderbolt fighters, one of which was piloted by Lieutenant Patsy Milligan had left on a daylight raid on Bremen at sixteen thirty hundred hours, the American theory, disapproved of by the British, being that if they flew high enough and in close enough formation, daylight raiding would prove less hazardous, and there would be less chance of suffering heavy casualties. The raiders were expected home any time after twenty thirty hundred hours, but no later than twenty one hundred, by which time they would have run out of fuel.

Artemis's call was logged in twenty forty one hundred hours, at which time the party had not yet returned. It was still daylight thanks to the government's new measure of introducing double summertime from the beginning of April.

By eleven o'clock, when she was beginning to get worried, she decided to ring her godmother. 'I know it's late,' she said, 'but is my father there?'

'Yes, darling,' Diana replied, obviously surprised. 'Is something the matter?'

'I was just wondering something, that's all,' Artemis said. 'It's just he knows about aeroplanes and that sort of thing. And I wondered if he knew how long a trip to Germany from Norfolk should take.'

'How long's a piece of string,' her father said, when Artemis repeated her question. 'It all depends first where you're flying and second, what you're flying.'

'I don't know the destination, I mean I hardly would, would I?' Artemis said, trying not to sound irritated. 'But I think he said something about flying something called a Thunderbolt. Would that be right?'

'Probably,' her father agreed. 'In fact almost certainly. Seeing this is their first sortie. Thunderbolt's a short range fighter. Useless. Practically obsolete. Maximum range probably no more than eight or nine hundred miles.'

Artemis felt a sudden chill, and pulled her cardigan round her. 'So suppose the planes left even as late as I don't know – ' Artemis looked at the clock, trying to remember when exactly she had called. 'I don't know,' she repeated. 'Say eight o'clock.'

'Given their declared policy, or from what I hear,' her father said, 'namely all this daylight bombing nonsense, I should imagine they'd have left a lot earlier. And that they should all have been home long ago.'

Artemis said nothing. She just held the phone to her ear and stared blankly down at the fire.

'Hullo?' her father's voice said in her ear. 'Look – is that any help?'

When she called again, the duty officer in the mess told her he was not empowered to give details, and Artemis was advised to call the proper authorities on the air base itself. Which she at once did, only to be told that the official list of casualties had not yet been posted. Losses had been sustained, but they had not yet been detailed. As soon as they had been the officer in charge assured her she would be notified.

Thirty two long and sleepless hours later the postman cycled up the long drive to Brougham with a telegram, addressed to Tanner. Porter brought it through to the 'sulking' room where Ellie and Artemis had been keeping vigil, and handed the small brown envelope on a silver tray to Ellie, to whom it was addressed.

Artemis avoided looking at her, but instead sat stroking her dog's head with meticulous concentration, while Ellie carefully opened the back of the envelope with a paper knife, and took out the telegram. There was a long silence.

'Yes?' Artemis said. 'Well?'

Ellie looked up and handed her the wire. 'He's missing,' she said. 'Missing presumed lost.'

21

As Artemis slept, sedated, Ellie allowed herself to grieve, the realization dawning on her that she would never again see Patsy, with his warm loving smile, and his infectious laugh. He was gone. She could hear his voice when they were little: 'Come on Ellie, we can do it, we can lick 'em.' It had always been Patsy and Ellie versus the rest of the world.

'No,' a voice suddenly said from the bed, and a hand sought hers. 'It only said "presumed", Eleanor. It didn't say definitely, did it?' Artemis was half sitting up in the bed, her eyes wide open.

Ellie looked down at her, not realizing how much in the half light she resembled her brother. 'I don't quite follow what you're saying,' she said.

'The telegram, Eleanor. It said "missing *presumed* lost". That's not exactly final, is it?'

'No,' Ellie said slowly, considering the possibility. 'I see.'

'Because he was – because he is a pilot,' Artemis corrected herself, 'because he was flying a plane, one assumes that missing on a raid presumed lost means that he's lost. As in killed. But if that was the case, then they'd say that, wouldn't they? That's what they say. They say "regret to inform you etc, etc, but so-and-so was lost" ie killed "in action".' She threw back the bedclothes and started to try and get out of bed. 'But presumed isn't that, is it?' she continued. 'Don't you see? He might have baled out!' By now she was sitting on the edge of the bed, looking for her stick, which she saw was propped up against a far wall. She eased herself on to the floor and started to try and cross the room but only managed a couple of steps before her legs buckled under her.

'What are you doing?' Ellie cried, catching her before she fell. 'Where do you think you're going?'

'To ring the base, Eleanor. Where do you think?'

'Oh no you're not, Artemis.' Ellie had her by the arms. 'You're in no state.'

'Let me go,' Artemis pleaded, looking at her with bright blue eyes which were beginning to flood with tears. 'Please, Eleanor.'

'No, darling,' Eleanor said quietly, leading her back to the bed. 'You're in no state. And neither am I. I think we ought to let things just take their course. Just for the moment.'

'Please.'

'I don't think it's wise.'

'I have to know, Eleanor. We both have to.'

'They'll tell us in due course, honey,' Ellie said, sitting down beside her on the bed. 'They do. They always do.'

While they were trying to comfort each other upstairs, the telephone rang in Ellie's office, and Matron stopped by to answer it. It was Diana Lanchester.

'I was rather hoping I'd get you,' Diana said down the telephone, 'or someone official, let's say. Lady Artemis's father was very worried by her call the day before yesterday or whenever, and he made a few enquiries. I'm afraid the news isn't good.'

'I see,' Matron said, leaning over to close the open door. 'You mean Mrs Tanner's brother is now officially lost.'

'No,' Diana replied, 'although it might be easier all round if that was the case. No the raid was a disaster, and the Americans lost seven out of twelve bombers, and five, I'm afraid, of the six escorting fighter planes. And only one of those returned undamaged. And it wasn't Mrs Tanner's brother.'

'Did anyone see him go down?' Matron asked.

'No. But the one surviving fighter pilot is pretty certain he saw Lieutenant Tanner's plane hit and catch fire.'

'So what would you like me to say, Lady Lanchester?' Matron enquired.

'If you want to say anything, Matron,' Diana replied, 'tell them what they were told is true. That Lieutenant Milligan is missing, presumed lost.'

Mr McCabe returned to see Brutus as promised at the end of the week. He had heard the sad news in the village and expressed his sympathy.

'Thank you,' Artemis said quickly, 'but let's hope it's premature. Lieutenant Milligan is only presumed missing, you know. There's a very good chance he could have baled out.'

'Of course, of course,' the vet replied, looking quickly away from his client's penetrating stare. Like everyone, he had seen the newsreels. He had seen what happened to fighter aircraft when they were hit in battle rather than by ack-ack fire. They burst into a ball of flames and disintegrated. Everyone knew when a fighter pilot went missing, he stayed missing. Naturally he said nothing of this to Artemis who was, like many others McCabe had seen, buoyed up by what could only be the very faintest of faint hopes.

'But as far as your old dog goes,' he told her, 'there is good news. Yes, his old ticker's not as strong as it was, but then he's no pup, we're agreed on that. And I was wrong about his leg, and you were right to suspect the paw. He's got something in his lower leg, and I've a feeling, because I found an entry wound, I've a feeling it's a splinter or thorn perhaps that's worked its way into the foot and up into the lower leg where it's set up an infection. Look.' He just touched the lower part of Brutus's leg and the dog at once lifted it up with a puzzled whine.

'You can't touch it now,' the vet said. 'And of course what with one thing and another, this last day or so you wouldn't have noticed the swelling most probably. So with your permission, if someone can bring him to the surgery this evening, I'll perform the necessary.'

Jenks returned Brutus the next morning. 'Right as rain,' he said with a grin. ' 'E'll live to drive you madder yet.'

Artemis sat on the floor and took the big front paw which was being held out on offer to her. 'I love you, Brutus,' she told him. 'Now let's hope that other person I love is safe.'

That was the end of the good news. With the arrival of an official communiqué the USAF sent to Ellie as named next of kin, which stated quite clinically that given the circumstances of the air battle, any chance that might be held for the safety of the Lieutenant Milligan must by necessity only be a slim one, hope effectively came to an end.

At the same time Ellie received a short letter from her father, from which she learned that her three eldest brothers had all been drafted into the Army, that her father was suffering from angina, and that no doubt she'd be seeing a lot of her youngest brother now that he was being posted to England. The letter was signed without love or affection 'Your Father'. Ellie put it on the fire and watched it burn.

It seemed not much more could happen when Mr Peake told her all the arrangements for Hugo's transfer to a private clinic up near Banbury in Oxfordshire had been made, and it was planned to move him there within the week.

'But he's made such great strides recently,' Ellie protested. 'You said so yourself, Mr Peake. All the tests you've run – '

'Mrs Tanner.' The consultant stopped her mid-sentence, and shook his head kindly. 'You know it's not my decision. And believe me, where your husband is going, there's every chance that with the proper care – '

It was Ellie's turn to interrupt. 'There's every chance, Mr Peake,' Ellie said turning away to look out over the parkland, 'that with moving my husband away from here we shall have lost our final hope.'

From the window, after the consultant had left, Ellie saw Hugo wandering out on the lawn with a group of fellow patients, and attendant nurses. He was about to hold his daily art class, his own idea, teaching the war-wounded how to draw and paint. He was laughing and joking with them, his straw hat pushed back from his eyes, his hands sunk deep in his trouser pockets as he wandered round while the men set up their easels or opened their sketchbooks. He looked over their shoulders at their efforts, encouraging them, helping them, instructing them, doing his best to help them mend, and to rediscover their self-esteem. Ellie watched him for a time, seeing the old Hugo.

At that moment, as Ellie was wondering what possible justification there could be for taking Hugo away from her to lock him away in a mental home, he looked up and seemed to catch her looking down at him from the house. He stared for a moment, then suddenly smiled and waved, and called up to her. Ellie opened the window to hear what he was saying.

'Come on out!' he was calling. 'Come down, darling, and see how well these chaps are doing!'

Ellie's heart gave a leap, and she turned to go out, only to find that Artemis had arrived and was standing by her shoulder. And it was to her that Hugo was calling.

'Tom!' he shouted up. 'Tom – come on! Come out here!'

Artemis ignored him. 'I've just been talking to Peake,' she said to Ellie. 'I think it's ridiculous.'

'But you knew,' Ellie said. 'You knew it was on the cards.'

'You can know things,' Artemis replied. 'But it doesn't mean you necessarily have to believe them.'

They looked at each other, and then Ellie took Artemis by the arm and walked across the hall with her. 'Have you been riding?' she asked, noting Artemis's riding habit. 'Or are you just about to go?'

'I'm just going, actually,' Artemis replied. 'I thought it might do me some good.'

They walked out of the house the back way and Ellie accompanied Artemis all the way to the stables where Jenks had her horse all ready for her.

'Who's this?' Ellie asked, looking at the tall immaculately turned out grey the old groom was holding. 'He's new isn't he?'

'It's a mare, actually, Eleanor,' Artemis said with a smile, as Jenks legged her up into her side-saddle. 'Shows what you know about horses.'

'Take care,' Ellie said, as Artemis turned the horse out of the yard. 'And come in and have a cup of tea when you come back!'

It was a perfectly glorious spring afternoon, warm but with a gentle breeze, the ideal weather for a canter through a parkland which was just coming back to life. Artemis chose her favourite ride, out across the bridge and then turning right, away from the house on a line on which she had so often followed her father's hounds, up the gentle rolling slopes of the first fields, through the open gates and on to open countryside. She would forget for the moment there was a war on, she would forget about the ever-present ache in her heart, and the ever recurring image of the smiling laughing tousle-haired young man burning to death in a crashing plane. And she would ride across the fields with hope again in her heart, because she still believed deep inside her that Patsy was out there somewhere, that he was alive and that he was thinking of her as at this moment she was thinking of him.

Today she would stop thinking he might be dead, because today she knew for a fact he wasn't. Today she believed he was restored to life, unblemished, unhurt, not burned alive, alive and handsome, with laughter in his eyes and a smile that stole hearts. Today, as her new mare took off and soared over a big hedge which was just bursting into life, Patsy lived and because he lived, Artemis could live again.

They walked home, a swinging easy walk, the mare happy and relaxed, having enjoyed her hack, her breath now easy and her ears pricked forwards, while Artemis ran her hand down her mane and patted her strong neck. At the bottom of Pease Field, she gathered her, trotted her, pushed on into a canter and popped her over the stile at the bottom. The grey landed ten feet beyond and as Artemis reined her back, to show how much she'd enjoyed herself, put in a good natured buck.

'How do I know, horse?' Artemis asked the mare as they resumed their walk. 'How do I know he's alive?' The horse paid her no attention, pretending instead to shy at something in the hedge. 'I don't know, horse,' Artemis said. 'I just do, that's all.'

She turned in through the last gate, across the perfectly flat field that led back to the stables. A moment later, the young mare lost a leg down a hole and as she stumbled and before Artemis could pull her head back up there was the terrible and sickening sound of breaking bone.

Artemis was out of her saddle in a moment, slipping down to the ground, dropping the reins on the horse's neck, holding on to a stirrup so that she did not lose her balance as she stared in horror at the mare's shattered leg. It was only a hole in the ground, a small hole, she could see it there, a half-dug rabbit hole, but a hole quite deep enough to catch and momentarily trap the horse's leg halfway up its cannon, long enough for the impetus to break it in two as a person would snap a branch across their knee.

The mare just stood there, suddenly bewildered as to why she couldn't put down on one leg. As yet there would be no pain, Artemis knew that, the pain would come later, in a minute, in two, three, four minutes, but the cannon bone was plainly and visibly shattered, and then and there all hope was gone.

There was a boy in the field, trying to restart a tractor. Artemis called to him, shouted at him until he heard, and came running quickly across to her, in answer to her urgent cries. She told him to hold the mare quite still, and not to panic, just to stand there and stroke the mare's neck while she went to the stables and that she would be back in one moment. The boy nodded dumbly, seeing what had happened, as the big grey stood quite still, as if she too knew her fate.

Artemis backed away the first few steps, then cursing her impediment, stumbled as fast as she could without the help of a stick across the last few yards of the field and on to the path which led to the nearby stables.

Ellie had seen the horse and its rider returning but had lost sight of them after they'd jumped the stile, disappearing as they did from view behind the long hedge that divided the field from the track to the stable yard. She had walked down to the lawn to watch Hugo's art class from a distance, and now the class was over, she had approached and got into idle conversation with her husband, who seemed to be in the very best of moods.

'Did you see Tom?' he asked her. 'She was out on her horse.'

'They've just got back I think,' Ellie said, as she helped Hugo pack up his box of paints and pencils. 'How about if we go across and see them in the stables? Maybe you could sketch her new horse.'

'I'll wander over to the stables, certainly,' Hugo replied. 'But I think even I've had quite enough art for one day, thanks.'

Together they ambled over towards the stable yard, talking about Hugo's art class and about the various and surprising talents of some of the students. At that moment, so relaxed and happy were they both, it was just like the old days.

Jenks kept his old service revolver in a locker in the tack room. She knew that. She also knew he cleaned and checked it regularly, particularly since the outbreak of war and the talk of invasion. But when she finally reached the tack room he was nowhere to be found.

Artemis called for him, but the yard was deserted, and realizing there was no time to spare, she took the key from the peg, unlocked the cupboard, and took out the loaded gun. She would have to despatch the animal herself.

Hurrying back out to the yard, she called once more for Jenks, but there was still no reply. She looked at the gun in her hand and tried to remember the procedure. She had seen it done often enough not to need too much reminding. Straight down, between the ears, and a quick and merciful death. She left the yard as quickly as she could go, and by the time Jenks had returned from checking the horses out at grass, there was no longer any sign of her.

Ellie was so busy talking and laughing with Hugo that she didn't notice Artemis as she hurried as fast as she could back across to the field.

Hugo did. All at once he stopped and stared ahead of them, as the sunlight caught the barrel of the gun.

'What's the matter, Hugo?' Ellie asked, turning back to see now Hugo was no longer at her side. He was standing behind her, with his eyes wide open, an odd, lost look about them. 'Hugo?' Ellie called to him again. 'What's the matter – don't you feel well?'

Above the noise of the engine, he could hear nothing. It was so hot, appallingly hot, so hot you could hardly breathe. And there was dust, no not dust, it was sand. Everywhere there was sand. And blood. There was blood everywhere as well, on him, all over him, blood everywhere, all over the inside of the boiling vehicle, and there was this dead man in his arms, across his lap, the blood still shooting out of his head and drenching him, soaking his shirt and his shorts and his bare arms and his hands as he held the dead man, this man who had been alive a moment ago and was now dead. Shot through the head by a sniper's bullet.

Through the haze of sunshine and the glare that was in his eyes, Hugo searched and stared, but there was no-one there now, just a gate to a field beyond swinging on its hinges, and the hot desert sun blinding his eyes. Hugo put a hand up as a shield from the sudden brightness of the light that seemed to have burst somewhere deep inside his head, as at that moment, that very moment he heard the unmistakeable crack of a gunshot.

'No!' he shouted suddenly, grabbing Ellie's hand. 'No! No quickly! She can't! She mustn't! Quickly – Tom can't shoot herself! Not without us! Remember? That was the agreement! If one goes, we all go! Quickly! Quickly – run, Ellie, run! Run!'

And running, running, running as fast as he could and as fast as he could take his wife with him, and before Ellie could say anything or ask anything, Hugo ran to find Artemis, who when they finally reached her was standing over the body of her dead horse.

The sorrow of losing the mare was drowned in the euphoria which followed Hugo's recovery. At first Hugo's sole concern was for Artemis, mindful of the love she had for her horses, while Ellie was torn between feelings of joy at Hugo's apparent return to normality and Artemis's loss.

'We have to keep things in perspective,' Artemis said, taking Ellie aside when the three of them had repaired to the Dower House. 'I've lost a horse, but you've recovered Hugo. Which is more important. And who knows? If the mare hadn't died like that, at that particular moment and everything, who knows? Hugo mightn't have got his memory back. Not ever.'

'I know,' Ellie agreed. 'It seems when he heard the shot –'

'Exactly,' Artemis interrupted. 'As Nanny was forever saying, reproaches are often blessings in disguise, or some such. So come on. Let's all get tight.'

Artemis despatched Rosie to her cellar to fetch two of her few remaining bottles of champagne, while Ellie sat with Hugo on the sofa.

'All I can remember, Ell,' he told her in answer to her question, 'is I remember the explosion. That's not true. I remember everything *up* to the explosion, the driver being shot, and his head – I can remember his . . .' Hugo stopped and stared silently at the unlit fire, before putting both his hands on both his knees and gripping them tightly. 'I remember us hitting what must have been a landmine, I suppose,' he continued, 'and then the next thing I remember is being in the field. And finding Artemis. With you.' He turned to Ellie and smiled at her, but there was great sadness in his eyes. 'What happened, Ell?' he asked. 'Something else must have happened. What happened to me – in between?'

Ellie took one of his hands in both of hers. 'You lost your memory, Hugo,' she told him.

'Altogether?'

'Yes,' Ellie said. 'Altogether.'

'I didn't even know you?'

'No, Hugo. It was as if we'd never even met.'

'My God,' Hugo sighed. 'God Almighty.'

Artemis, who had been standing with her back to them at the window, crossed the room and tipping Brutus out of her chair, sat down opposite.

'Didn't I know anyone, Tom?' he pleaded. 'No-one at all?'

'Not a person, Hugo,' Artemis replied. 'You had no idea who or where you were.'

'My God,' Hugo repeated. 'How terrible for you both. You must have despaired.'

'Yes,' Artemis said. 'We did.'

The champagne changed the mood. That and the findings of Mr Peake when he arrived half an hour later to examine Hugo in order to try and ascertain whether or not his recovery was complete.

'I told him what we told Hugo,' Artemis said to Ellie, on her return after settling Hugo and his doctor in her morning room. 'You don't mind, do you?'

'On the contrary,' Ellie replied, taking Artemis's hand and sitting her down beside her on the sofa. 'I wasn't quite sure what we should tell Hugo. I didn't want to confuse him.'

'Quite,' Artemis agreed. 'I'd say we'd had quite enough confusion, wouldn't you?'

The two women looked at each other, and then raised their glasses of champagne in celebration.

'Cheers,' said Ellie.

'Absolutely,' said Artemis.

Mr Peake's initial diagnosis was guarded but optimistic. He told Ellie that Hugo appeared to have recovered his memory totally, with the exception of the period between the incident in the desert and the death of Artemis's horse. 'Over that period, his illness and confinement both in Cairo and here his mind is a complete blank,' he assured Ellie, 'which I hasten to add is no bad thing. And I would guess, and it's only a guess because heaven alone knows how the mind works, I would guess that period of his life will always remain unremembered, probably because his brain has decided it is really of no importance.'

'There's no chance of my husband losing his memory again, is there?' Ellie enquired anxiously. 'Through another shock? Or – or an accident or anything?'

'That I can't guarantee, I'm afraid,' Mr Peake replied with a smile. 'After all, there's a war on, and even were there not, who knows what tricks the mind might play? But provided he doesn't overtax himself, and given your husband's intelligence, I would say there is every chance of a full and total recovery.'

And in fact once he had accepted that there was a period in his life which was and would remain a total blank, Hugo never looked back, so much so that within two months he was determined to return to work. Ellie not unnaturally opposed such a notion, and lobbied for him to remain at Brougham and help her run the hospital.

'Sorry, Ell,' Hugo grinned. 'No offence, but that's really girls' work.'

'You're not for a moment even thinking about going abroad again, are you?' Ellie asked in horror.

'There's a war on, Ellie!' Hugo laughed. 'I'll go where I'm told and do what I'm told!'

'They won't send him abroad,' Artemis retorted when Ellie told her. 'I mean he's really still one of the walking wounded.'

'Where there's a will, Artemis,' Ellie sighed. 'You know Hugo. No of course they won't send him abroad, but he might persuade them to give him a desk job in Whitehall.'

'He could get killed anywhere, Eleanor,' Artemis replied. 'They're dropping bombs all over the place.'

'This might seem ridiculous, Artemis,' Ellie said. 'But I'm just as worried about him being in the middle of an air raid, and not being killed, but . . . well. Losing his mind again. But this time for good.'

'I see,' Artemis said thoughtfully. 'In that case, I'd better ring Diana. And she can have a word with my father.'

A month later Hugo was offered a job by the War Office.

'In Whitehall?' Ellie asked innocently.

'No,' Hugo replied. 'In Woodstock. Blenheim Palace actually. I asked if there wasn't anything in London, but apparently there isn't. At least not anything suitable.'

'Oh dear,' said Artemis, scratching Brutus's head between his ears. 'What hard luck.'

22

The car had been the break he needed. After the first night in the woods outside the town, the initial elation had given way to a more realistic appraisal of his fortunes, and he realized that one slice of luck wasn't going to be enough to see him through.

But then, two hours after darkness fell the second night, to his surprise he heard a car. Yes, there was a track below, he knew that. He'd seen it in the daylight, below the tree. But from where he was hidden, deep in the woods, the track looked hardly used. So perhaps the car was military. Perhaps it was a search party. He held his breath, hidden up among the high branches, and waited.

But the car was small, with a high revving engine, a private car. After a moment, the driver killed the engine and the lights, and then after another moment, a longer moment, opened his door. His passenger opened his door as well.

Or rather her door. He could see them below, in the moonlight, a man and a woman. He saw them embrace, and kiss passionately, and then strip down to their underwear before running off to make love in the woods. Availing himself of his good fortune, he stole all the man's clothes.

On the third day he ran into a patrol. In response, he started to sing the verse of a song the extras in *The Mortal Storm* had sung, a song he had been delegated to teach them, while smiling and waving casually at the men on the opposite side of the road. The men passing him by were also singing. Most of them laughed and waved back.

Later that day he was stopped. The man who stopped him leaned out of his car and asked him something, something which he didn't understand. So he shrugged, and as he shrugged the idea came to him to be deaf and dumb. So he pointed to his mouth, putting a finger on his lips, and then to his ears, while shaking his head.

The man opened the door of his car and gave him a lift to a village eighty miles north, talking to him non-stop, even though he was pretending to be deaf and dumb. Beyond the village he crossed the river hidden in a barge, and then over the next three days walked sixty miles across country with the help of the map he had stolen from the man who had given him a lift. He took food where he could, and wine or beer also, discovering that the more brazenly you stole something, the less chance there was of being apprehended.

The last leg was the hardest. The weather had turned cold, freezing at night and sleeting by day. For four days he had to stay hidden while waiting to stow away on a fishing boat which would take him to the island. But the boat didn't dock. Instead it turned back, two or three miles from the coast, and so he had to slip overboard and swim ashore.

Half dead with hunger and cold and ready to concede defeat, he stumbled on a remote farmhouse where they fed him and hid him for two weeks until he could cross to the mainland on the far side of the sea. There he was safe, and there Patsy stayed, until the time finally came for his return.

23

Rosie gave her a set of hand stitched napkins.

'Drawn threads *and* embroidery,' Artemis said admiringly. 'Whenever did you find the time, Rosie?'

'In the evenings,' Rosie told her, shyly. 'I was as sure as anythin' you'd noticed.'

'They're absolutely lovely, Rosie,' Artemis said, showing them off to her guests. 'Thank you.'

It was only a small birthday party, just Artemis, and Ellie, Hugo and Rosie. But it was a perfect one, exactly how a birthday should be. The four of them had lunch, cooked by Rosie from specially saved rations and laid out in the panelled dining room of the Dower House. Then they moved to the drawing room, where they all sat warmed by the log fire while Artemis opened her gifts.

There were cards and hand-made gifts from the nurses and the patients, as there were from all the staff and the ever faithful Jenks. Diana, as always, hadn't forgotten, and had sent her a funny card and bottle of Scotch whisky.

'She must have her own distillery,' Hugo said. 'She's the only person we know who's never short of a drop.'

Most surprisingly of all, there was a card and a gift from Artemis's father. The card was a hunting print, naturally enough, signed 'With best wishes, Papa'. But the present was much less predictable. It was a deep red leather bound book.

'Surtees, I bet,' said Hugo with a puckish grin. '*Mr Sponge's Sporting Tour.*'

'Who's Surtees for goodness sake?' Ellie asked.

'Wrote all about hunting in the nineteenth century,' Hugo told her. 'Marvellous stuff. Well?' he asked Artemis.

'Wrong,' Artemis smiled, holding the book to her. 'It's poetry.'

'John Masefield,' guessed Hugo.

'Percy Bysshe Shelley,' Artemis replied.

Quickly she turned to opening her gift from Ellie, which was a gorgeous old hat Ellie had found in the attics of the house and which she'd retrimmed herself.

'It must have been one of your ancestor's, I guess,' Ellie told her as Artemis tried it on. 'Anyway, it's just the kind of mad thing you like.'

'You're right,' Artemis agreed. 'I love it.'

Artemis was so delighted with it, she wore it while she opened Hugo's present, which after giving a sigh of admiration she held up for all to see. It was a perfectly exquisite watercolour of Brutus, whom he'd pictured lying in the middle of a field of buttercups, and which he'd entitled 'Brutus Absolutely Refusing To Fetch Any More Sticks'.

'Thank you, Ellie,' Artemis said. 'And thank you, Hugo.' She kissed them both.

For a while, after Rosie had cleared away lunch, time stood still, and the war-torn world seemed an age away. There was idle talk round the fire, reminiscences, moments fondly recalled of other birthdays and moments shared, and most importantly there was laughter, something that had too long been absent from their three lives, and which had only returned to Brougham with the restoration of Hugo's memory.

After tea, in the late afternoon, Ellie and Hugo made their excuses and slipped away, leaving Artemis sad because the main part of the celebrations were over, but content that it had been such a happy day. She threw another log on the fire, and settled back with her shoeless feet up on the sofa, to read her much thumbed copy of *The Secret Garden* which Diana had given to her many birthdays ago. Brutus, now very deaf but otherwise in sturdy health, sighed deeply with contentment as he settled back down in front of the fire, and within minutes he was snoring deeply, fast asleep.

Artemis prodded him with her stick. 'Sssshhhh, dog,' she said. 'Or I'll only fall asleep as well.'

The dog looked round at her quizzically, and then settled down. Within seconds he was snoring again. This time Artemis smiled, and leaned over to ruffle his coat. Then she lay back on the cushions and opened her book.

'I do love this book, Brutus,' she murmured. 'It's odd. But one's childhood books are rather comforting at a time like this.'

The dog snored ever more deeply, while the logs settled on to the fire with a hiss and a sigh. Artemis yawned and stared at the words in front of her, doing her best to keep awake. But the warmth of the fire and the sound of her dog sleeping finally proved too much for her.

The corridor she was in was long and dark, lit only by the candle in the palm of her hand. Like Mary, she knew this wasn't the right corridor, that the door she wanted was in a shorter passage, and that the door was covered in a sort of fabric. There was a crying sound somewhere, but it might be a bird, because she knew she was somewhere near the sea, and then there were some steps, a double set of steps which swept up to a wooden house. Opening the door she could still hear the crying but she knew the plane was down there somewhere, just the body of it, no wings, just the broken fuselage, while the light flickering in the palm of her hand sputtered and grew dim.

She was in the room. She had found it and she was in it. But all the furniture which had been so fine was burned and broken, and still she could hear the crying, and she knew who it was. The crying was her crying, and as she looked at the bed she saw Patsy sitting there, in his flying jacket and helmet, under which tumbled out some of his brown hair, over his forehead, dark against the paleness of his face with huge grey brown eyes which seemed too big. And although he was smiling, she knew he'd been tired, and exhausted, and close to death.

She drew nearer while the wax from the candle fell on to the palm of her hand. But now she was in the bed, she was lying on the pillows looking up and seeing him, turning her head round to him, opening her eyes wide to see him as he bent nearer and nearer to her, and she could feel the tears running from the corners of her eyes, tears which came from her heart, tears which she didn't want to spill in case she woke up, and if she woke up he would be gone.

'Who are you?' she said at last, in a half-frightened whisper. 'Are you a ghost?'

'No,' Patsy said. 'Are you?'

It was Cousin Rose's idea they should get married in Ireland, a notion with which Artemis was only too happy to concur.

'I'd have thought you'd have wanted to get married here,' Ellie had said, after she had spoken to Cousin Rose on the telephone. 'I'd have thought you'd have chosen Brougham.'

'I'd like Patsy to meet your Cousin Rose,' Artemis had replied. 'And Tutti. I want him to see Strand House before it's too late.'

Nothing had changed at Strand House. As the taxi pulled up the drive, the four of them could see Cousin Rose stooped over the flower bed by the front door, with the gum-booted and bowler-hatted Tutti behind her, shading her under his large black umbrella.

'Will you just look who it is, Tutti!' Cousin Rose exclaimed as Ellie and Artemis, Hugo and Patsy climbed out of the cab. 'Will you just look who it is now!'

'Sure don't I know well enough?' Tutti replied, looking heavenwards. 'For haven't you been telling me all day?'

Ellie kissed her relative fondly, and Cousin Rose, seizing her by both arms, kissed her twice in return and even more fondly. Artemis was also seized, before she could introduce Patsy, and hugged until the breath was all but squeezed out of her.

'We've no need for introductions, child!' Cousin Rose admonished. 'Sure Patsy and I are blood!' Patsy too was seized and hugged, and then held at arm's length, before being seized and hugged again. 'Will you look at him, Tutti?' Cousin Rose sighed. 'Will you just look? Isn't he a ringer for that lovely man in the fillums?'

'He is not,' Tutti replied. 'You must be thinking of somebody different altogether.'

'Who?' Cousin Rose challenged. 'I'd just love to hear.'

'Wouldn't you just?' said Tutti. 'Maybe next time we go to the fillums you'll take your spectacles.'

Finally it was Hugo's turn, and then with one hand in his and the other in Patsy's, Cousin Rose led them up the steps. 'Will you help with the bags, Tutti!' she called over her shoulder. 'Instead of standing there like an orange!'

'I will not!' Tutti called in return. 'That's the jarvey's vocation! Isn't that right, my man?' he asked the cabman.

'It is not,' the driver replied. 'Now will you help take these in, my man?'

The little church in which they were to be married stood in a field full of grazing sheep, on a hill overlooking the bay. It was hard to know if there were more flowers packed in it or people, Ellie thought, as she looked at the sea of shining faces, and the innumerable jugs of flowers picked by Cousin Rose and Tutti from the garden. The heavy smell of roses filled the air, accompanied by the drone of fat bees who had found their way in through the open door and were lazily gorging themselves on the still succulent flowers.

There were people outside the church as well, well wishers and sightseers, come to see the English Lady marry the Yank, and when Tutti finally drew Cousin Rose's big Humber up at the foot of the hill, a cheer went up from the crowds as Artemis stepped out into the sunshine.

'They'll not have seen anyone prettier,' Tutti said, holding the car door open. 'And I've a mind to say that they're not the only ones.'

In the unavoidable absence of her father and Diana, Tutti had been nominated unanimously to give the bride away, and for once he showed no signs of objecting. Now he offered Artemis his arm, once she had reached into the car for her stick, and steadied herself.

'The white flag is up, your ladyship,' Tutti said, as Artemis adjusted her veil. 'And they're off.'

Patsy stared as hard as he could at the altar, not daring to look round. Behind him he heard a cheer outside the church, then a slight gasp from the people behind him. Out of the corner of his eye he could see Ellie, who was half turned to look down the aisle. The organist began to play and still Patsy dared not look. He hadn't been allowed sight or sound of Artemis since tea time the day before, and it seemed like a lifetime.

Hugo, his best man, took hold of his hand and squeezed it. '*Bon voyage*, pal,' he whispered in his best American. 'Happy days.'

Now Artemis was by his side and still Patsy didn't look. He thought if he turned now and saw his bride, his heart was so full of love it would burst. So he waited until the priest took a step towards them before he looked at Artemis.

She was dressed in a cream silk dress which had belonged to Ellie's grandmother and which had been worn by her the day she was married in this very same church. Patsy knew that because Cousin Rose had promised her on the telephone she would fetch it down from the attic where she had it in safe keeping, and have it ready for her when she arrived. But he had no idea of quite how beautiful the old dress was, and how perfectly it would fit Artemis. The sleeves were full and half puffed above the elbows, the crinoline was covered by an overskirt which was caught up at regular intervals by orange blossom, and on her head she wore a simple lace cap from which fell a veil of old lace.

Artemis turned to Patsy and as she did so, through the fine veil he could see her smiling at him, and Patsy had to swallow hard to stop the tears from flooding his eyes.

'Here in the sight of God, and in the face of this congregation,' the priest exhorted, to which the congregation gave a great sigh before being asked for the last time whether or not any of them knew cause or just impediment why the two people before them should not be joined in Holy Matrimony.

'They do not!' Tutti pronounced, earning himself a glare from Cousin Rose, while the congregation earned a glare from Tutti.

His final demand being greeted with silence, the priest then proceeded to marry the English Lady to the Yank, bidding them to live together after God's ordinance, forsaking all others, for better or for worse, to love, and to cherish and to obey, until death parted them. And on the will of those gathered behind them in the church, strangers till that moment, but now part of the large eternal family, and for the love that they felt for each other, Patsy Milligan and Artemis Deverill were wed.

'Those whom God hath joined together,' said the priest, 'let no man put asunder.'

'Let them not!' boomed Tutti. 'Nor no woman either!'

The little organ then piped out the 'Wedding March', its bellows barely big enough to sustain each chord, while Patsy and Artemis Milligan turned together and walked down the aisle as man and wife. And as they went, walking out into the sunshine which danced off the sea, the people gathered in the tiny church wished them God speed and good luck as they showered them with petals plucked from the multitude of cut roses.

When the war was over, Hugo recorded the events on the repainted mural in the back hall.

Today, guides make Hugo's wall-painting the last stop on the tours around Brougham, since it has become one of the major talking points of visits to the stately home. But when Hugo was repainting it, it was much more than that. For the family and residents of Brougham it was a lifeline, a defiant statement that despite everything, they would all survive and endure. Everyone who passed through the portals of Brougham during those critical years and who stayed to make their mark or play their part or had come there just simply to recover, they were all included: Matron, the nursing sisters, the nurses and their patients, Mr Peake and Doctor Leigh, Porter and his staff, Cook, Mrs Byrne, and Jenks, the cats and Boot, Brutus and the foals and their mothers, Jamie as a baby, and Jamie growing as a child, painted from pictures sent from Nanny in America, and Jamie back home, old Nanny and new Nanny, all the people and their children and their animals and pets, all part of a time that is now gone, and yet because of the painting is there for evermore.

As indeed are Artemis and Ellie, Patsy and Hugo.

THE END

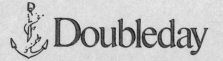

CONJURE ME
by
Jack Curtis

In his most chilling novel to date, Curtis lays deception on deception, illusion on illusion. He evokes an extraordinary world of magic, murder, dark secrets and darker dreams.

BANTAM
PRESS

New in hardcover.